AQA CERTIFICATE

Further Mathematics

DAVID PRITCHARD
with Val Hanrahan
and Roger Porkess

HODDER
EDUCATION
AN HACHETTE UK COMPANY

Hachette UK's policy is to use papers that are natural, renewable and recyclable products and made from wood grown in sustainable forests. The logging and manufacturing processes are expected to conform to the environmental regulations of the country of origin.

Orders: please contact Bookpoint Ltd, 130 Milton Park, Abingdon, Oxon OX14 4SB. Telephone: (44) 01235 827720. Fax: (44) 01235 400454. Lines are open 9.00–5.00, Monday to Saturday, with a 24-hour message answering service. Visit our website at www.hoddereducation.com

© David Pritchard, Val Hanrahan 2013
First published in 2013 by
Hodder Education,
a Hachette UK company,
Carmelite House,
50 Victoria Embankment,
London, EC4Y 0DZ

Impression number   12
Year   2018

Cover photo © *Michael Smith/iStock photo*
Typeset in *10.5/14 in Minion Regular* by Aptara, Inc.
Printed in Great Britain by CPI Group (UK) Ltd, Croydon, CR0 4YY

A catalogue record for this title is available from the British Library

ISBN 978 1444 18112 8

Introduction

This book supports the AQA Level 2 Certificate in Further Mathematics.

The qualification is designed for high achieving students who have already achieved, or are expected to achieve, grades A or A* in GCSE Mathematics. Many of these students are likely to progress to study Mathematics at A-level and beyond.

Higher order mathematical skills will be studied in greater depth with an emphasis on algebraic reasoning, rigorous argument and problem solving skills. Students following this course will be able to achieve their maximum potential at Level 2 and be well prepared to tackle a Level 3 Mathematics qualification.

The content is split into Algebra, Geometry, Calculus and Matrices with each section containing work that stretches and challenges, and which goes beyond the Key Stage 4 Programme of Study. The topic areas are frequently linked together as progress is made through the book, highlighting the beauty and inter-connectedness of mathematics. The problem-solving questions will often involve more than one topic area.

Two symbols are used throughout the book:

? This denotes a 'discussion point'. These are prompts to help you to understand the theory that has been, or is about to be, introduced. Answers to these are also included.

⚠ This 'warning sign' alerts you either to restrictions that need to be imposed or to possible pitfalls.

In addition the book includes a number of activities. These are often used to introduce a new concept, or to reinforce the examples in the text. Throughout the book the emphasis is on understanding the mathematics being used rather than merely being able to perform the calculations but the exercises do, nonetheless, provide plenty of scope for practising basic techniques.

It is hoped that students (and teachers) will be inspired and challenged by the rigorous nature of the course and be able to appreciate the power of mathematics for its own sake as well as a problem-solving tool.

Contents

ALGEBRA

Number and algebra I

The only thing that separates successful people from the ones who aren't is the willingness to work very, very hard.

Helen Gurley Brown (American Businesswoman)

Numbers and the number system

Number will be tested implicitly throughout the course. Apart from manipulation of surds (pages 14–18), examination questions will always test number with at least one of algebra, calculus or geometry. These questions will appear at appropriate times in the book. The following exercise provides practice of some number skills that may be needed.

EXERCISE 1A

Do not use a calculator.

1 ABCD is a straight line. AB = 4 cm, AC = 10 cm, AD = 22 cm.

A   B   C   D

Work out these ratios, giving your answers in their simplest form.

    (i)   AC : AB   **(ii)** AB : BC   **(iii)** AD : AB

    (iv) BC : CD   **(v)** BD : BC

*2 Work out
    (i)   60% of £115   **(ii)** $33\frac{1}{3}$% of 780   **(iii)** 17.5% of 64 cm.

3 Work out
    (i)   95% of 7540   **(ii)** $12\frac{1}{2}$% of 53.76   **(iii)** 4.2% of £150.

*4 **(i)**   Increase 80 by 5%.   **(ii)** Increase £240 by 75%.

    (iii) Decrease £20 by 40%.   **(iv)** Decrease 36 by $66\frac{2}{3}$%.

5 **(i)**   Increase 650 by 14%.   **(ii)** Decrease 3250 by 3.5%.

    (iii) Decrease £3650 by 64%.   **(iv)** Increase £46 by $5\frac{1}{2}$%.

*6 Work out, giving your answers as fractions in their simplest form

    (i) $\dfrac{3}{5} + \dfrac{2}{3} \times \dfrac{5}{6}$ **(ii)** $\left(\dfrac{1}{2}\right)^3 \div 4$ **(iii)** $3\dfrac{2}{5} - \dfrac{3}{4}$

7 A bag contains blue, green and white beads. The ratio of blue beads to green beads is 4 : 3.

The ratio of green beads to white beads is 2 : 7.

Work out the smallest possible number of beads in the bag.

8 (i) Work out, giving your answer to 3 significant figures $52.7 \div 4.93$

(ii) Work out, giving your answer to 2 significant figures $5.9 - 0.53 \times 1.8$

(iii) Work out, giving your answer to 1 significant figure $0.23 \times 0.14 + 0.09^2$

(iv) Work out, giving your answer to 2 decimal places $\dfrac{19 + 36}{144 - 52}$

9 55% of teachers in a school are female. 36 teachers are male.
Work out the number of teachers in the school.

? A large ice cream costs 40p more than a small one. Two large ice creams cost the same as three small ones. What is the cost of each size of ice cream?

This is an example of the type of question that you might find in a puzzle book or the puzzle section of a newspaper or magazine. How would you set about tackling it?

? You may think that the following question appears to be very similar. What happens when you try to solve it?

A large ice cream costs 40p more than a small one. Five small ice creams plus three large ones cost 80p less than three small ice creams plus five large ones. What is the cost of each size of ice cream?

Simplifying expressions

When you are asked to *simplify* an algebraic expression you need to write it in its most compact form. This will involve techniques such as collecting like terms, removing brackets, factorising and finding a common denominator (if the expression includes fractions).

EXAMPLE 1.1

Simplify this expression.

$$3a + 4b - 2c + a - 3b - c$$

SOLUTION

Expression $= 3a + a + 4b - 3b - 2c - c$ collecting like terms
$= 4a + b - 3c$

EXAMPLE 1.2

Simplify this expression.

$$2(3x - 4y) - 3(x + 2y)$$

Notice that $(-3)(2y) = -6y$.

SOLUTION

Expression $= 6x - 8y - 3x - 6y$ removing the brackets

$$= 3x - 14y$$

EXAMPLE 1.3

Simplify this expression.

$$3x^2yz \times 2xy^3$$

SOLUTION

Expression $= (3 \times 2) \times (x^2 \times x) \times (y \times y^3) \times z$ collecting like terms

$$= 6x^3y^4z$$

EXAMPLE 1.4

Simplify this expression.

$$\frac{6a^2b^3c}{3ab^4c^3}$$

SOLUTION

Look where the higher powers of a, b and c occur. You may find that it helps if you split them up like this.

$$\frac{6a^2b^3c}{3ab^4c^3} = \frac{\cancel{3} \times 2 \times \cancel{a} \times a \times \cancel{b^3} \times \cancel{c}}{\cancel{3} \times \cancel{a} \times \cancel{b^3} \times b \times \cancel{c} \times c^2}$$

You can then cancel as indicated to give

$$\frac{2a}{bc^2}$$

EXAMPLE 1.5

Factorise this expression.

$$3a^2b + 6ab^2$$

SOLUTION

First you need to look for the highest common factor of the two terms, which is $3ab$ here.

$$3a^2b + 6ab^2 = 3ab(a + 2b)$$

Since $3a^2b = 3ab \times a$ and $6ab^2 = 3ab \times 2b$.

❓ Explain what the word *factorise* means.

Simplify this expression.

$$\frac{2x^2}{3yz} \div \frac{4xy^2}{5z^2}$$

SOLUTION

Expression $= \dfrac{2x^2}{3yz} \times \dfrac{5z^2}{4xy^2}$

$= \dfrac{5xz}{6y^3}$

Simplify this expression.

$$\frac{x}{4t} - \frac{2y}{5t} + \frac{z}{2t}$$

SOLUTION

Expression $= \dfrac{5x}{20t} - \dfrac{8y}{20t} + \dfrac{10z}{20t}$

$20t$ is the common denominator for $4t$, $5t$ and $2t$.

$= \dfrac{5x - 8y + 10z}{20t}$

1 Simplify the following expressions.

(i) $12a + 3b - 7c - 2a - 4b + 5c$

(ii) $4x - 5y + 3z + 2x + 2y - 7z$

(iii) $3(5x - y) + 4(x + 2y)$

(iv) $2(p + 5q) - (p - 4q)$

(v) $x(x + 3) - x(x - 2)$

(vi) $a(2a + 3) + 3(3a - 4)$

(vii) $3p(q - p) - 3q(p - q)$

(viii) $5f(g + 2h) - 5g(h - f)$

2 Factorise the following expressions by taking out the highest common factor.

(i) $8 - 10x^2$

(ii) $6ab + 8bc$

(iii) $2a^2 + 4ab$

(iv) $pq^3 - p^3q$

(v) $3x^2y + 6xy^4$

(vi) $6p^3q - 4p^2q^2 + 2pq^3$

(vii) $15lm^2 - 9l^3m^3 + 12l^2m^4$

(viii) $84a^5b^4 - 96a^4b^5$

3 Simplify the following expressions and factorise the answers.

(i) $4(3x + 2y) + 8(x - 3y)$

(ii) $x(x - 2) - x(x - 8) + 6$

(iii) $x(y + z) - y(x + z)$

(iv) $p(2q - r) + r(p - 2q)$
(v) $k(l + m + n) - km$
(vi) $a(a - 2) - a(a + 4) + 2(a - 4)$
(vii) $3x(x + y) - 3y(x - 2y)$
(viii) $a(a - 2) - a(a - 4) + 8$

4 Simplify the following expressions as much as possible.

(i) $2a^2b \times 5ab^3$
(ii) $6p^3q \times 2q^3r$
(iii) $lm \times mn \times np$
(iv) $3r^3 \times 6s^2 \times 2rs$
(v) $ab \times 2bc \times 4cd \times 8de$
(vi) $3xy^2 \times 4yz^2 \times 5x^2z$
(vii) $2ab^3 \times 6a^4 \times 7b^6$
(viii) $6p^2q^3r \times 7pq^5r^4$

5 Simplify the following fractions as much as possible.

(i) $\dfrac{4a^2b}{2ab}$

(ii) $\dfrac{p^2}{q} \times \dfrac{q^2}{p}$

(iii) $\dfrac{8a}{3b^2} \times \dfrac{6b^3}{4a^2}$

(iv) $\dfrac{3ab}{2c^2} \times \dfrac{4cd}{6a^2}$

(v) $\dfrac{8xy^3z^2}{12yz}$

(vi) $\dfrac{3a^2}{9b^3} \div \dfrac{2a^4}{15b}$

(vii) $\dfrac{5p^3q}{8rs^2} \div \dfrac{15pq^5}{28r^4}$

6 Simplify the following expressions as single fractions.

(i) $\dfrac{2a}{3} + \dfrac{a}{4}$

(ii) $\dfrac{2x}{5} - \dfrac{x}{2} + \dfrac{3x}{4}$

(iii) $\dfrac{4p}{3} - \dfrac{3p}{4}$

(iv) $\dfrac{2s}{5} - \dfrac{s}{3} + \dfrac{4s}{15}$

(v) $\dfrac{3b}{8} - \dfrac{b}{6} + \dfrac{5b}{24}$

(vi) $\dfrac{3a}{b} - \dfrac{2a}{3b}$

(vii) $\dfrac{5}{2p} - \dfrac{3}{2q}$

(viii) $\dfrac{2x}{3y} - \dfrac{3x}{2y}$

Solving linear equations

? What is an equation?
What does solving an equation mean?

Since both sides of an equation are equal, you may do what you wish to the equation, provided that you do exactly the same thing to both sides. The examples that follow illustrate this in great detail. In practice you would expect to omit some of the working.

EXAMPLE 1.8

Solve this equation.

$$3(3x - 17) = 2(x - 1)$$

SOLUTION

Open the brackets	$\Rightarrow 9x - 51$	$= 2x - 2$
Subtract $2x$ from both sides	$\Rightarrow 9x - 51 - 2x$	$= 2x - 2 - 2x$
Tidy up	$\Rightarrow 7x - 51$	$= -2$
Add 51 to both sides	$\Rightarrow 7x - 51 + 51$	$= -2 + 51$
Tidy up	$\Rightarrow 7x$	$= 49$
Divide both sides by 7	$\Rightarrow x$	$= 7$

EXAMPLE 1.9

Solve this equation.

$$\tfrac{1}{2}(x + 8) = 2x + \tfrac{1}{3}(4x - 5)$$

SOLUTION

Start by clearing the fractions by multiplying by 6 (the least common multiple of 2 and 3).

Multiply both sides by 6	$\Rightarrow 6 \times \tfrac{1}{2}(x + 8)$	$= 6 \times 2x + 6 \times \tfrac{1}{3}(4x - 5)$
Tidy up	$\Rightarrow 3(x + 8)$	$= 12x + 2(4x - 5)$
Open the brackets	$\Rightarrow 3x + 24$	$= 12x + 8x - 10$
Tidy up	$\Rightarrow 3x + 24$	$= 20x - 10$
Subtract $3x$ from both sides	$\Rightarrow 24$	$= 17x - 10$
Add 10 to both sides	$\Rightarrow 34$	$= 17x$
Divide both sides by 17	$\Rightarrow x$	$= 2$

? Why have the variable and the number changed sides on the last line?

Sometimes you will need to set up the equation as well as solve it. When you are doing this, make sure that you define any variables that you introduce.

EXAMPLE 1.10

In a triangle, the largest angle is nine times as big as the smallest. The third angle is 60°.

(i) Write this information in the form of an equation for a, the size in degrees of the smallest angle.

(ii) Solve the equation to find the sizes of the three angles.

SOLUTION

Let the smallest angle = $a°$.

So the largest angle is $9a°$.

The sum of all three angles is $180°$

$$\Rightarrow a + 9a + 60 = 180$$
$$\Rightarrow 10a \qquad = 120$$
$$\Rightarrow a \qquad = 12$$

This gives $9a = 108$, so the angles are $12°$, $60°$ and $108°$.

1 Solve the following equations.

(i) $2x - 3 = x + 4$

(ii) $5a + 3 = 2a - 3$

(iii) $2(x + 5) = 14$

(iv) $7(2y - 5) = -7$

(v) $5(2c - 8) = 2(3c - 10)$

(vi) $3(p + 2) = 4(p - 1)$

(vii) $3(2x - 1) = 6(x + 2) + 3x$

(viii) $\dfrac{x}{3} + 7 = 5$

(ix) $\dfrac{5y - 2}{11} = 3$

(x) $\dfrac{k}{2} + \dfrac{k}{3} = 35$

(xi) $\dfrac{2t}{3} - \dfrac{3t}{5} = 4$

(xii) $\dfrac{5p - 4}{6} - \dfrac{2p + 3}{2} = 7$

(xiii) $p + \dfrac{1}{3}(p + 1) + \dfrac{1}{4}(p + 2) = \dfrac{5}{6}$

2 The length, l metres, of a field is $80\,\text{m}$ greater than the width. The perimeter is $600\,\text{m}$.

(i)   Write the information in the form of an equation for l.

(ii)   Solve the equation and so find the area of the field.

3 Louise and Molly are twins and their brother Jonathan is four years younger. The total of their three ages is 17 years.

(i)   Write this information in the form of an equation in j, Jonathan's age in years.

(ii)   What are all their ages?

4 In a multiple-choice examination of 20 questions, four marks are given for each correct answer and one mark is deducted for each wrong answer. There is no penalty for not attempting a question. A candidate attempts a questions and gets c correct.

(i)   Write down, and simplify, an expression for the candidate's total mark in terms of a and c.

(ii)   A candidate attempts three-quarters of the questions and scores 40. Write down, and solve, an equation for the number of correct questions.

5 John is three times as old as his son, Michael, and in x years' time he will be twice as old as him.

   (i)   Write down expressions for John's and Michael's age in x years' time.

   (ii) Write down, and solve, an equation in x.

6 A square has sides of length $2a$ metres, and a rectangle has length $3a$ metres and breadth 3 metres.

   (i)   Find, in terms of a, the perimeter of the square.

   (ii) Find, in terms of a, the perimeter of the rectangle.

   (iii) The perimeters of the square and the rectangle are equal. Find a.

7 The sum of five consecutive numbers is equal to 105. Let m represent the middle number.

   (i)   Write down the five numbers in terms of m.

   (ii) Form an equation in m and solve it.

   (iii) What are the five consecutive numbers?

8 One rectangle has a length of $(x + 2)$ cm and a breadth of 2 cm, and another, of equal area, has a length of 5 cm and a breadth of $(x - 3)$ cm.

   (i)   Write down an equation in x and solve it.

   (ii) What is the area of each of the rectangles?

Algebra and number

Some algebra questions will involve using number skills.

EXAMPLE 1.11 a is 75% of b and $b : c = 3 : 2$.

Show that $8a = 9c$.

SOLUTION

a is 75% of b 　　　 $a = \dfrac{75}{100} b$

$$a = \frac{3}{4} b \qquad\qquad ①$$

$b : c = 3 : 2$ 　　　 $\dfrac{b}{c} = \dfrac{3}{2}$

$$b = \frac{3}{2} c \qquad\qquad ②$$

Substitute ② in ① $a = \dfrac{3}{4} \times \dfrac{3}{2}c$

$$a = \dfrac{9}{8}c$$

$$8a = 9c$$

EXAMPLE 1.12

$p : q = 4 : 5$

Work out $p + 2q : 4q$, giving your answer in the simplest form.

SOLUTION

Think in terms of parts.

p is 4 parts, q is 5 parts.

$p + 2q$ is $4 + 2 \times 5 = 14$ parts

$4q$ is 20 parts

$p + 2q : 4q = 14 : 20$

$= 7 : 10$

EXERCISE 1D

1 Write expressions for the following, giving your answers in the simplest form.

(i) 30% of b (ii) $y\%$ of 450   (iii) $c\%$ of d

2 60% of p = 40% of q
Work out p as a percentage of q.

3 Write expressions for the following, giving your answers in the simplest form.
(i) a increased by 20%   (ii) b increased by 5%
(iii) k decreased by 35%   (iv) m decreased by 2%

4 a increased by 80% is equal to b increased by 50%.
Show that $\dfrac{b}{a} = 1.2$.

5 p increased by 25% is equal to q decreased by 25%.
Work out p as a percentage of q.

6 $x : y = 2 : 3$ and $y : z = 4 : 9$
Work out $x : y : z$, giving your answer in the simplest form.

7 $a : b = 5 : 2$
(i) Write a in terms of b.
(ii) Work out $2a + b : b$, giving your answer in the simplest form.
(iii) Work out $7a - 5b : 4a$, giving your answer in the simplest form.

8 $m : n = 3 : 8$ and r is 20% of n.
Work out $m : r$.

Expanding brackets

A quadratic expression is one in which the highest power of its terms is 2. For example,

$$x^2 + 3$$
$$a^2$$
$$2y^2 - 3y + 5$$

are all quadratic expressions.

? Why is $(x + 5)(2x - 3)$ a quadratic expression?

EXAMPLE 1.13 Expand $(x + 5)(2x - 3)$.

SOLUTION

$$\begin{aligned} \text{Expression} &= x(2x - 3) + 5(2x - 3) \\ &= 2x^2 - 3x + 10x - 15 \\ &= 2x^2 + 7x - 15 \end{aligned}$$

This method has multiplied everything in the second bracket by each term in the first bracket. An alternative way of setting this out is used in the next example.

EXAMPLE 1.14 Expand $(3x - 5)^2$.

SOLUTION

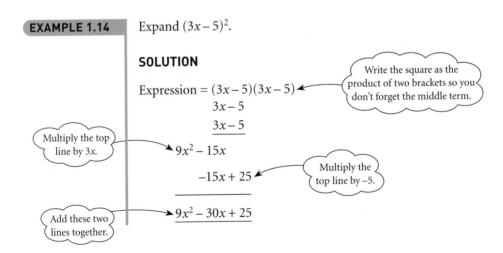

Write the square as the product of two brackets so you don't forget the middle term.

$$\text{Expression} = (3x - 5)(3x - 5)$$
$$3x - 5$$
$$3x - 5$$

Multiply the top line by $3x$.

$$9x^2 - 15x$$

$$-15x + 25$$

Multiply the top line by -5.

Add these two lines together.

$$9x^2 - 30x + 25$$

EXAMPLE 1.15   Multiply $(x^3 + 2x - 4)$ by $(x^2 - x + 3)$.

> Leave a gap here, since there is no x^2 term.

SOLUTION

$$
\begin{array}{r}
x^3 \qquad\ + 2x\ -\ 4 \\
x^2\ -\ \ x\ +\ 3 \\
\times \hline
\end{array}
$$

Multiply top line by x^2 $x^5 \qquad + 2x^3 - 4x^2$

Multiply top line by $(-x)$ $-\ x^4 \qquad\ - 2x^2 +\ 4x$

Multiply top line by 3 $3x^3 \qquad\ + 6x - 12$

$$x^5 - x^4 + 5x^3 - 6x^2 + 10x - 12$$

⚠ Keep a separate column for each power of x. Sometimes it is necessary to leave gaps. In arithmetic zeros are placed in the gaps. For example four thousand and five is written 4005.

EXAMPLE 1.16   Expand and simplify $(a - 2)^3$.

SOLUTION

$$(a - 2)^3 = (a - 2)(a - 2)^2$$

Work out $(a - 2)^2$

$$
\begin{aligned}
(a - 2)\ (a - 2) &= a(a - 2) - 2(a - 2) \\
&= a^2 - 2a - 2a + 4 \\
&= a^2 - 4a + 4
\end{aligned}
$$

Multiply by $(a - 2)$

$$
\begin{aligned}
(a - 2)(a^2 - 4a + 4) &= a(a^2 - 4a + 4) - 2(a^2 - 4a + 4) \\
&= a^3 - 4a^2 + 4a - 2a^2 + 8a - 8 \\
&= a^3 - 6a^2 + 12a - 8
\end{aligned}
$$

EXERCISE 1E   **1** Expand the following expressions.

     (i) $(x + 5)(x + 4)$ **(ii)** $(x + 3)(x + 1)$

     (iii) $(a + 5)(2a - 1)$ **(iv)** $(2p + 3)(3p - 2)$

     (v) $(x + 3)^2$ **(vi)** $(2x + 3)(2x - 3)$

     (vii) $(2 - 3m)(m - 4)$ **(viii)** $(6 + 5t)(2 - t)$

     (ix) $(4 - 3x)^2$ **(x)** $(m - 3n)^2$

  2 **(i)**   Multiply $(x^3 - x^2 + x - 2)$ by $(x^2 + 1)$.

     (ii)   Multiply $(x^4 - 2x^2 + 3)$ by $(x^2 + 2x - 1)$.

     (iii)   Multiply $(2x^3 - 3x + 5)$ by $(x^2 - 2x + 1)$.

     (iv)   Multiply $(x^5 + x^4 + x^3 + x^2 + x + 1)$ by $(x - 1)$.

(v) Expand $(x + 2)(x - 1)(x + 3)$. (Hint: expand two brackets first)

(vi) Expand $(2x + 1)(x - 2)(x + 4)$.

(vii) Expand and simplify $(x + 1)^3$.

(viii) Expand and simplify $(p - 5)^3$.

(ix) Expand and simplify $(2a + 3)^3$.

(x) Simplify $(2x^2 - 1)(x + 2) - 4(x + 2)^2$.

(xi) Simplify $(x^2 - 1)(x + 1) - (x^2 + 1)(x - 1)$.

Manipulating surds

Simplifying expressions containing square roots

In mathematics there are times when it is helpful to be able to manipulate square roots, rather than just find their values from your calculator. This ensures that you are working with the exact value, not just a rounded version.

EXAMPLE 1.17

Simplify the following.

(i) $\sqrt{8}$

(ii) $\sqrt{6} \times \sqrt{3}$

(iii) $\sqrt{32} - \sqrt{18}$

(iv) $(4 + \sqrt{3})(4 - \sqrt{3})$

SOLUTION

(i) $\sqrt{8} = \sqrt{2 \times 2 \times 2}$

$\qquad = \sqrt{2} \times \sqrt{2} \times \sqrt{2}$

$\qquad = (\sqrt{2})^2 \times \sqrt{2}$

$\qquad = 2\sqrt{2}$

(ii) $\sqrt{6} \times \sqrt{3} = \sqrt{6 \times 3}$

$\qquad = \sqrt{2 \times 3 \times 3}$

$\qquad = (\sqrt{3})^2 \times \sqrt{2}$

$\qquad = 3\sqrt{2}$

(iii) $\sqrt{32} - \sqrt{18} = \sqrt{16 \times 2} - \sqrt{9 \times 2}$

$\qquad = 4\sqrt{2} - 3\sqrt{2}$

$\qquad = \sqrt{2}$

(Start by looking for the largest square number factors of 32 and 18.)

(iv) $(4 + \sqrt{3})(4 - \sqrt{3}) = 16 - 4\sqrt{3} + 4\sqrt{3} - (\sqrt{3})^2$

$\qquad = 16 - 3$

$\qquad = 13$

Notice that in this last example there is no square root in the answer.

In the next example, all the numbers involve fractions with a square root on the bottom line. It is easier to work with numbers if any square roots are only on the top line. Manipulating a number to that form is called *rationalising the denominator*.

What is a rational number?

EXAMPLE 1.18 Simplify the following by rationalising their denominators.

(i) $\dfrac{2}{\sqrt{3}}$ (ii) $\sqrt{\dfrac{3}{5}}$ (iii) $\sqrt{\dfrac{3}{8}}$

SOLUTION

(i) $\dfrac{2}{\sqrt{3}} = \dfrac{2}{\sqrt{3}} \times \dfrac{\sqrt{3}}{\sqrt{3}}$

$= \dfrac{2\sqrt{3}}{(\sqrt{3})^2}$

$= \dfrac{2\sqrt{3}}{3}$

(ii) $\sqrt{\dfrac{3}{5}} = \dfrac{\sqrt{3}}{\sqrt{5}}$

$= \dfrac{\sqrt{3}}{\sqrt{5}} \times \dfrac{\sqrt{5}}{\sqrt{5}}$

$= \dfrac{\sqrt{3} \times \sqrt{5}}{(\sqrt{5})^2}$

$= \dfrac{\sqrt{15}}{5}$

(ii) $\sqrt{\dfrac{3}{8}} = \dfrac{\sqrt{3}}{\sqrt{8}}$

$= \dfrac{\sqrt{3}}{2\sqrt{2}}$

$= \dfrac{\sqrt{3}}{2\sqrt{2}} \times \dfrac{\sqrt{2}}{\sqrt{2}}$

$= \dfrac{\sqrt{3} \times \sqrt{2}}{2(\sqrt{2})^2}$

$= \dfrac{\sqrt{6}}{4}$

Number and algebra

EXERCISE 1F

Do not use a calculator for this exercise.

1 Simplify the following.

(i) $\sqrt{32}$ (ii) $\sqrt{125}$

(iii) $\sqrt{5} \times \sqrt{15}$ (iv) $\sqrt{8} - \sqrt{2}$

(v) $3\sqrt{27} - 6\sqrt{3}$ (vi) $4(3 + \sqrt{2}) - 3(5 - \sqrt{2})$

(vii) $4\sqrt{32} - 3\sqrt{8}$ (viii) $5(6 - \sqrt{3}) + 2(3 + 4\sqrt{3})$

(ix) $2\sqrt{125} + 6\sqrt{5}$ (x) $3(2\sqrt{2} - 3\sqrt{3}) - 2(3\sqrt{2} - 5\sqrt{3})$

2 Simplify the following.

(i) $(\sqrt{2} - 1)^2$ (ii) $(4 - \sqrt{5})(2 + \sqrt{5})$

(iii) $(2 - \sqrt{7})(\sqrt{7} - 1)$ (iv) $(\sqrt{5} - \sqrt{3})(\sqrt{5} + \sqrt{3})$

(v) $(3 + \sqrt{2})(5 - 2\sqrt{2})$ (vi) $(\sqrt{7} - 3)(2\sqrt{7} + 3)$

(vii) $(3\sqrt{3} - 2)(2\sqrt{3} - 3)$ (viii) $(\sqrt{5} - \sqrt{3})^2$

(ix) $(5 - 3\sqrt{2})(2\sqrt{2} - 1)$ (x) $(2\sqrt{2} + 3)^2$

3 Simplify the following by rationalising their denominators.

(i) $\dfrac{1}{\sqrt{3}}$ (ii) $\dfrac{5}{\sqrt{5}}$

(iii) $\dfrac{8}{\sqrt{6}}$ (iv) $\sqrt{\dfrac{2}{3}}$

(v) $\dfrac{2\sqrt{2}}{\sqrt{8}}$ (vi) $\sqrt{\dfrac{3}{7}}$

(vii) $\dfrac{21}{\sqrt{7}}$ (viii) $\dfrac{5}{3\sqrt{5}}$

(ix) $\dfrac{\sqrt{75}}{\sqrt{125}}$ (x) $\dfrac{8}{\sqrt{128}}$

Rationalising denominators with two terms

The next examples show how to rationalise denominators that have two terms.

EXAMPLE 1.19

Simplify the following by rationalising the denominator.

$$\frac{3\sqrt{2}}{4 - \sqrt{5}}$$

SOLUTION

$$\frac{3\sqrt{2}}{4-\sqrt{5}} = \frac{3\sqrt{2}}{4-\sqrt{5}} \times \frac{4+\sqrt{5}}{4+\sqrt{5}}$$

$$= \frac{12\sqrt{2}+3\sqrt{2}\sqrt{5}}{16+4\sqrt{5}-4\sqrt{5}-(\sqrt{5})^2}$$

$$= \frac{12\sqrt{2}+3\sqrt{10}}{16-5}$$

$$= \frac{12\sqrt{2}+3\sqrt{10}}{11}$$

EXAMPLE 1.20 Write $\dfrac{2\sqrt{3}-4}{3\sqrt{3}+5}$ in the form $a+b\sqrt{3}$, where a and b are integers.

SOLUTION

$$\frac{2\sqrt{3}-4}{3\sqrt{3}+5} = \frac{2\sqrt{3}-4}{3\sqrt{3}+5} \times \frac{3\sqrt{3}-5}{3\sqrt{3}-5}$$

$$= \frac{6(\sqrt{3})^2-10\sqrt{3}-12\sqrt{3}+20}{9(\sqrt{3})^2-15\sqrt{3}+15\sqrt{3}-25}$$

$$= \frac{18-22\sqrt{3}+20}{27-25}$$

$$= \frac{38-22\sqrt{3}}{2}$$

$$= 19-11\sqrt{3}$$

EXERCISE 1G   *Do not use a calculator for this exercise.*

1 Simplify the following by rationalising the denominator.

(i) $\dfrac{2\sqrt{3}}{5+\sqrt{2}}$

(ii) $\dfrac{\sqrt{7}}{4-\sqrt{2}}$

(iii) $\dfrac{3\sqrt{3}}{\sqrt{3}+1}$

(iv) $\dfrac{2+\sqrt{2}}{3-\sqrt{2}}$

(v) $\dfrac{\sqrt{7}-3}{1-\sqrt{7}}$

(vi) $\dfrac{10+\sqrt{3}}{\sqrt{3}+\sqrt{2}}$

2 Write $\dfrac{3\sqrt{2}+6}{\sqrt{2}-1}$ in the form $a + b\sqrt{2}$, where a and b are integers.

3 Write $\dfrac{2\sqrt{5}}{4\sqrt{5}+9}$ in the form $c\sqrt{5} + d$, where c and d are integers.

4 Write $\dfrac{1+\sqrt{3}}{3+2\sqrt{3}}$ in the form $p + \dfrac{q}{r}\sqrt{3}$, where p, q and r are integers.

KEY POINTS

Each chapter in this book ends with KEY POINTS, a summary of the essential ideas that you should have understood in the chapter. Chapter 1, however, is fundamental to mathematics and you will need to be confident on all of the techniques covered in this chapter if you are to understand the rest of your course. These are:

1 Simplifying algebraic expressions by
  - collecting like terms
  - removing brackets
  - cancelling by common factors
  - expressing them as a single fraction.

2 When simplifying expressions involving square roots you should
  - make the number under the square root sign as small as possible
  - rationalise the denominator.

Algebra II

If *A* equals success, then the formula is *A* equals *X* plus *Y* plus *Z*, with *X* being work, *Y* play, and *Z* keeping your mouth shut.

Albert Einstein

Factorising

Factorising an expression involves writing the expression as a product using brackets. Simple cases of this were seen in Chapter 1 in Algebra and number. Here, pairs of brackets will be needed. If you have already learnt another method, and use it quickly and accurately, then you should stick with it. With practice, you may be able to factorise some of these expressions *by inspection*.

EXAMPLE 2.1

Factorise $xa + xb + ya + yb$.

SOLUTION

First take out a common factor of each pair of terms.

$$\Rightarrow \quad xa + xb + ya + yb = x(a + b) + y(a + b)$$

Next notice that $(a + b)$ is now a common factor.

$$\Rightarrow \quad x(a + b) + y(a + b) = (a + b)(x + y)$$

In practice this relates to areas of rectangles.

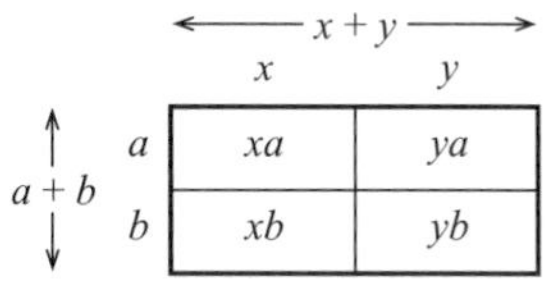

Figure 2.1

The idea illustrated in figure 2.1 can be used to factorise a quadratic expression containing three terms, but first you must decide how to split up the middle term.

Factorise $x^2 + 6x + 8$.

SOLUTION

Splitting the $6x$ as $4x + 2x$ gives

$$x^2 + 6x + 8 = x^2 + 4x + 2x + 8$$
$$= x(x + 4) + 2(x + 4)$$
$$= (x + 4)(x + 2).$$

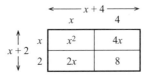

Figure 2.2

The crucial step is knowing how to split up the middle term.

? Is the illustration in figure 2.2 the only possibility?

To answer this question, notice that

- the numbers 4 and 2 have a sum of 6, which is the *coefficient* of x (i.e. the number multiplying x) in $x^2 + 6x + 8$

- the numbers 4 and 2 have a product of 8 which is the *constant term* in $x^2 + 6x + 8$.

There is only one pair of numbers that satisfies both of these conditions.

Factorise $x^2 - 7x - 18$.

SOLUTION

Pairs of numbers with a product of (-18) are:

$$1 \text{ and } (-18)$$
$$2 \text{ and } (-9)$$
$$3 \text{ and } (-6)$$
$$6 \text{ and } (-3)$$
$$9 \text{ and } (-2)$$
$$18 \text{ and } (-1)$$

There is only one pair, 2 and (-9) with a sum of (-7), so use these.

$$x^2 - 7x - 18 = x^2 + 2x - 9x - 18$$
$$= x(x + 2) - 9(x + 2)$$
$$= (x + 2)(x - 9)$$

Notice the sign change due to the $-$ sign in front of the 9.

? Do you get the same factors if the order in which you use the 2 and the (-9) is reversed so that you write it $x^2 - 9x + 2x - 18$?

NOTE Since the pair of numbers that you are looking for is unique, you can stop listing products when you find one that has the correct sum.

EXAMPLE 2.4

Factorise $x^2 - 16$.

SOLUTION

First write

$$x^2 - 16 = x^2 + 0x - 16.$$

Pairs of numbers with a product of (-16) are:

1 and (-16)

2 and (-8)

4 and (-4),…(stop here) ◄———— The only pair with a sum of 0 is 4 and (-4).

$$x^2 - 16 = x^2 + 4x - 4x - 16$$
$$= x(x + 4) - 4(x + 4)$$
$$= (x + 4)(x - 4)$$

This is an example of a special case called *the difference of two squares* since you have

$$x^2 - 4^2 = (x + 4)(x - 4)$$

In general

$$a^2 - b^2 = (a + b)(a - b)$$

Most people recognise this when it occurs and write down the answer straight away.

? Does $x^2 + 16$ factorise to $(x + 4)\ (x + 4)$?

EXAMPLE 2.5

Factorise $4x^2 - 9y^2$.

SOLUTION

$$4x^2 - 9y^2 = (2x)^2 - (3y)^2$$
$$= (2x + 3y)(2x - 3y)$$

EXAMPLE 2.6

Factorise fully $y^5 - 36y^3$.

SOLUTION

The instruction to factorise fully tells you that there is likely to be more than one step involved.

Take out the highest common factor of the two terms

$$y^5 - 36y^3 = y^3(y^2 - 36)$$

Use the difference of two squares

$$y^3(y^2 - 36) = y^3(y + 6)(y - 6)$$

The technique for finding how to split the middle term needs modifying for examples where the expression starts with a multiple of x^2. The difference is that you now multiply the two outside numbers together to give the product you want.

EXAMPLE 2.7

Factorise $2x^2 - 11x + 15$.

SOLUTION

Here the sum is (-11) and the product is $2 \times 15 = 30$.

Options are:

> A negative sum and a positive product means that both numbers are negative.

(-1) and (-30) (-5) and (-6)

(-2) and (-15) (-6) and $(-5) \ldots$ (repeats)

> (-5) and (-6) is the only option.

(-3) and (-10)

$$2x^2 - 11x + 15 = 2x^2 - 5x - 6x + 15$$
$$= x(2x - 5) - 3(2x - 5)$$
$$= (2x - 5)(x - 3)$$

EXAMPLE 2.8

Factorise $3x^2 - 10xy - 8y^2$.

SOLUTION

This expression can be factorised using the same method used in the previous example.

Here the sum is (-10) and the product is $3 \times -8 = -24$.

Option needed is (-12) and 2.

> A negative product means that one number is positive and the other is negative.

$$3x^2 - 10xy - 8y^2 = 3x^2 - 12xy + 2xy - 8y^2$$
$$= 3x(x - 4y) + 2y(x - 4y)$$
$$= (3x + 2y)(x - 4y)$$

1 Factorise the following expressions.

(i) $ab - ac + db - dc$ (ii) $2xy + 2x + wy + w$

(iii) $2pq - 8p - 3rq + 12r$ (iv) $5 - 5m - 2n + 2nm$

2 Factorise the following expressions.

(i) $x^2 + 5x + 6$ (ii) $y^2 - 5y + 4$

(iii) $m^2 - 8m + 16$ (iv) $m^2 - 8m + 15$

(v) $x^2 + 3x - 10$ (vi) $a^2 + 20a + 96$

(vii) $x^2 - x - 6$ (viii) $y^2 - 16y + 48$

(ix) $k^2 + 10k + 24$ (x) $k^2 - 10k - 24$

(xi) $x^2 + 3xy + 2y^2$ (xii) $x^2 + 4xy - 5y^2$

(xiii) $a^2 - ab - 12b^2$ (xiv) $c^2 - 11cd + 24d^2$

3 Each of these is a difference of two squares. Factorise them.

(i) $x^2 - 4$ (ii) $a^2 - 25$

(iii) $9 - p^2$ (iv) $x^2 - y^2$

(v) $t^2 - 64$ (vi) $4x^2 - 1$

(vii) $4x^2 - 9$ (viii) $4x^2 - y^2$

(ix) $16x^2 - 25$ (x) $9a^2 - 4b^2$

(xi) $(2a + 1)^2 - a^2$ (xii) $(3x + 1)^2 - (x + 4)^2$

(xiii) $(2p - 3)^2 - (p + 1)^2$ (xiv) $16 - (5y - 2)^2$

4 Factorise the following expressions.

(i) $2x^2 + 5x + 2$ (ii) $2a^2 + 11a - 21$

(iii) $15p^2 + 2p - 1$ (iv) $3x^2 + 8x - 3$

(v) $5a^2 - 9a - 2$ (vi) $2p^2 + 5p - 3$

(vii) $8x^2 + 10x - 3$ (viii) $2a^2 - 3a - 27$

(ix) $9x^2 - 30x + 25$ (x) $4x^2 + 4x - 15$

(xi) $2x^2 + 5xy + 2y^2$ (xii) $3x^2 + 5xy - 2y^2$

(xiii) $5a^2 - 8ab + 3b^2$ (xiv) $6c^2 + 5cd - 4d^2$

5 Factorise fully the following expressions.

(i) $x^3 - 4x$ (ii) $a^4 - 16a^2$

(iii) $9y^3 - y^5$ (iv) $2x^3 - 2x$

(v) $4p^4 - 9p^2$ (vi) $100x - x^3$

(vii) $18c^3 - 2c$ (viii) $8x^3 - 50xy^2$

(i) Work out 9^2 and $(a^2)^2$.

Remember that $(a^p)^q = a^{pq}$.

(ii) Show that $a^4 - 81$ is the difference of two squares.

(iii) Factorise fully $a^4 - 81$.

Rearranging formulae

The circumference of a circle is given by

$$C = 2\pi r$$

where r is the radius. An equation such as this is often called a formula.

? C is called the *subject* of the formula. Explain what this means.

In some cases, you want to calculate r directly from C. You want r to be the subject of the formula.

EXAMPLE 2.9   Make r the subject of $C = 2\pi r$.

SOLUTION

Divide both sides by $2\pi \Rightarrow \quad \dfrac{C}{2\pi} = r$

$$\Rightarrow \quad r = \dfrac{C}{2\pi}$$

⚠ Notice how the new subject should be on its own on the left-hand side of the new formula.

EXAMPLE 2.10   Make x the subject of this formula.

$$h = \sqrt{(x^2 + y^2)}$$

SOLUTION

Square both sides $\qquad\qquad \Rightarrow \qquad h^2 = x^2 + y^2$

Subtract y^2 from both sides $\qquad \Rightarrow h^2 - y^2 = x^2$

Lead with the x^2 term $\qquad\qquad \Rightarrow \qquad x^2 = h^2 - y^2$

Take the square root of both sides $\Rightarrow \qquad x = \pm\sqrt{(h^2 - y^2)}$

? What would you do with the $\pm$ sign in the case where h is the hypotenuse of a right-angled triangle with x and y as the other two sides?

EXAMPLE 2.11   Make a the subject of this formula.

$$v = u + at$$

SOLUTION

Subtract u from both sides $\Rightarrow \quad v - u = at$

Divide both sides by $t \qquad \Rightarrow \dfrac{v - u}{t} = a$

Write the answer with $a \qquad \Rightarrow \quad a = \dfrac{v - u}{t}$
on the left-hand side

EXERCISE 2B

In this exercise all the equations refer to real situations. How many of them can you recognise?

1 Make   **(i)** u **(ii)** a the subject of $v = u + at$.

2 Make b the subject of $A = \frac{1}{2}bh$.

3 Make l the subject of $P = 2(l + b)$.

4 Make r the subject of $A = \pi r^2$.

5 Make c the subject of $A = \frac{1}{2}(b + c)h$.

6 Make h the subject of $A = \pi r^2 + 2\pi rh$.

7 Make l the subject of $T = \dfrac{\lambda e}{l}$.

8 Make   **(i)** u **(ii)** a the subject of $s = ut + \frac{1}{2}at^2$.

9 Make x the subject of $v^2 = \omega^2(a^2 - x^2)$.

The following examples show how to rearrange a formula when the letter that is to be the subject appears more than once.

EXAMPLE 2.12

Make t the subject of this formula.

$$at = 3(t + 2)$$

SOLUTION

Expand the brackets $\Rightarrow$ $at = 3t + 6$

Collect all the terms in t on one side $\Rightarrow$ $at - 3t = 6$

Factorise $\Rightarrow t(a - 3) = 6$

Divide both sides by $(a - 3)$ $\Rightarrow$ $t = \dfrac{6}{a - 3}$

> The brackets are not needed in the denominator.

EXAMPLE 2.13

Make x the subject of this formula.

$$y = \frac{x + 2}{1 + 3x}$$

SOLUTION

Multiply both sides by $(1 + 3x)$ $\Rightarrow y(1 + 3x) = x + 2$

Expand the brackets $\Rightarrow$ $y + 3xy = x + 2$

Collect all the terms in x on one side with all the other terms on the other side $\Rightarrow$ $3xy - x = 2 - y$

Factorise $\Rightarrow x(3y - 1) = 2 - y$

Divide both sides by $(3y - 1)$ $\Rightarrow$ $x = \dfrac{2 - y}{3y - 1}$

EXERCISE 2C

1 Make m the subject of $3m = x(m + 2)$.

2 Make y the subject of $5y - 2x = xy$.

3 Make b the subject of $4(a + b) = 3(a - b)$.

4 Make h the subject of $S = 2\pi r^2 + 2\pi rh$.

5 Make x the subject of $y = \dfrac{x + 1}{2 + x}$.

6 Make c the subject of $d(2 + c) = 1 - 3c$.

7 (i) Make t the subject of $x = \dfrac{t}{t - 3}$.

   (ii) Hence, or otherwise, work out the value of t when $x = 3$.

8 (i) Make p the subject of $r = \dfrac{3p + 2}{2p + 3}$.

   (ii) Hence, or otherwise, work out the value of p when $r = -1$.

ACTIVITY 2.2

(i) Show that $(x + 3)^2 = x^2 + 6x + 9$.

(ii) Hence, make x the subject of $y = x^2 + 6x + 9$.

ACTIVITY 2.3

(i) Show that $(x - 5)^2 + 4 = x^2 - 10x + 29$.

(ii) Hence, make x the subject of $p = x^2 - 10x + 29$.

Simplifying algebraic fractions

? What is a fraction in arithmetic?
What about in algebra?

Fractions in algebra obey the same rules as fractions in arithmetic.
These cover two pairs of operations: $\times$ and $\div$, and $+$ and $-$.

? When can you cancel fractions in arithmetic?
What about in algebra?
What is a factor in arithmetic?
What about in algebra?

EXAMPLE 2.14

Simplify the following.

(i) $\dfrac{18}{24}$ (ii) $\dfrac{2x+2}{3x+3}$ (iii) $\dfrac{a^2-a-6}{a^2-8a+15}$

SOLUTION

(i) $\dfrac{18}{24} = \dfrac{\overset{1}{\cancel{6}} \times 3}{\underset{4}{\cancel{16}} \times 4} = \dfrac{3}{4}$

(ii) $\dfrac{2x+2}{3x+3} = \dfrac{2\overset{1}{\cancel{(x+1)}}}{3\underset{1}{\cancel{(x+1)}}} = \dfrac{2}{3}$

⚠ ❓ Look at this calculation for (ii). Why is it wrong?

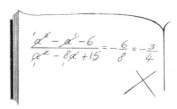

$$\dfrac{2\cancel{x}+2}{3\cancel{x}+3} = \dfrac{4}{6} = \dfrac{2}{3} \quad \times$$

(iii) $\dfrac{a^2-a-6}{a^2-8a+15} = \dfrac{\overset{1}{\cancel{(a-3)}}(a+2)}{\underset{1}{\cancel{(a-3)}}(a-5)} = \dfrac{a+2}{a-5}$

⚠ ❓ Look at this answer to (iii). Why is it wrong?

$$\dfrac{\cancel{a^2}-\cancel{a}-6}{\cancel{a^2}-8\cancel{a}+15} = -\dfrac{6}{8} = -\dfrac{3}{4} \quad \times$$

EXAMPLE 2.15

Simplify the following.

(i) $\dfrac{2}{3} \times \dfrac{9}{14}$ (ii) $\dfrac{3}{4} \div \dfrac{9}{16}$ (iii) $\dfrac{3a^2b}{2c} \times \dfrac{4c^3}{9ab}$ (iv) $\dfrac{4n^2-9}{n+1} \div \dfrac{2n+3}{n^2-1}$

SOLUTION

(i) $\dfrac{2}{3} \times \dfrac{9}{14} = \dfrac{1 \times 3}{1 \times 7} = \dfrac{3}{7}$

(ii) $\dfrac{3}{4} \div \dfrac{9}{16} = \dfrac{3}{4} \times \dfrac{16}{9} = \dfrac{4}{3}$

(iii) $\dfrac{3a^2b}{2c} \times \dfrac{4c^3}{9ab} = \dfrac{2ac^2}{3}$

(iv) $\dfrac{4n^2-9}{n+1} \div \dfrac{2n+3}{n^2-1} = \dfrac{(2n+3)(2n-3)}{\underset{1}{\cancel{(n+1)}}} \times \dfrac{\overset{1}{\cancel{(n+1)}}(n-1)}{\underset{1}{\cancel{(2n+3)}}}$

$$= (2n-3)(n-1)$$

? **⚠** Look at this answer to **(iv)**.
Why is it wrong?

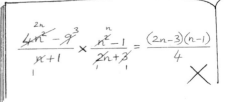

? What is a common denominator?

To add or subtract fractions it is first necessary to find a *common denominator*.

EXAMPLE 2.16

Simplify the following.

(i) $\dfrac{2}{3} + \dfrac{3}{4}$

(ii) $\dfrac{5x}{6} + \dfrac{x}{4}$

(iii) $\dfrac{2}{(x+1)} + \dfrac{5}{(x-1)}$

(iv) $\dfrac{a}{a^2 - 1} - \dfrac{2}{a+1}$

SOLUTION

(i) $\dfrac{2}{3} + \dfrac{3}{4} = \dfrac{8}{12} + \dfrac{9}{12} = \dfrac{17}{12}$

(ii) $\dfrac{5x}{6} + \dfrac{x}{4} = \dfrac{10x}{12} + \dfrac{3x}{12} = \dfrac{13x}{12}$

⚠ Notice that the common denominator is the lowest common multiple of the original denominators.

(iii) $\dfrac{2}{(x+1)} + \dfrac{5}{(x-1)} = \dfrac{2(x-1)}{(x+1)(x-1)} + \dfrac{5(x+1)}{(x+1)(x-1)}$

$= \dfrac{2x - 2 + 5x + 5}{(x+1)(x-1)}$

$= \dfrac{7x + 3}{(x+1)(x-1)}$

(iv) $\dfrac{a}{a^2 - 1} - \dfrac{2}{a+1} = \dfrac{a}{(a-1)(a+1)} - \dfrac{2}{a+1}$

$= \dfrac{a}{(a-1)(a+1)} - \dfrac{2(a-1)}{(a-1)(a+1)}$

$= \dfrac{a - 2a + 2}{(a-1)(a+1)}$

$= \dfrac{2 - a}{(a-1)(a+1)}$

? What is the lowest common multiple of the following?
(a) 6 and 4
(b) $(x^2 - 1)$ and $(x^2 - 4x + 3)$

1 Simplify the following.

(i) $\dfrac{2(x + 3)}{4x + 12}$

(ii) $\dfrac{4x - 8}{(x - 2)(x + 8)}$

(iii) $\dfrac{3(x + y)}{x^2 - y^2}$

(iv) $\dfrac{6x^2 y^3}{9xy^4}$

(v) $\dfrac{2p}{6p - 2p^2}$

(vi) $\dfrac{4ab^3}{10a^3 b}$

(vii) $\dfrac{x^2 - 4x + 3}{2x - 6}$

(viii) $\dfrac{x^2 + xy}{x^2 - y^2}$

(ix) $\dfrac{a + 2}{a^2 - a - 6}$

(x) $\dfrac{3x^2 + 15x}{10x + 2x^2}$

(xi) $\dfrac{9x^2 - 1}{9x + 3}$

(xii) $\dfrac{3x^2 + 3xy}{6xy + 6y^2}$

2 Simplify the following.

(i) $\dfrac{3a}{b^2} \times \dfrac{b^3}{6a}$

(ii) $\dfrac{xy - y^2}{y} \times \dfrac{x}{x - y}$

(iii) $\dfrac{x + 1}{2x} \div \dfrac{4x^2 - 4}{x^2}$

(iv) $\dfrac{3a^2 + a - 2}{2} \div \dfrac{6a^2 - a - 2}{8a + 4}$

(v) $\dfrac{x^2 - 4x + 4}{x^2 - 2x} \times \dfrac{x - 2}{x^2 - 4}$

(vi) $\dfrac{2x - 1}{x + 1} \div \dfrac{2x^2 - x - 1}{x^2 + 3x + 2}$

(vii) $\dfrac{4p^2 + 12}{p - 3} \times \dfrac{p^2 - 9}{p^2 + 3}$

(viii) $\dfrac{3x^2 - 9}{x + 2} \div \dfrac{x^2 - 6x + 9}{x^2 + x - 2}$

3 Simplify the following.

(i) $\dfrac{3a}{5} - \dfrac{a}{4}$

(ii) $\dfrac{5}{3a} - \dfrac{4}{a}$

(iii) $\dfrac{2}{(m + n)} - \dfrac{1}{(m - n)}$

(iv) $\dfrac{4}{p - 2} - \dfrac{3}{2p + 1}$

(v) $\dfrac{2}{a^2 + a} + \dfrac{3}{a^2 - a}$

(vi) $\dfrac{2x}{x - y} + \dfrac{2y}{y - x}$

(vii) $\dfrac{p}{p^2 - 1} - \dfrac{1}{p + 1}$

(viii) $\dfrac{a - b}{a + b} + \dfrac{a + b}{a - b}$

? What is the difference between *simplifying* fractions and *solving* an equation involving fractions?

Solving equations involving fractions

When you solved the equations in Chapter 1, you used mathematical operations such as $+, -, \times$ and $\div$ to find the value of the variable. The same principle applies for solving equations involving fractions.

EXAMPLE 2.17

Solve the following.

$$\frac{x + 2}{6} = \frac{x - 6}{2}$$

SOLUTION

The LCM of 6 and 2 is 6, so multiply by 6.

$$^1 6 \times \frac{(x + 2)}{6_1} = {}^3 6 \times \frac{(x - 6)}{2_1}$$

⚠ ? When you multiply a fraction, you only multiply its numerator (top line). Why?

? How does this help?

$$\begin{aligned} \Rightarrow \quad x + 2 &= 3x - 18 \\ \Rightarrow \quad 20 &= 2x \\ \Rightarrow \quad x &= 10 \end{aligned}$$

EXAMPLE 2.18

Solve the following.

$$\frac{x + 2}{6} + 3 = \frac{x}{5}$$

SOLUTION

The LCM of 6 and 5 is 30, so multiply by 30.

$$^5 30 \times \frac{(x + 2)}{6_1} + 30 \times 3 = {}^6 30 \times \frac{x}{5_1}$$

⚠ ❓   Look at this version of the first stage of the solution.
Why is it wrong?

$$30 \times \frac{(x+2)}{6} + 3 = 30 \times \frac{x}{5}$$ ✗

$\Rightarrow \quad 5x + 10 + 90 = 6x$

$\Rightarrow \qquad\qquad x = 100$

EXAMPLE 2.19   Solve the following.

$$\frac{5}{a+1} - \frac{2a}{a^2 - 1} = \frac{1}{2}$$

SOLUTION

First factorise $(a^2 - 1)$ as $(a+1)(a-1)$.

❓   How does this help?

$$\frac{5}{a+1} - \frac{2a}{(a+1)(a-1)} = \frac{1}{2}$$

Multiply by $2\,(a+1)(a-1)$

$$\Rightarrow \quad 2\,\cancel{(a+1)}^{1}\,(a-1) \times \frac{5}{\cancel{(a+1)}_{1}} - 2\,\cancel{(a+1)}^{1}\,\cancel{(a-1)}^{1} \times \frac{2a}{\cancel{(a+1)}_{1}\,\cancel{(a-1)}_{1}}$$

$$= \cancel{2}^{1}(a+1)(a-1) \times \frac{1}{\cancel{2}_{1}}$$

$\Rightarrow \quad 10(a-1) - 4a = (a+1)(a-1)$

$\Rightarrow \quad 10a - 10 - 4a = a^2 - 1$

$\Rightarrow \qquad\qquad 0 = a^2 - 6a + 9$

$\Rightarrow \qquad\qquad 0 = (a-3)(a-3)$

$\Rightarrow \qquad\qquad a = 3 \text{ (repeated root)}$

EXERCISE 2E   **1** Solve the following equations.

(i) $x - \dfrac{x}{5} = \dfrac{2}{3}$

(ii) $\dfrac{2}{a} - \dfrac{3}{4a} = 2$

(iii) $\dfrac{1}{x} = 3 - \dfrac{2}{x+1}$

(iv) $\dfrac{3x+2}{2} - \dfrac{x-1}{5} = 3$

(v) $\dfrac{2}{3x-1} + \dfrac{1}{x+8} = \dfrac{1}{2}$

(vi) $\dfrac{2}{a} - \dfrac{5}{2a-1} = 0$

(vii) $\dfrac{1}{p} + p + 1 = \dfrac{13}{3}$

(viii) $1 + \dfrac{1}{x-1} = \dfrac{2x}{x+1}$

2 A formula used in physics is

$$\frac{1}{f} = \frac{1}{u} + \frac{1}{v}$$

where f is the focal length of a mirror, u is the distance of the object from the mirror, and v is the distance of the image from the mirror.

For a mirror with focal length 20 cm, find the distance of the object from the mirror when the image is twice as far away from the mirror as is the object.

Quadratic identities

When considering a quadratic expression it will sometimes be useful to write it using $(x - a)^2$, where a is a constant. Some uses of this approach will be seen later in sections on quadratic equations and quadratic graphs.

NOTE The identity symbol ($\equiv$) is used when two expressions are equal for all values of x.

For example $x + x \equiv 2x$.

EXAMPLE 2.20 Work out the values of p and q such that $x^2 - 6x + 2 \equiv (x - p)^2 + q$.

SOLUTION

Expand the bracket $x^2 - 6x + 2 \equiv x^2 - 2px + p^2 + q$

Equate coefficients of x $\qquad -6 = -2p$

$$3 = p$$

$$(x - p)^2 = (x - p)(x - p)$$
$$= x^2 - px - px + p^2$$
$$= x^2 - 2px + p^2$$

Equate constants $\qquad\qquad 2 = p^2 + q$

$$2 = 9 + q$$

$$-7 = q$$

Equate coefficients of x means making equal the number of x on each side of the identity.

$$p = 3 \text{ and } q = -7$$

EXAMPLE 2.21 Work out the values of a, b and c such that $2x^2 + bx + 5 \equiv a(x - 3)^2 + c$.

SOLUTION

Expand the bracket $2x^2 + bx + 5 \equiv a(x^2 - 6x + 9) + c$

$$\equiv ax^2 - 6ax + 9a + c$$

Equate coefficients of x^2 $\qquad\qquad 2 = a$

Equate coefficients of x $\qquad\qquad b = -6a$

$$b = -12$$

Equate constants $\qquad\qquad\qquad 5 = 9a + c$

$$5 = 18 + c$$

$$-13 = c$$

$$a = 2, b = -12 \text{ and } c = -13.$$

EXAMPLE 2.22

Work out the values of a, b and c such that $3x^2 + 5x - 1 \equiv a(x + b)^2 + c$.

SOLUTION

Expand the bracket

$$3x^2 + 5x - 1 \equiv a(x^2 + 2bx + b^2) + c$$
$$\equiv ax^2 + 2abx + ab^2 + c$$

Equate coefficients of x^2

$$3 = a$$

Equate coefficients of x

$$5 = 2ab$$
$$5 = 6b$$
$$\frac{5}{6} = b$$

Equate constants

$$-1 = ab^2 + c$$

$$-1 = 3 \times \left(\frac{5}{6}\right)^2 + c$$

$$-1 = 3 \times \frac{25}{36} + c$$

$$-1 = \frac{25}{12} + c$$

$$-\frac{37}{12} = c$$

$$a = 3, \quad b = \frac{5}{6} \quad \text{and} \quad c = -\frac{37}{12}$$

EXERCISE 2F

1 Work out the values of a and b such that $x^2 + 8x + 10 \equiv (x + a)^2 + b$.

2 Work out the values of c and d such that $x^2 - cx + 7 \equiv (x - 1)^2 + d$.

3 Work out the values of p and q such that $x^2 - 12x - 4 \equiv (x - p)^2 + q$.

4 Work out the values of a and b such that $x^2 + 5x - 2 \equiv (x + a)^2 + b$.

5 Work out the values of p and q such that $5 + 4x - x^2 \equiv p - (x - q)^2$.

6 Work out the values of c and d such that $2 - x - x^2 \equiv c - (x + d)^2$.

7 Work out the values of a, b and c such that $2x^2 + bx + 5 \equiv a(x + 2)^2 + c$.

8 Work out the values of a, b and c such that $5x^2 + 30x + 10 \equiv a(x + b)^2 + c$.

9 Work out the values of p, q and r such that $3x^2 - 12x + 14 \equiv p(x + q)^2 + r$.

10 Work out the values of a, b and c such that $3x^2 - bx + 1 \equiv a(x - 4)^2 + c$.

11 Work out the values of a, b and c such that $6 + bx - 2x^2 \equiv c - a(x - 1)^2$.

12 Work out the values of p, q and r such that $5 - 12x - 2x^2 \equiv p - q(x + r)^2$.

13 (i) Work out the values of a and b such that $x^2 - 8x + 20 \equiv (x - a)^2 + b$.

   (ii) Hence, make x the subject of $y = x^2 - 8x + 20$.

14 (i) Work out the values of p, q and r such that $3x^2 + 6x + 1 \equiv p(x + q)^2 + r$.

   (ii) Hence, make x the subject of $y = 3x^2 + 6x + 1$.

KEY POINTS

1 Factorising quadratic expressions.
2 Changing the subject of an equation.
3 When simplifying an algebraic fraction involving addition or subtraction you need to find a common denominator.
4 When solving an equation involving fractions you start by multiplying through by the LCM of all the denominators to eliminate the fractions.
5 Quadratic expressions can be written in the form $a(x - b)^2 + c$.

Algebra III

Others have done it before me. I can, too.

Corporal John Faunce (American soldier)

Function notation

Here is a flow chart.

Figure 3.1

For an input of 5, $\quad 5 \to 25 \to 27 \quad$ the output is 27.

For an input of -2, $\quad -2 \to 4 \to 6 \quad$ the output is 6.

For an input of x, $\quad x \to x^2 \to x^2 + 2 \quad$ the output is $x^2 + 2$.

This leads to the use of function notation $\quad f(x) = x^2 + 2$

For an input of 5, $\quad f(5) = 5^2 + 2$
$$= 25 + 2$$
$$= 27$$

For an input of -2, $\quad f(-2) = (-2)^2 + 2$
$$= 4 + 2$$
$$= 6$$

EXAMPLE 3.1

$f(x) = 10 - 4x$ and $g(x) = x^3$

(i) Work out $f(-1)$ and $g\left(\dfrac{1}{2}\right)$. **(ii)** Work out an expression for $f(3x)$.

(iii) Solve $g(x) = -64$.

SOLUTION

(i) $f(-1) = 10 - 4(-1)$
$$= 10 + 4$$
$$= 14$$

$$g\left(\frac{1}{2}\right) = \left(\frac{1}{2}\right)^3$$

$$= \frac{1}{2} \times \frac{1}{2} \times \frac{1}{2}$$

$$= \frac{1}{8}$$

35

(ii) $f(3x) = 10 - 4(3x)$

$\qquad = 10 - 12x$

(iii) $g(x) = -64$

$\qquad x^3 = -64$

$\qquad x = \sqrt[3]{-64}$

$\qquad = -4$

EXERCISE 3A

1 $f(x) = 2x - 1$ and $g(x) = x^2 + 2x$

Work out

(i) $f(-4)$ **(ii)** $f(0.6)$ **(iii)** $g(3)$ **(iv)** $g(-1)$ **(v)** $f(0)$ **(vi)** $g(0)$.

2 $f(x) = 3x^2$ and $g(x) = \dfrac{6}{x}$

Work out

(i) $f(2)$ **(ii)** $f(-5)$ **(iii)** $g(2)$ **(iv)** $g(-1.5)$ **(v)** $g\left(\dfrac{1}{2}\right)$ **(vi)** $g\left(-\dfrac{2}{3}\right)$.

3 $f(x) = 8 - 3x$ and $g(x) = 4(x + 3)$.

Solve

(i) $f(x) = 0$ **(ii)** $g(x) = 20$ **(iii)** $f(x) = g(x)$.

4 $h(x) = 3x - 2$

Work out expressions, giving answers in the simplest form, for

(i) $h(2x)$ **(ii)** $h(x + 1)$ **(iii)** $h(x^2)$.

5 $f(x) = x^2 + 5x - 1$

Work out expressions, giving answers in the simplest form, for

(i) $f(3x)$ **(ii)** $f(x - 2)$.

6 $g(x) = \dfrac{x + 6}{2x}$

(i) Work out $g(3)$. **(ii)** Solve $g(x) = 3$. **(ii)** Solve $g(2x) = 1$.

Domain and range of a function

Domain of f(x)

The set of input values is the domain of $f(x)$.

When a function is defined it will include a domain. If a domain is not stated it can be assumed that the domain is all real values of x.

$f(x) = 2x - 3 \quad x > 1$ $\qquad$ The domain is $x > 1$.

$g(x) = \dfrac{1}{x} \qquad x \neq 0$ $\qquad$ The domain is all real values of x apart from 0.

? Why is it not possible for $x = 0$ to be in the domain of $g(x) = \dfrac{1}{x}$?

Range of f(x)

The set of output values is the range of f(x).

The range will always depend on the domain.

The range is given as a set of f(x) values as shown in the following examples.

EXAMPLE 3.2 $f(x) = x^2$ for all real values of x.

Work out the range of f(x).

SOLUTION

The value of x^2 is positive or zero for all real values of x.

Range is $f(x) \geqslant 0$.

NOTE Domain and range can be seen on a sketch graph of $f(x) = x^2$.

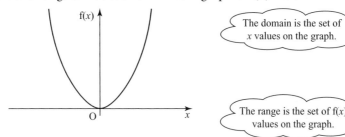

The domain is the set of x values on the graph.

The range is the set of f(x) values on the graph.

Figure 3.2

ACTIVITY 3.1   Sketch the graph of $g(x) = \dfrac{1}{x} \, x \neq 0$.

Use the graph to work out the range of g(x).

EXAMPLE 3.3 $f(x) = 6 - 4x$ $-2 \leqslant x \leqslant 3$

Work out the range of f(x).

SOLUTION

A sketch of $f(x) = 6 - 4x$ for the given domain is

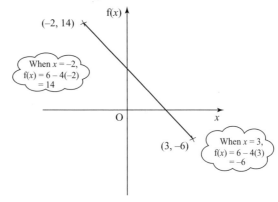

$(-2, 14)$

When $x = -2$,
$f(x) = 6 - 4(-2)$
$= 14$

$(3, -6)$

When $x = 3$,
$f(x) = 6 - 4(3)$
$= -6$

Figure 3.3

Range is $-6 \leqslant f(x) \leqslant 14$.

1 Work out the range of f(x) in each of the following.

(i)   f(x) = 3x $x < 2$

(ii)   f(x) = x + 4 $x \geqslant 1$

(iii)   f(x) = 2x + 4 $x \geqslant -1$

(iv)   f(x) = 10 − x $x \leqslant 4$

(v)   f(x) = 2x $1 \leqslant x \leqslant 5$

(vi)   f(x) = x − 3 $0 < x < 10$

(vii)   f(x) = 5 − 2x $x \geqslant -3$

(viii)   f(x) = 3 − 4x $-2 \leqslant x \leqslant 3$

2 Work out the range of f(x) in each of the following.

(i)   f(x) = x^2 $-2 \leqslant x \leqslant 2$

(ii)   f(x) = x^2 $0 < x < 4$

(iii)   f(x) = x^3 $x \geqslant 0$

(iv)   f(x) = x^3 $-1 \leqslant x \leqslant 3$

3 In each of the following, a sketch of a function, f(x), is shown.

Write down the domain and the range for f(x).

(i)

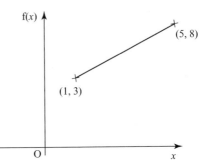

(ii)

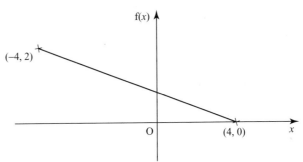

(iii)

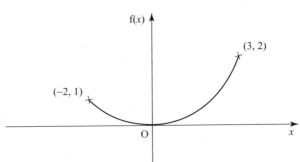

Graphs of functions

Drawing a graph

If asked to draw a graph you should use graph paper. The axes should be numbered. The graph should be drawn passing through the correct points.

Here is a drawing of the graph of $y = 2x + 1$ for values of x from -2 to 4.

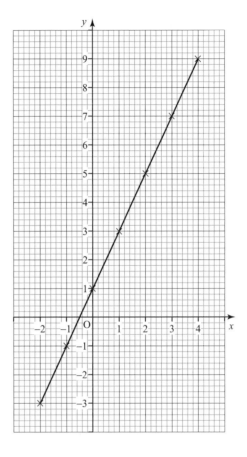

Figure 3.4

Sketching a graph

If asked to sketch a graph you should *not* use graph paper. Axes should be drawn and only certain numbers need to be marked on the axes (e.g. points where the graph crosses the axes).

The correct shape of the graph should be shown and it should be in the correct position relative to the axes.

This means that the main features of the graph are shown although there is no requirement to plot points accurately.

Here is a sketch of the graph of $y = 2x + 1$.

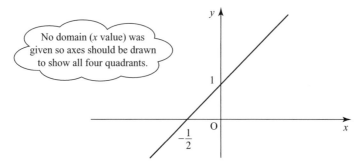

No domain (x value) was given so axes should be drawn to show all four quadrants.

Figure 3.5

Graphs of linear functions

The gradient of a line

In mathematics the word *line* refers to a straight line. The slope of a line is measured by its *gradient* and the letter m is often used to represent this.

? What information do you need to have in order to fix the position of a line?

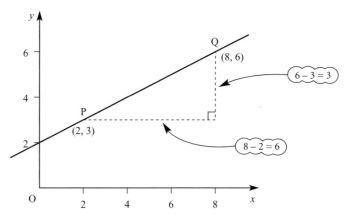

Figure 3.6

$$\text{gradient} = \frac{\text{change in } y \text{ co-ordinate from P to Q}}{\text{change in } x \text{ co-ordinate from P to Q}}$$

In figure 3.6, gradient $= \dfrac{6-3}{8-2} = \dfrac{3}{6} = \dfrac{1}{2}$.

ACTIVITY 3.2

On each line in figure 3.7, take any two points and use them to calculate the gradient of the line.

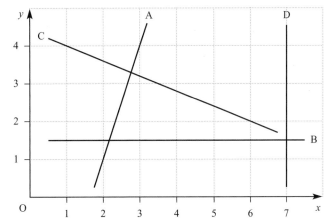

Figure 3.7

You can generalise the previous activity to find the gradient m of the line joining (x_1, y_1) to (x_2, y_2).

$$m = \frac{y_2 - y_1}{x_2 - x_1}$$

? Does it matter which point you call (x_1, y_1) and which (x_2, y_2)?

You can easily tell by looking at a line if its gradient is positive, negative, zero or infinite.

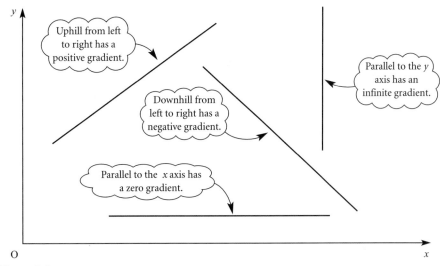

Figure 3.8

The equation of a straight line

EXAMPLE 3.4

Find the equation of the straight line with gradient 2 through the point with co-ordinates $(0, 1)$.

SOLUTION

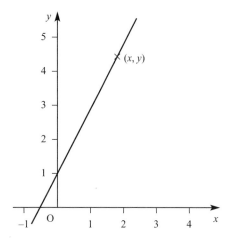

Figure 3.9

Take a general point (x, y) on the line, as shown in figure 3.9. The gradient of the line joining $(0, 1)$ to (x, y) is given by

$$\text{gradient} = \frac{y - 1}{x - 0} = \frac{y - 1}{x}.$$

Since you are given that the gradient of the line is 2, you have

$$\frac{y - 1}{x} = 2 \implies y = 2x + 1.$$

Since (x, y) is a general point on the line, this holds for any point on the line and is therefore the equation of the line.

This example can be generalised to give the result that the equation of the line with gradient m cutting the y axis at the point $(0, c)$ is

$$\frac{y - c}{x - 0} = m$$

$$\implies \quad y = mx + c.$$

This is a well known standard form for the equation of a straight line.

Drawing or sketching a line given its equation

There are several standard forms for the equation of a straight line. When you need to draw or sketch a line, look at its equation and see if it fits one of these.

Equations of the form $x = a$

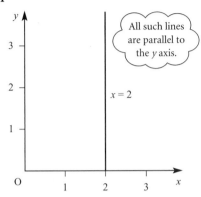

All such lines are parallel to the y axis.

$x = 2$

Equations of the form $y = b$

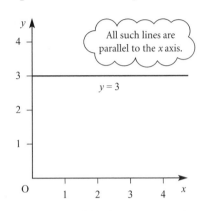

All such lines are parallel to the x axis.

$y = 3$

Equations of the form $y = mx$

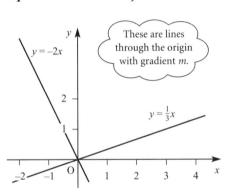

These are lines through the origin with gradient m.

$y = -2x$

$y = \frac{1}{3}x$

Equations of the form $y = mx + c$

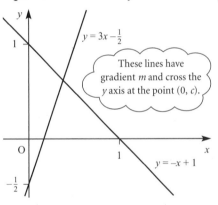

$y = 3x - \frac{1}{2}$

These lines have gradient m and cross the y axis at the point $(0, c)$.

$y = -x + 1$

Equations of the form $px + qy + r = 0$

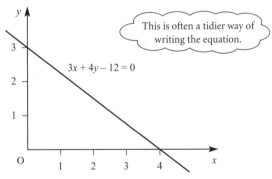

This is often a tidier way of writing the equation.

$3x + 4y - 12 = 0$

Figure 3.10

Graphs of equations in this form will usually be sketched by finding the co-ordinates of the points where the line crosses the x and y axes.

? (i) Rearrange the equation $3x + 4y - 12 = 0$ into the form $\dfrac{x}{a} + \dfrac{y}{b} = 1$.

(ii) What are the values of a and b?

(iii) What do these numbers represent?

EXAMPLE 3.5

Sketch the lines $y = -2$, $y = 3x - 2$ and $x + 3y - 9 = 0$ on the same axes.

SOLUTION

The line $y = -2$ is parallel to the x axis and passes through $(0, -2)$.
The line $y = 3x - 2$ has gradient 3 and passes through $(0, -2)$.
To sketch the line $x + 3y - 9 = 0$ find two points on it.

$$x = 0 \implies 3y - 9 = 0 \implies y = 3 \qquad (0, 3) \text{ is on the line}$$

$$y = 0 \implies x - 9 = 0 \implies x = 9 \qquad (9, 0) \text{ is on the line}$$

Figure 3.11 shows the triangle ABC formed by the three lines.

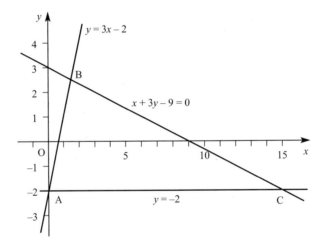

Figure 3.11

EXERCISE 3C

1 For each of the following pairs of points, A and B, calculate the gradient of the line AB.

(i)   A(4, 3)   B(8, 11)   (ii)   A(3, 4)   B(0, 13)
(iii) A(5, 3)   B(10, -8)   (iv)   A(-6, -14)   B(1, 7)
(v)   A(6, 0)   B(8, 15)   (vi)   A(-2, -4)   B(3, 9)
(vii) A(-3, -6) B(2, -7)   (viii) A(4, 7)   B(7, -4)

2 Sketch these lines.

(i)	$x = 5$	**(ii)**	$y = -3$	**(iii)**	$y = 4x$
(iv)	$y = -3x$	**(v)**	$y = 2x + 3$	**(vi)**	$y = -x + 2$
(vii)	$y = \frac{1}{2}x - 1$	**(viii)**	$y = -2x - 1$	**(ix)**	$y = \frac{1}{3}x + \frac{2}{3}$
(x)	$y = 3x - 2$	**(xi)**	$y = 2x - 3$	**(xii)**	$x + y - 1 = 0$
(xiii)	$2x + y - 4 = 0$	**(xiv)**	$x - 3y + 6 = 0$	**(xv)**	$2x - 3y = 12$
(xvi)	$y - 3x + 9 = 0$	**(xvii)**	$3x = 2y - 6$	**(xviii)**	$5x - 4y + 3 = 0$

If you have access to a graphic calculator, you can use it to check your results.

Finding the equation of a line

The simplest way of finding the equation of a straight line depends on what information you have been given.

Given the gradient, *m*, and the co-ordinates (x_1, y_1) of one point on the line

Take the general point (x, y) on the line, as shown in figure 3.12.

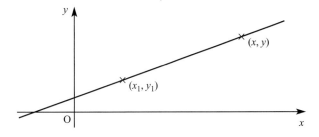

Figure 3.12

The gradient *m* of the line joining (x_1, y_1) to (x, y) is given by

$$m = \frac{y - y_1}{x - x_1}$$

$$\Rightarrow y - y_1 = m(x - x_1).$$

This is a standard result, and one you will find very useful.

EXAMPLE 3.6

Find the equation of the line with gradient 2 which passes through the point $(-1, 3)$.

SOLUTION

Using $y - y_1 = m(x - x_1)$

$$\Rightarrow y - 3 = 2(x - (-1))$$
$$\Rightarrow y - 3 = 2x + 2$$
$$\Rightarrow y = 2x + 5.$$

In the formula

$$y - y_1 = m(x - x_1)$$

two positions of the point (x_1, y_1) lead to results you have met already.

45

(x_1, y_1) is at $(0, 0)$ (x_1, y_1) is at $(0, c)$

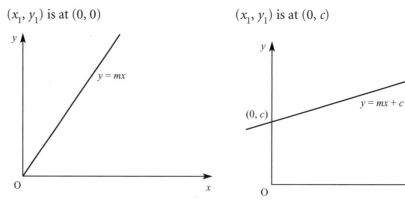

Figure 3.13

Given two points (x_1, y_1) and (x_2, y_2)

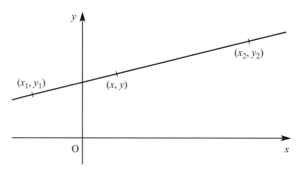

Figure 3.14

The two points are used to find the gradient

$$m = \frac{y_2 - y_1}{x_2 - x_1}.$$

This value is then substituted in the equation

$$y - y_1 = m(x - x_1).$$

This gives

$$y - y_1 = \frac{y_2 - y_1}{x_2 - x_1}(x - x_1).$$

Rearranging this gives

$$\frac{y - y_1}{y_2 - y_1} = \frac{x - x_1}{x_2 - x_1} \quad \text{or}$$

$$\frac{y - y_1}{x - x_1} = \frac{y_2 - y_1}{x_2 - x_1}.$$

EXAMPLE 3.7

Find the equation of the line joining $(-1, 4)$ to $(2, -3)$.

SOLUTION

Let (x_1, y_1) be $(-1, 4)$ and (x_2, y_2) be $(2, -3)$.

Substituting these values in $\dfrac{y - y_1}{y_2 - y_1} = \dfrac{x - x_1}{x_2 - x_1}$

gives $\qquad \dfrac{y - 4}{(-3) - 4} = \dfrac{x - (-1)}{2 - (-1)}$

$\Rightarrow \qquad \dfrac{y - 4}{(-7)} = \dfrac{x + 1}{3}$

$\Rightarrow \qquad 3(y - 4) = (-7)(x + 1)$

$\Rightarrow \qquad 7x + 3y - 5 = 0.$

Applying the different techniques

The following examples illustrate the different techniques, and show how these can be used to solve a practical problem.

EXAMPLE 3.8

Find the equations of the lines **(a)** to **(e)** in figure 3.15.

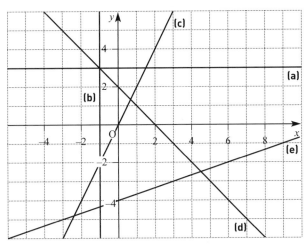

Figure 3.15

SOLUTION

Line **(a)** is parallel to the x axis and passes though $(0, 3)$

$\qquad \Rightarrow \qquad$ equation of **(a)** is $y = 3$.

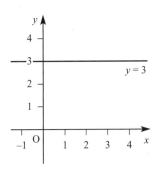

Line **(b)** is parallel to the y axis and passes through $(-1, 0)$

$\Rightarrow$ equation of **(b)** is $x = -1$.

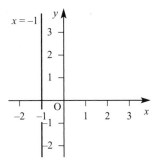

Line **(c)** passes through $(0, 0)$ and has gradient 2

$\Rightarrow$ equation of **(c)** is $y = 2x$.

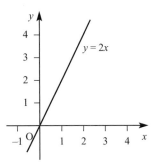

Line **(d)** passes through $(0, 2)$ and has gradient (-1)

$\Rightarrow$ equation of **(d)** is $y = -x + 2$.

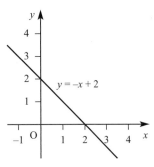

Line **(e)** passes through $(0, -4)$ and has gradient $\frac{1}{3}$

$\Rightarrow$ equation of **(e)** is $y = \frac{1}{3}x - 4$.

This can be rearranged to give

$x - 3y - 12 = 0$.

Figure 3.16

EXERCISE 3D

1 Find the equations of the lines **(a)** – **(j)** in these diagrams.

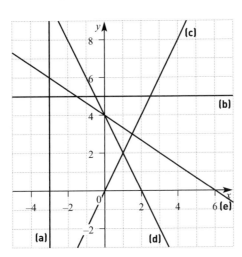

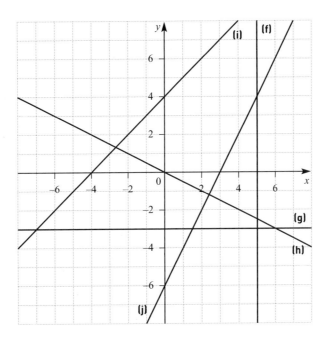

2 Find the equations of these lines.
  (i)   Gradient 3 and passing through $(2, -1)$.
  (ii) Gradient 2 and passing through $(0, 0)$.
  (iii) Gradient 3 and passing through $(2, -7)$.
  (iv) Gradient 4 and passing through $(4, 0)$.
  (v)   Gradient $-\frac{3}{2}$ and passing through $(1, -2)$.
  (vi) Gradient $-\frac{1}{2}$ and passing through $(0, 6)$.

3 Find the equation of the line AB in each of these cases.

    (i)   A(2, 0)   B(3, 1)

    (ii)   A(3, −1)   B(0, 4)

    (iii) A(2, −3)   B(3, −2)

    (iv) A(−1, 3)   B(4, 0)

    (v)   A(3, −5)   B(10, −6)

    (vi) A(−1, −2)   B(−4, −8)

Graphs of quadratic functions

ACTIVITY 3.3

Copy and complete the table of values and draw the graph of $y = x^2 - 5$ for values of x from −3 to 4.

x	−3	−2	−1	0	1	2	3	4
y	4			−5		−1	4	

ACTIVITY 3.4

Copy and complete the table of values and draw the graph of $y = 4x - x^2$ for values of x from −2 to 6.

x	−2	−1	0	1	2	3	4	5	6
y	−12	−5			4				−12

The shape of the graph of $y = ax^2 + bx + c$ is a parabola.

The sign of the coefficient of x^2 determines the direction of the curve.

$a > 0$

P is the lowest point on the graph.
P is the vertex.

Figure 3.17

$a < 0$

Q is the highest point on the graph.
Q is the vertex.

Figure 3.18

Symmetry

Quadratic graphs will have a line of symmetry when drawn using an appropriate domain.

Here is the graph of $y = x^2 - 2x - 3$ for domain $-2 \leqslant x \leqslant 4$.

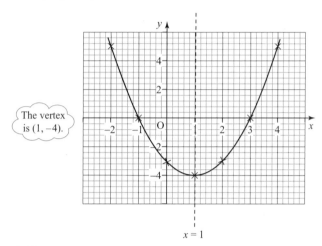

The vertex is $(1, -4)$.

Figure 3.19

The line of symmetry has equation $x = 1$ and passes through the vertex.

Here is a sketch of the graph of $y = 9 - x^2$ for domain $-4 \leqslant x \leqslant 4$.

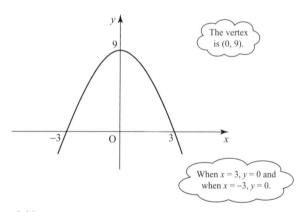

The vertex is $(0, 9)$.

When $x = 3$, $y = 0$ and when $x = -3$, $y = 0$.

Figure 3.20

The line of symmetry is the y axis and passes through the vertex.

The following example shows how completing the square can be used to find the vertex and the line of symmetry of a quadratic graph.

EXAMPLE 3.9

For the graph of $y = x^2 + 6x + 11$, state

(i) the vertex

(ii) the equation of the line of symmetry

(iii) the co-ordinates of the point where the graph intersects the y axis.

Sketch the graph.

SOLUTION

Write the quadratic expression in the form $(x + a)^2 + b$.

$$x^2 + 6x + 11 \equiv (x + a)^2 + b$$
$$\equiv x^2 + 2ax + a^2 + b$$

Equate coefficients of x $6 = 2a$
                              $3 = a$

> Equate coefficients of x means making equal the number of x on each side of the identity.

Equate constants $11 = a^2 + b$
                         $11 = 9 + b$
                         $2 = b$

$$y = x^2 + 6x + 11$$
$$= (x + 3)^2 + 2$$

> $(x + 3)^2$ is always positive or zero. The lowest value of $(x + 3)^2 + 2$ is 2 and this occurs when $x = -3$.

(i) The vertex is $(-3, 2)$.

(ii) The equation of the line of symmetry is $x = -3$.

(iii) When $x = 0$, $y = 11$, co-ordinates of the point are $(0, 11)$.

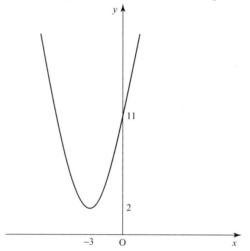

Figure 3.21

1 Which equation fits each of the quadratic curves **(a)** and **(b)**?
Choose from the equations shown.

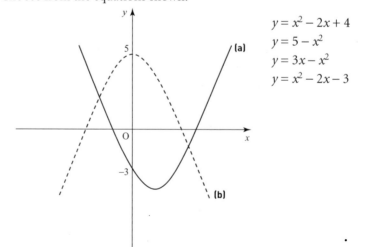

$$y = x^2 - 2x + 4$$
$$y = 5 - x^2$$
$$y = 3x - x^2$$
$$y = x^2 - 2x - 3$$

2 Which equation fits each of the quadratic curves **(a)** and **(b)**?
Choose from the equations shown.

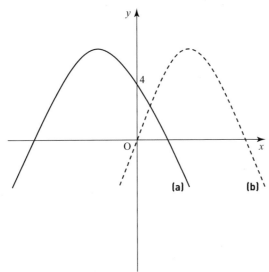

$$y = x^2 + 3x + 4$$
$$y = 4 - 7x - 2x^2$$
$$y = x^2 + 2x$$
$$y = 4x - x^2$$

3 For the graph of $y = x^2 + 2x + 3$, work out
(i)   the vertex
(ii)   the equation of the line of symmetry
(iii) the co-ordinates of the point where the graph intersects the y axis.
Sketch the graph.

4 For the graph of $y = x^2 - 4x + 5$, work out
(i)   the vertex
(ii)   the equation of the line of symmetry
(iii) the co-ordinates of the point where the graph intersects the y axis.
Sketch the graph.

5 For the graph of $y = x^2 - 6x + 7$, work out
(i)   the vertex
(ii)   the equation of the line of symmetry
(iii) the co-ordinates of the point where the graph intersects the y axis.
Sketch the graph.

6 (i)   Show that $6 - 4x - x^2 = 10 - (x + 2)^2$.
(ii)   Write down the vertex of the graph of $y = 6 - 4x - x^2$.
(iii) Write down the equation of the line of symmetry of $y = 6 - 4x - x^2$.
(iv)   Write down the co-ordinates of the point where the graph $y = 6 - 4x - x^2$
         intersects the y axis.
(v)   Sketch the graph of $y = 6 - 4x - x^2$.

Graphs of functions with up to three parts to their domains

A function may be defined with more than one part to its domain.

Here are two examples.

$$f(x) = x + 1 \qquad -2 \leqslant x < 1$$
$$ = 2 \qquad\quad 1 \leqslant x \leqslant 4$$

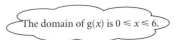 The domain of f(x) is $-2 \leqslant x \leqslant 4$.

$$g(x) = 3 \qquad\qquad 0 \leqslant x < 2$$
$$ = 7 - 2x \qquad 2 \leqslant x < 5$$
$$ = 3x + 12 \qquad 5 \leqslant x \leqslant 6$$

The domain of g(x) is $0 \leqslant x \leqslant 6$.

EXAMPLE 3.10

Draw the graph of $y = $ f(x) where

$$f(x) = 4 \qquad\quad -4 \leqslant x < -2$$
$$ = x^2 \qquad\quad -2 \leqslant x < 2$$
$$ = 8 - 2x \qquad 2 \leqslant x \leqslant 4$$

SOLUTION

The graph is drawn for each part of the given domain.

$y = 4$ is a horizontal line.
$y = x^2$ is a quadratic curve.
$y = 8 - 2x$ is a straight line with gradient -2.

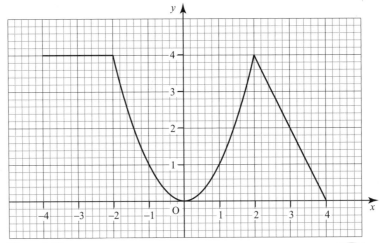

Figure 3.22

Because the three parts do not have any gaps between them, the graph is continuous.

Not all graphs are continuous.

EXAMPLE 3.11 Here is the graph of $y = f(x)$.

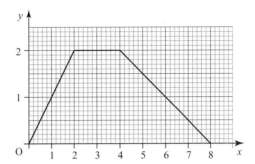

Figure 3.23

(i) Define $f(x)$, stating clearly the domain for each part.

(ii) State the range of $f(x)$.

SOLUTION

(i) For $0 \leqslant x < 2$ $\qquad$ gradient $= \dfrac{2 - 0}{2 - 0}$

$\qquad\qquad\qquad\qquad\qquad = 1$

$\qquad\qquad$ Line passes through $(0, 0)$ so $\qquad y = x$

$\quad$ For $2 \leqslant x < 4$ $\qquad$ horizontal line so $\qquad y = 2$

$\quad$ For $4 \leqslant x \leqslant 8$ $\qquad$ gradient $= \dfrac{2 - 0}{4 - 8}$

$\qquad\qquad\qquad\qquad\qquad = \dfrac{2}{-4}$

$\qquad\qquad\qquad\qquad\qquad = -\dfrac{1}{2}$

$\qquad\qquad$ Line passes through $(8, 0)$ so $\qquad y - 0 = -\dfrac{1}{2}(x - 8)$

$\qquad\qquad\qquad\qquad\qquad\qquad\qquad\qquad y = -\dfrac{1}{2}x + 4$

$\quad f(x) = x \qquad\qquad\qquad 0 \leqslant x < 2$

$\qquad = 2 \qquad\qquad\qquad 2 \leqslant x < 4$

$\qquad = -\dfrac{1}{2}x + 4 \qquad\quad 4 \leqslant x \leqslant 8$

> No x value should be included more than once in the domain.

(ii) The range is obtained by looking at the y values on the graph.

$\qquad 0 \leqslant f(x) \leqslant 2$

1 Draw the graph of $y = f(x)$ where
$$f(x) = 2 \qquad -2 \leqslant x < 1$$
$$= 2x \qquad 1 \leqslant x \leqslant 3$$

2 Draw the graph of $y = f(x)$ where
$$f(x) = x^2 \qquad 0 \leqslant x < 3$$
$$= 9 \qquad 3 \leqslant x \leqslant 5$$

3 Draw the graph of $y = g(x)$ where
$$g(x) = x + 3 \qquad -3 \leqslant x < 0$$
$$= 3 - x \qquad 0 \leqslant x \leqslant 3$$

4 Draw the graph of $y = f(x)$ where
$$f(x) = 3x - 1 \qquad -2 \leqslant x < 1$$
$$= 3 - x \qquad 1 \leqslant x < 4$$
$$= -1 \qquad 4 \leqslant x \leqslant 6$$

5 Draw the graph of $y = f(x)$ where
$$f(x) = 2x \qquad -2 \leqslant x < 0$$
$$= \frac{1}{2}x \qquad 0 \leqslant x < 2$$
$$= 5 - 2x \qquad 2 \leqslant x \leqslant 4$$

6 Draw the graph of $y = g(x)$ where
$$g(x) = -4 \qquad -3 \leqslant x < -2$$
$$= -x^2 \qquad -2 \leqslant x < 2$$
$$= 3x - 10 \qquad 2 \leqslant x \leqslant 4$$

7 Here is the graph of $y = f(x)$.

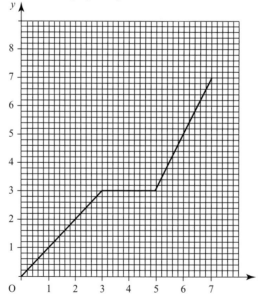

(i) Define $f(x)$, stating clearly the domain for each part.

(ii) State the range of $f(x)$.

(iii) Solve $f(x) = 5$.

8 Here is the graph of $y = f(x)$.

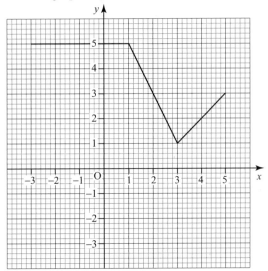

(i) Define $f(x)$, stating clearly the domain for each part.
(ii) State the range of $f(x)$.
(iii) Solve $f(x) = 3$.

9 The graph of $y = f(x)$ is shown.

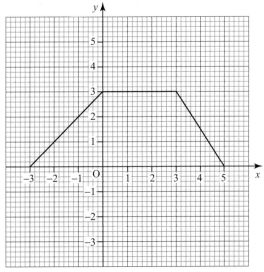

(i) Define $f(x)$, stating clearly the domain for each part.
(ii) Work out the area between the graph and the x axis.

10 The graph of $y = g(x)$ is shown.

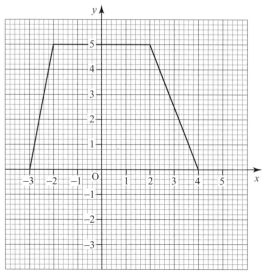

(i) Define $g(x)$, stating clearly the domain for each part.

(ii) Work out the area between the graph and the x axis.

KEY POINTS

1 A function maps an input, x, to an output, $f(x)$.

2 The set of input values is the domain of $f(x)$.

The set of output values is the range of $f(x)$.

3 To draw a graph, use graph paper.

4 To sketch a graph, do not use graph paper.

5 The gradient of the straight line joining the points (x_1, y_1) and (x_2, y_2) is given by

$$\text{gradient} = \frac{y_2 - y_1}{x_2 - x_1}$$

6 The equation of a straight line may take any of these forms.
- line parallel to the y axis: $x = a$
- line parallel to the x axis: $y = b$
- line through the origin with gradient m: $y = mx$
- line through $(0, c)$ with gradient m: $y = mx + c$
- line through (x_1, y_1) with gradient m: $y - y_1 = m(x - x_1)$
- line through (x_1, y_1) and (x_2, y_2):

$$\frac{y - y_1}{y_2 - y_1} = \frac{x - x_1}{x_2 - x_1} \quad \text{or} \quad \frac{y - y_1}{x - x_1} = \frac{y_2 - y_1}{x_2 - x_1}$$

7 The shape of a quadratic graph is a parabola.

4 Algebra IV

Cogito ergo sum. (I think, therefore I am.)

René Descartes (1596–1650)

Quadratic equations

Solving a quadratic equation by factorising

EXAMPLE 4.1

Solve $x^2 + 3x - 18 = 0$.

SOLUTION

$$x^2 + 3x - 18 = 0$$
$$\Rightarrow \quad x^2 + 6x - 3x - 18 = 0$$
$$\Rightarrow x(x + 6) - 3(x + 6) = 0$$
$$\Rightarrow \quad (x + 6)(x - 3) = 0$$

The only way this expression can ever equal zero is if one of the brackets equals zero

$\Rightarrow$ either $(x + 6) = 0$ or $(x - 3) = 0$
$\Rightarrow x = -6$ or $x = 3$

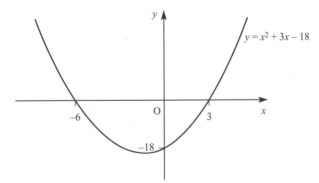

Figure 4.1

NOTE The *solution* of the equation is the *pair* of values $x = -6$ or $x = 3$. The *roots* of the equation are the *individual* values $x = -6$ and $x = 3$.

⚠ Before starting to solve a quadratic equation, you must make sure that all terms of the quadratic expression are on the left-hand side of the equation.

EXAMPLE 4.2 Solve $8x^2 + 10x = 3$.

SOLUTION

First, rewrite the equation as

Sum of $+10$ and product $8 \times (-3) = -24$ gives (12) and (-2).

$$8x^2 + 10x - 3 = 0.$$
$$\Rightarrow \quad 8x^2 + 12x - 2x - 3 = 0$$
$$\Rightarrow \quad 4x(2x+3) - 1(2x+3) = 0$$
$$\Rightarrow \quad (2x+3)(4x-1) = 0$$
$$\Rightarrow (2x+3) = 0 \text{ or } (4x-1) = 0$$
$$\Rightarrow \quad 2x = -3 \text{ or } 4x = 1$$
$$\Rightarrow \quad x = \frac{3}{2} \text{ or } x = \frac{1}{4}$$

Common factor of $-2x$ and -3 is -1.

Sometimes you need to solve a quadratic equation that does not factorise.

Solving a quadratic equation by completing the square

EXAMPLE 4.3 Solve $x^2 - 8x + 3 = 0$.

SOLUTION

Subtract the constant term from both sides of the equation

$$\Rightarrow \quad x^2 - 8x = -3$$

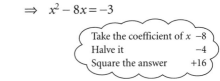

Take the coefficient of x -8
Halve it -4
Square the answer $+16$

Add 16 to both sides of the equation $\Rightarrow \quad x^2 - 8x + 16 = -3 + 16$

Factorise the left-hand side $\Rightarrow \quad (x-4)^2 = 13$

This will always be a perfect square.

Take the square root of both sides $\Rightarrow \quad (x-4) = \pm\sqrt{13}$

Add 4 to both sides $\Rightarrow \quad x = 4 + \sqrt{13} \text{ or } x = 4 - \sqrt{13}$

$$\Rightarrow \quad x = 7.6055\ldots \text{ or } x = 0.3944\ldots$$

This technique is called completing the square.

Solving a quadratic equation using the quadratic formula

EXAMPLE 4.4   Solve $2x^2 + 3x - 7 = 0$.

SOLUTION

$$2x^2 + 3x - 7 = 0$$

$$\Rightarrow x^2 + \frac{3}{2}x - \frac{7}{2} = 0$$

$$\Rightarrow x^2 + \frac{3}{2}x = \frac{7}{2}$$

$$\Rightarrow x^2 + \frac{3}{2}x + \left(\frac{3}{4}\right)^2 = \frac{7}{2} + \left(\frac{3}{4}\right)^2$$

$$\Rightarrow \left(x + \frac{3}{4}\right)^2 = \frac{65}{16}$$

$$\Rightarrow \left(x + \frac{3}{4}\right) = \pm\sqrt{\frac{65}{16}}$$

$$\Rightarrow x = -\frac{3}{4} \pm \sqrt{\frac{65}{16}}$$

GENERALISATION

$$ax^2 + bx + c = 0$$

$$\Rightarrow x^2 + \frac{b}{a}x + \frac{c}{a} = 0$$

$$\Rightarrow x^2 + \frac{b}{a}x = -\frac{c}{a}$$

$$\Rightarrow x^2 + \frac{b}{a}x + \left(\frac{b}{2a}\right)^2 = -\frac{c}{a} + \left(\frac{b}{2a}\right)^2$$

$$\Rightarrow \left(x + \frac{b}{2a}\right)^2 = \frac{b^2}{4a^2} - \frac{c}{a} = \frac{b^2 - 4ac}{4a^2}$$

$$\Rightarrow \left(x + \frac{b}{2a}\right) = \pm\sqrt{\frac{b^2 - 4ac}{4a^2}} = \frac{\sqrt{b^2 - 4ac}}{2a}$$

$$\Rightarrow x = -\frac{b}{2a} \pm \frac{\sqrt{b^2 - 4ac}}{2a} = \frac{-b \pm \sqrt{b^2 - 4ac}}{2a}$$

The result

$$x = \frac{-b \pm \sqrt{b^2 - 4ac}}{2a}$$

is known as the *quadratic formula*. It allows you to solve any quadratic equation. One root is found by taking the + sign, and the other by taking the − sign. Figure 4.2 shows you the general curve and its line of symmetry.

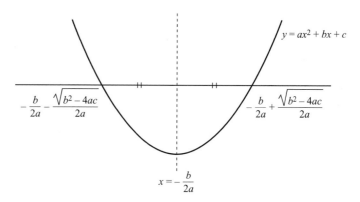

Figure 4.2

EXAMPLE 4.5

Use the quadratic formula to solve $2x^2 - 3x - 7 = 0$.

SOLUTION

Comparing
$$2x^2 - 3x - 7 = 0$$
with
$$ax^2 + bx + c = 0$$
gives
$$a = 2, b = -3, c = -7.$$

Using these values in the formula
$$x = \frac{-b \pm \sqrt{b^2 - 4ac}}{2a}$$

gives
$$x = \frac{-(-3) \pm \sqrt{(-3)^2 - 4 \times 2 \times (-7)}}{2 \times 2}$$

> When you use the quadratic formula and no level of accuracy is specified it is common practice to give the roots rounded to 2 decimal places.

$$\Rightarrow \quad x = \frac{3 \pm \sqrt{65}}{4}$$

$$\Rightarrow \quad x = \frac{3 + 8.0623}{4} = 2.77 \text{ or } x = \frac{3 - 8.0623}{4} = -1.27.$$

EXAMPLE 4.6

The length of a carpet is 1 m more than its width. Its area is $9\,m^2$. Find the dimensions of the carpet to the nearest centimetre.

SOLUTION

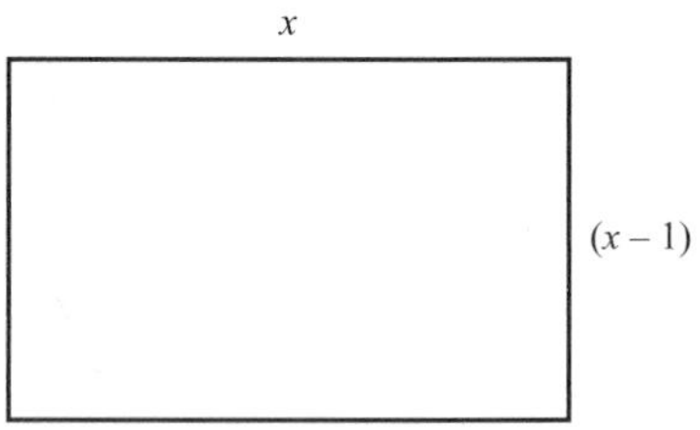

Let the length be x metres, so the width is $(x - 1)$ metres.

x

$(x - 1)$

length $\times$ width = area

$$\Rightarrow \quad x(x - 1) = 9$$
$$\Rightarrow \quad x^2 - x = 9$$
$$\Rightarrow \quad x^2 - x - 9 = 0 \text{ (collect everything on the left-hand side)}$$

Figure 4.3

Substituting $a = 1, b = -1, c = -9$ into the formula
$$x = \frac{-b \pm \sqrt{b^2 - 4ac}}{2a}$$

$$\Rightarrow \quad x = \frac{-(-1) \pm \sqrt{(-1)^2 - 4 \times 1 \times (-9)}}{2 \times 1}$$

$$\Rightarrow \quad x = \frac{1 \pm \sqrt{37}}{2}$$

$$\Rightarrow \quad x = 3.541\ldots \text{ or } x = -2.541\ldots$$

Clearly a negative answer is not suitable here, so the dimensions are

length = 3.54 m
width = 2.54 m (to the nearest cm).

EXERCISE 4A

1 Solve the following equations by factorising.

(i) $x^2 - 8x + 12 = 0$ (ii) $m^2 - 4m + 4 = 0$

(iii) $p^2 - 2p - 15 = 0$ (iv) $a^2 + 11a + 18 = 0$

(v) $2x^2 + 5x + 2 = 0$ (vi) $4x^2 + 3x - 7 = 0$

(vii) $15t^2 + 2t - 1 = 0$ (viii) $24r^2 + 19r + 2 = 0$

(ix) $3x^2 + 8x = 3$ (x) $3p^2 = 14p - 8$

2 Solve the following equations

(a) by completing the square

(b) by using the quadratic formula.

Give your answers correct to 2 decimal places.

(i) $x^2 - 2x - 10 = 0$ (ii) $x^2 + 3x - 6 = 0$

(iii) $x^2 + x - 8 = 0$ (iv) $2x^2 + x - 8 = 0$

(v) $2x^2 + 2x - 9 = 0$ (vi) $x^2 + x = 10$

(vii) $x^2 = 4x + 1$ (viii) $2x^2 - 8x + 5 = 0$

3 Solve the following equations by using the quadratic formula.
Give your answers correct to 2 decimal places.

(i) $3x^2 + 5x + 1 = 0$ (ii) $4x^2 + 9x + 3 = 0$

(iii) $2x^2 + 11x - 4 = 0$ (iv) $4x^2 - 9x + 4 = 0$

(v) $5x^2 - 10x + 1 = 0$ (vi) $3x^2 + 11x + 9 = 0$

4 The sides of a right-angled triangle, in centimetres, are x, $2x - 2$, and $x + 2$, where $x + 2$ is the hypotenuse.
Use Pythagoras' theorem to find their lengths.

5 A rectangular lawn measures 8 m by 10 m and is surrounded by a path of uniform width x m.
The total area of the path is 63 m². Find x.

6 The difference between two positive numbers is 2 and the difference between their squares is 40.
Taking x to be the smaller of the two numbers, form an equation in x and solve it.

7 The formula $h = 15t - 5t^2$ gives the height h metres of a ball, t seconds after it is thrown up into the air.

(i) Find the times when the height is 10 m.

(ii) After how long does the ball hit the ground?

8 The area of this triangle is 68 cm².

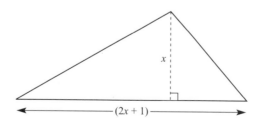

(i) Show that x satisfies the equation
$$2x^2 + x - 136 = 0.$$

(ii) Solve the equation to find the length of the base of the triangle.

9 Boxes are made by cutting 8 cm squares from the corners of sheets of cardboard and then folding. The sheets of cardboard are 6 cm longer than they are wide.

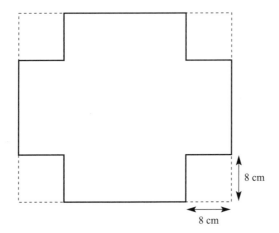

(i) For a sheet of cardboard whose width is x cm, find expressions, in terms of x, for
  (a) the length of the sheet
  (b) the length of the finished box
  (c) the width of the finished box.
(ii) Show that the volume of the box is $8x^2 - 208x + 1280$ cm^3.
(iii) Find the dimensions of the sheet of cardboard needed to make a box with a volume of 1728 cm^3.

Simultaneous equations

The equations you have met so far have only involved one variable, for example

$$2x + 2 = x - 5 \ \text{ or } \ a^2 - 3a + 2 = 0.$$

? When an equation involves two variables, for example $x + y = 4$, how many possible pairs of values are there for x and y?

Figure 4.4 shows the line $x + y = 4$.

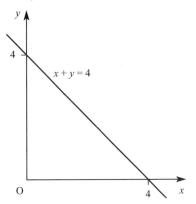

Figure 4.4

The co-ordinates of every point on that line give a pair of possible values for x and y. If you add the line $y = 2x + 1$, as in figure 4.5, you will see that the two lines intersect at a single point.

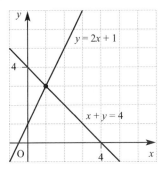

Figure 4.5

The co-ordinates of this point are the solution to the *simultaneous equations*

$$x + y = 4$$
and $\quad y = 2x + 1.$

There are several ways of solving simultaneous equations. You have just seen one method, that of drawing graphs. This is valid, but it has two drawbacks

(i) it is tedious

(ii) it may not be very accurate, particularly if the solution does not have integer values.

Solving simultaneous equations by substitution

EXAMPLE 4.7 Solve the simultaneous equations

$$x + y = 4$$
$$y = 2x + 1$$

by substitution.

> This method is particularly suitable when y is already the subject of one of the equations.

SOLUTION

Take the expression for y from the second equation and substitute it into the first. This gives

$$x + (2x + 1) = 4$$
$$\Rightarrow \quad 3x = 3$$
$$\Rightarrow \quad x = 1.$$

Since $y = 2x + 1$, when $x = 1$, $y = 3$, as before.

EXAMPLE 4.8

Figure 4.6 shows the graphs of $y = x^2 + x$ and $2x + y = 4$.

Solve the simultaneous equations

$$y = x^2 + x$$
$$\text{and} \quad 2x + y = 4$$

using the method of substitution.

> This method is also particulary suitable when one of the equations represents a curve.

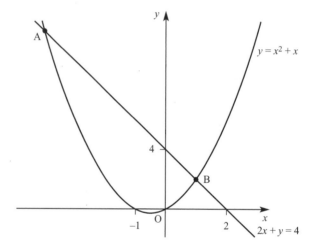

Figure 4.6

SOLUTION

⚠ Notice from figure 4.6 that there are two points of intersection, A and B, so expect the solution to be two pairs of values for x and y.

$$y = x^2 + x \qquad ①$$
$$2x + y = 4 \qquad ②$$

Substitute for y from equation ① into equation ②.

$$2x + (x^2 + x) = 4$$
$$\Rightarrow \quad x^2 + 3x - 4 = 0$$
$$\Rightarrow \quad (x + 4)(x - 1) = 0$$
$$\Rightarrow \quad x = -4 \text{ or } x = 1$$

Substituting in $2x + y = 4$ ← Always substitute back into the linear equation. ②

$$x = -4 \quad \Rightarrow \quad -8 + y = 4 \quad \Rightarrow \quad y = 12$$
$$x = 1 \quad \Rightarrow \quad 2 + y = 4 \quad \Rightarrow \quad y = 2$$

The solution is $x = -4$, $y = 12$ (the point A) and $x = 1$, $y = 2$ (the point B). ← Check your solution also fits equation ①.

⚠ The solution must always be given as pairs of values. It is wrong to write $x = -4$ or 1, $y = 12$ or 2, since not all pairs of values are possible.

❓ Having found the values of x in the example above, the values of y were found by substituting into the equation of the line. What would happen if, instead, you were to substitute into the equation of the curve?

Solving linear simultaneous equations by elimination

An alternative method that you may prefer to use when neither equation has y as the subject is called *solution by elimination*.

EXAMPLE 4.9

Solve the simultaneous equations

$$2x + y = 8 \qquad ①$$
$$5x + 2y = 21 \qquad ②$$

SOLUTION

Notice that multiplying throughout equation ① by 2 gives you another equation containing $2y$.

$$5x + 2y = 21 \qquad \text{equation ②}$$
$$4x + 2y = 16 \qquad 2 \times \text{equation ①}$$

Subtracting $\Rightarrow \quad x \quad = 5$

Substitute $x = 5$ into equation ①

$$10 + y = 8 \quad \Rightarrow \quad y = -2$$

The solution is $x = 5$, $y = -2$.

Sometimes you need to manipulate both equations to eliminate one of the variables, as in the following example.

EXAMPLE 4.10

Solve the simultaneous equations

$$2x + 3y = -1 \quad ①$$
$$3x - 2y = 18 \quad ②$$

SOLUTION

It is equally easy to eliminate x or y. It is up to you to choose which. The following method eliminates y.

$$\begin{array}{ll} 4x + 6y = -2 & 2 \times \text{equation } ① \\ 9x - 6y = 54 & 3 \times \text{equation } ② \end{array}$$

Adding $\Rightarrow \quad 13x \quad = 52$

$\Rightarrow \quad x = 4$

Substitute $x = 4$ into equation ①

$$8 + 3y = -1 \quad \Rightarrow \quad y = -3$$

The solution is $x = 4$, $y = -3$.

? In Example 4.9 the equations were subtracted; in Example 4.10 they were added. How do you decide whether to add or subtract?

Simultaneous equations may arise in everyday problems.

EXAMPLE 4.11

Nisha has £2.20 to spend on fruit for a picnic and can buy either five apples and four pears or two apples and six pears.

(i) Write this information as a pair of simultaneous equations.

(ii) Solve your equations to find the cost of each type of fruit.

SOLUTION

Let a pence be the cost of an apple and p pence be the cost of a pear.

> Make sure you introduce your variables.

(i)
$$5a + 4p = 220 \quad ①$$
$$2a + 6p = 220 \quad ②$$

> The cost of each piece of fruit will be a number of pence, so writing £2.20 as 220 pence avoids working with decimals.

$$\Rightarrow \quad \begin{array}{ll} 15a + 12p = 660 & 3 \times \text{equation } ① \\ 4a + 12p = 440 & 2 \times \text{equation } ② \end{array}$$

Subtracting $\quad 11a \quad = 220$

$\Rightarrow \quad a \quad = 20$

Substitute $a = 20$ into equation ①

$$100 + 4p = 220$$
$$\Rightarrow \quad p = 30$$

An apple costs 20 pence and a pear costs 30 pence.

EXAMPLE 4.12   A flag consists of a purple cross on a white background. Each white rectangle measures $2x$ cm by x cm, and the cross is y cm wide.

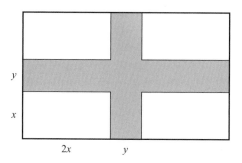

Figure 4.7

(i)   Write down the total area of the flag in terms of x and y.

(ii) Show that the area of the cross is $6xy + y^2$.

(iii) The total area of the flag is $4500\,\text{cm}^2$ and the area of the cross is $1300\,\text{cm}^2$. Find x and y.

SOLUTION

(i)   length $= 4x + y$ and width $= 2x + y$.

$$\Rightarrow \quad \text{area} = (4x + y)(2x + y)$$
$$= 8x^2 + 6xy + y^2 \qquad \qquad ①$$

(ii) Each white rectangle has an area of

$$2x \times x = 2x^2.$$
$$\Rightarrow \quad \text{area of cross} = 8x^2 + 6xy + y^2 - (4 \times 2x^2)$$
$$= 6xy + y^2 \qquad \qquad ②$$

(iii)

$$8x^2 + 6xy + y^2 = 4500 \qquad ①$$
$$6xy + y^2 = 1300 \qquad ②$$

Subtracting $8x^2 \qquad\qquad\quad = 3200$

$$\Rightarrow \quad x^2 = 400$$
$$\Rightarrow \quad x = 20 \quad \text{(positive answer only)}$$

Substitute $x = 20$ into equation ②

$$120y + y^2 = 1300$$
$$\Rightarrow \quad y^2 + 120y - 1300 = 0$$
$$\Rightarrow \quad (y + 130)(y - 10) = 0$$
$$\Rightarrow \quad y = -130 \text{ (reject since } y \text{ is a length) or } y = 10$$
$$\Rightarrow \quad x = 20 \text{ and } y = 10$$

1 Solve the following pairs of simultaneous equations using the substitution method.

(i) $y = x - 3$
    $3x + 2y = 19$

(ii) $y = 2x - 9$
    $4x - y = 17$

(iii) $y = 11 - 2x$
    $2x + 5y = 37$

(iv) $y = 3x + 3$
    $x - 2y = 4$

(v) $y = 7 - 2x$
    $2x + 3y = 15$

(vi) $y = 3x - 5$
    $x + 3y = -20$

2 Solve the following pairs of simultaneous equations using the elimination method.

(i) $3x + 2y = 12$
    $4x - y = 5$

(ii) $3x - 2y = 6$
    $5x + 6y = 38$

(iii) $3x + 2y = 22$
    $4x - 3y = 18$

(iv) $5x + 4y = 11$
    $2x + 3y = 9$

(v) $4x + 5y = 33$
    $3x + 2y = 16$

(vi) $4x - 3y = 2$
    $5x - 7y = 9$

3 Solve the following pairs of simultaneous equations.

(i) $x + y = 5$
    $x^2 + y^2 = 17$

(ii) $x - y + 1 = 0$
    $3x^2 - 4y = 0$

(iii) $x^2 + xy = 8$
    $x - y = 6$

(iv) $2x - y + 3 = 0$
    $y^2 - 5x^2 = 20$

(v) $x = 2y$
    $x^2 - y^2 + xy = 20$

(vi) $x + 2y = -3$
    $x^2 - 2x + 3y^2 = 11$

4 For each of the following situations, form a pair of simultaneous equations and solve them to answer the question.

(i) Three chews and four lollipops cost 72p. Five chews and two lollipops cost 64p. Find the cost of a chew and the cost of a lollipop.

(ii) A taxi firm charges a fixed amount plus so much per mile. A journey of five miles costs £5.00 and a journey of seven miles costs £6.60. How much does a journey of three miles cost?

(iii) Three packets of crisps and two packets of nuts cost £1.45. Two packets of crisps and five packets of nuts cost £2.25. How much does one packet of crisps and four packets of nuts cost?

(iv) Two adults and one child paid £37.50 to go to the theatre. The cost for one adult and three children was also £37.50. How much does it cost for two adults and five children?

5 The diagram shows the circle $x^2 + y^2 = 25$ and the line $x + y = 7$. Find the co-ordinates of A and B.

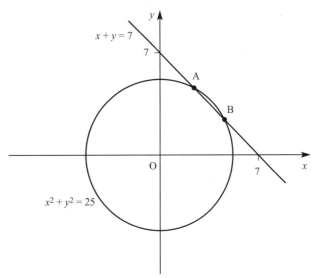

Factor theorem

Examination questions that only involve using the factor theorem are likely to appear on the non-calculator paper (Paper 1). It is therefore important to be able to factorise cubic expressions without using a calculator.

The factor theorem is an important result which allows you to find factors of polynomials of any order (if they factorise), and so to solve polynomial equations.

Look at this quadratic equation.

$$x^2 - 5x - 6 = 0$$
$$\text{Factorising} \Rightarrow (x - 6)(x + 1) = 0$$
$$\Rightarrow (x - 6) = 0 \text{ or } (x + 1) = 0$$
$$\Rightarrow x = 6 \text{ or } x = -1$$

? What happens if you substitute $x = 6$ in $x^2 - 5x - 6$?

What about $x = -1$?

NOTE If $f(x) = x^2 - 5x - 6$, you use the notation $f(6)$ to mean the value of $f(x)$ when $x = 6$.

The factor theorem states this result in a general form.

> If $(x - a)$ is a factor of the polynomial $f(x)$, then
> - $f(a) = 0$
> - $x = a$ is a root of the equation $f(x) = 0$.
> Conversely, if $f(a) = 0$, then $(x - a)$ is a factor of $f(x)$.

EXAMPLE 4.13

Given that

$$f(x) = x^3 + 2x^2 - x - 2$$

(i) find $f(-2)$, $f(-1)$, $f(0)$, $f(1)$, $f(2)$

(ii) factorise $x^3 + 2x^2 - x - 2$.

SOLUTION

(i) $f(-2) = (-2)^3 + 2(-2)^2 - (-2) - 2$
    $= -8 + 8 + 2 - 2$
    $= 0$ $\Rightarrow$ $(x + 2)$ is a factor

    $f(-1) = (-1)^3 + 2(-1)^2 - (-1) - 2$
    $= -1 + 2 + 1 - 2$
    $= 0$ $\Rightarrow$ $(x + 1)$ is a factor

    $f(0)\ = 0 + 0 - 0 - 2$
    $= -2$

    $f(1)\ = 1 + 2 - 1 - 2$
    $= 0$ $\Rightarrow$ $(x - 1)$ is a factor

    $f(2)\ = 8 + 8 - 2 - 2$
    $= 12$

(ii) Since $(x - 1)(x + 1)(x + 2)$ would expand to give a polynomial of order 3, you can say that

$$x^3 + 2x^2 - x - 2 = k(x - 1)(x + 1)(x + 2)$$

where k is a constant.

? The value of k is 1. How can you show this?

EXAMPLE 4.14

Given that

$$f(x) = x^3 + 3x^2 - x - 3$$

(i) show that $(x + 1)$ is a factor of $f(x)$

(ii) suggest other values of x you should try when looking for another factor

(iii) solve the equation $f(x) = 0$.

SOLUTION

(i) $(x + 1)$ is a factor if $f(-1) = 0$.
    $f(-1) = -1 + 3 + 1 - 3$
    $= 0$
    $\Rightarrow$ $(x + 1)$ is a factor of $x^3 + 3x^2 - x - 3$

(ii) Any other linear factor will be of the form $(x - a)$ where a is a factor of the constant term (-3).

This means that the only other values of x which are worth trying are 1, 3 and −3.

? Explain why.

(iii) $\text{f}(1) = 1 + 3 - 1 - 3$

$\qquad = 0 \qquad\qquad \Rightarrow \qquad (x - 1)$ is a factor

$\quad \text{f}(3) = 27 + 27 - 3 - 3$

$\qquad = 48$

$\quad \text{f}(-3) = -27 + 27 + 3 - 3$

$\qquad = 0 \qquad\qquad \Rightarrow \qquad (x + 3)$ is a factor

$\text{f}(-1) = 0$, $\text{f}(1) = 0$ and $\text{f}(-3) = 0$ and the equation is a cubic, so has at most three roots. The solution is $x = -1$, 1 or −3.

Sometimes you may only be able to find one linear factor for the cubic and, in this case, you then need to use long division.

EXAMPLE 4.15

Given that

$$\text{f}(x) = x^3 - x^2 - 3x - 1$$

(i) show that $(x + 1)$ is a factor

(ii) factorise $\text{f}(x)$

(iii) solve $\text{f}(x) = 0$.

SOLUTION

(i) $\text{f}(-1) = (-1)^3 - (-1)^2 - 3(-1) - 1$

$\qquad\quad = -1 - 1 + 3 - 1$

$\qquad\quad = 0$

$\quad \Rightarrow (x + 1)$ is a factor of $x^3 - x^2 - 3x - 1$

? What happens when you try $x = 1$?

Is there any other value you should try?

(ii) Since $(x + 1)$ is a factor, divide $\text{f}(x)$ by $(x + 1)$.

$$
\begin{array}{r}
x^2 - 2x - 1 \\
x + 1 \overline{\smash{)}\; x^3 - x^2 - 3x - 1} \\
\underline{x^3 + x^2} \\
-2x^2 - 3x \\
\underline{-2x^2 - 2x} \\
-x - 1 \\
\underline{-x - 1} \\
0
\end{array}
$$

So

$$f(x) = (x+1)(x^2 - 2x - 1)$$

(iii) $f(x) = 0 \Rightarrow (x+1)(x^2 - 2x - 1) = 0$
$\Rightarrow$ either $x = -1$ or $x^2 - 2x - 1 = 0$

Using the quadratic formula on

$$x^2 - 2x - 1 = 0$$

gives

$$x = \frac{2 \pm \sqrt{4 - (4 \times 1 \times (-1))}}{2}$$

$$= \frac{2 \pm \sqrt{8}}{2}$$

$$= 2.414 \text{ or } -0.414$$

The complete solution is $x = -1, -0.414$ or 2.414 (to 3 d.p.).

EXERCISE 4C

1 Determine whether the following linear functions are factors of the given polynomials.
   (i) $x^3 - 8x + 7$ $(x - 1)$ (ii) $x^3 - 7x^2 - 5x + 1$ $(x + 1)$
   (iii) $x^3 + x^2 - 4x - 5$ $(x + 2)$ (iv) $x^3 - 6x^2 + 10x - 4$ $(x - 2)$
   (v) $x^3 + 27$ $(x + 3)$ (vi) $x^3 - ax^2 + a^2x - a^3$ $(x - a)$

2 Factorise the following functions as a product of three linear factors.
   (i) $x^3 - 3x^2 - x + 3$ (ii) $x^3 - 7x - 6$
   (iii) $x^3 - x^2 - 2x$ (iv) $x^3 - 2x^2 - 13x - 10$
   (v) $x^3 - x^2 - 14x + 24$ (vi) $x^3 + 5x^2 - x - 5$
   (vii) $x^3 + 2x^2 - 4x - 8$ (viii) $x^3 + 5x^2 + 3x - 9$
   (ix) $x^3 + 3x^2 - 9x + 5$ (x) $x^3 + 7x^2 + 14x + 8$

3 Solve the following equations. Any solutions that are not integers should be given to 3 significant figures.
   (i) $x^3 - 2x^2 - 5x + 6 = 0$ (ii) $x^3 + 3x^2 - 6x - 8 = 0$
   (iii) $x^3 - 2x^2 - 21x - 18 = 0$ (iv) $x^3 - 3x^2 - 4x + 12 = 0$
   (v) $x^3 + 2x^2 - 4x + 1 = 0$ (vi) $x^3 - 9x - 10 = 0$

4 $f(x) = x^3 + 2x^2 + ax - 76$
   $(x - 4)$ is a factor of $f(x)$.
   Work out the value of a.

5 $f(x) = x^3 + px^2 + qx + 6$
   $(x - 1)$ and $(x + 3)$ are both linear factors of $f(x)$.
   (i)   Work out a third linear factor of $f(x)$.
   (ii)   Work out the values of p and q.

6 (i)   Find the value of k for which $x = 2$ is a root of $x^3 + kx + 6 = 0$.
   (ii)   Find the other roots when k has this value.

7 The diagram shows an open rectangular tank whose base is a square of side x metres and whose volume is $8\,\text{m}^3$.

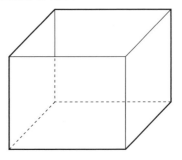

(i) Write down an expression in terms of x for the height of the tank.

(ii) Show that the surface area of the tank is $\left(x^2 + \frac{32}{x}\right)\,\text{m}^2$.

(iii) Given that the surface area is $24\,\text{m}^2$ show that
$$x^3 - 24x + 32 = 0.$$

(iv) Solve $x^3 - 24x + 32 = 0$ to find the possible values of x.

Linear inequalities

? What is the difference between an equation and an inequality?

? The radius of the Earth's orbit round the Sun is approximately $1.5 \times 10^8\,\text{km}$; that of Mars is about $2.3 \times 10^8\,\text{km}$. The Earth takes 365 days for one orbit and Mars takes 687 days.

At some time the distance from Earth to Mars is $x\,\text{km}$. What can you say about x?

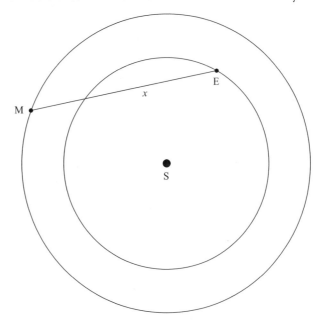

Figure 4.8

EXAMPLE 4.16

Solve $2y + 6 < 5y + 12$.

SOLUTION

Method 1

$$2y + 6 < 5y + 12$$

Subtract $2y$	$\Rightarrow$	$6 < 3y + 12$
Subtract 12	$\Rightarrow$	$-6 < 3y$
Divide by 3	$\Rightarrow$	$-2 < y$
Make y the subject	$\Rightarrow$	$y > -2$

Method 2

$$2y + 6 < 5y + 12$$

Subtract $5y$	$\Rightarrow$	$-3y + 6 < 12$
Subtract 6	$\Rightarrow$	$-3y < 6$
Divide by (-3)	$\Rightarrow$	$y > -2$

? In what ways is solving an inequality like solving an equation?
In what ways is it different?

? Explain, with examples, why you need to reverse the inequality sign when you multiply or divide an inequality by a negative number.

EXAMPLE 4.17

Solve the inequality $5 < 3x - 1 \leqslant 17$.

SOLUTION

| Add 1 throughout | $\Rightarrow$ | $6 < 3x \leqslant 18$ |
| Divide by 3 | $\Rightarrow$ | $2 < x \leqslant 6$ |

The following example, although algebraic, is solved by using knowledge of number operations and number facts.

EXAMPLE 4.18

(i) Given that $-2 < x < 5$, work out an inequality for x^2.

(ii) Given that $1 \leqslant a \leqslant 4$ and $-3 \leqslant b \leqslant 2$, work out an inequality for $a - b$.

SOLUTION

(i) Squaring a negative number results in a positive number.

So, $0 < x^2 < 25$

(ii) The least value for $a - b$ will occur when a takes its least value and b takes its greatest value.

Least value $= 1 - 2$
$= -1$

The greatest value for $a - b$ will occur when a takes its greatest value and b takes its least value.

Greatest value $= 4 - (-3)$
$$= 4 + 3$$
$$= 7$$

So, $-1 \leqslant a - b \leqslant 7$

EXERCISE 4D

1 Solve the following inequalities.

(i) $2x - 3 < 7$ (ii) $5 + 3x \geqslant 11$

(iii) $6y + 1 \leqslant 4y + 9$ (iv) $y - 4 > 3y - 12$

(v) $4x + 1 \geqslant 3x - 2$ (vi) $b - 3 \leqslant 5b + 9$

(vii) $\dfrac{x + 5}{2} > 1$ (viii) $\dfrac{2x - 3}{3} < 7$

(ix) $\dfrac{5 - 3x}{4} \leqslant 5$ (x) $\dfrac{2 - 4x}{3} \geqslant 6$

(xi) $4 \leqslant 5x - 6 \leqslant 14$ (xii) $11 \leqslant 3x + 5 \leqslant 20$

(xiii) $5 < 7 - 2x < 13$ (xiv) $5 > 9 - 4x > 1$

2 Given that $0 \leqslant p \leqslant 3$ and $2 \leqslant q \leqslant 5$, work out the inequality for $p - q$.

3 Given that $-2 < x < 4$ and $1 < y < 3$, work out the inequality for $x + y$.

4 Given that $1 \leqslant a \leqslant 6$ and $-3 \leqslant b \leqslant 3$, work out inequalities for

(i) $a + b$ (ii) $a - b$.

5 Given that $-3 \leqslant a \leqslant 0$ and $-1 \leqslant b \leqslant 10$, work out inequalities for

(i) $a + b$ (ii) $a - b$ (iii) $2a + 3b$.

6 Given that $x > 2$ and $y < 0$, decide whether each of the following statements are ALWAYS TRUE, SOMETIMES TRUE or NEVER TRUE.

(i) $4x > 8$ (ii) $2y > 0$ (iii) $x + y < 2$

(iv) $x^2 > 10$ (v) $y^2 < 0$ (vi) $x - y > 2$

7 Given that $0 < x < 1$ and $y > 0$, decide whether each of the following statements are ALWAYS TRUE, SOMETIMES TRUE or NEVER TRUE.

(i) $\dfrac{1}{x} > 1$ (ii) $\dfrac{y}{x} > 0$ (iii) $x + y < 0$

(iv) $xy > 4$ (v) $x^2 > 1$ (vi) $x - y < 0$

8 The square and rectangle have dimensions in centimetres.

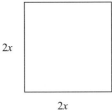
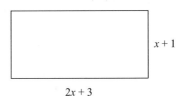

2x

x + 1

2x

2x + 3

The perimeter of the square is greater than the perimeter of the rectangle.

Work out an inequality for x.

Quadratic inequalities

The quadratic inequalities in this section all involve quadratic expressions that factorise. This means that you can either find a solution by sketching the appropriate graph, or you can use line segments to reduce the quadratic inequality to two simultaneous linear inequalities.

EXAMPLE 4.19

Solve

(i) $x^2 - 2x - 3 < 0$
(ii) $x^2 - 2x - 3 \geqslant 0$.

SOLUTION

Method 1

$$x^2 - 2x - 3 = (x + 1)(x - 3)$$

So the graph of $y = x^2 - 2x - 3$ crosses the x axis when $x = -1$ and $x = 3$.

Look at the two graphs in figure 4.9.

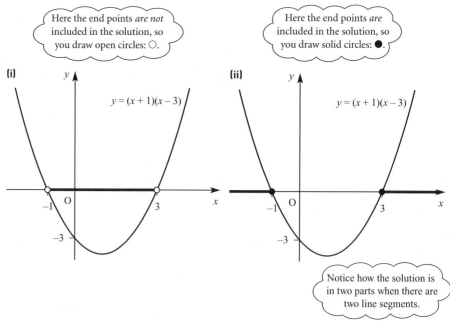

Figure 4.9

(i)   You want the values of x for which $y < 0$, that is where the curve is below the x axis. The solution is $-1 < x < 3$.

(ii) You want the values of x for which $y \geqslant 0$, that is where the curve crosses or is above the x axis. The solution is $x \leqslant -1$ or $x \geqslant 3$.

An alternative method identifies the values of x for which each of the factors is zero and considers the sign of each factor in the intervals between these critical values.

Method 2

	$x < -1$	$x = -1$	$-1 < x < 3$	$x = 3$	$x > 3$
sign of $(x + 1)$	$-$	0	$+$	$+$	$+$
sign of $(x - 3)$	$-$	$-$	$-$	0	$+$
sign of $(x+1)(x-3)$	$(-)\times(-)$ $= +$	$(0)\times(-)$ $= 0$	$(+)\times(-)$ $= -$	$(+)\times(0)$ $= 0$	$(+)\times(+)$ $= +$

From the table the solution to $(x + 1)(x - 3) < 0$ is $-1 < x < 3$.

The solution to $(x + 1)(x - 3) \geq 0$ is $x \leq -1$ or $x \geq 3$.

NOTE If the inequality to be solved contains $>$ or $<$, then the solution is described using $>$ and $<$, but if the original inequality contains $\geq$ or $\leq$, then the solution is described using $\geq$ and $\leq$.

Both of these are valid methods, and you should decide which you prefer. This may depend on how easily you sketch graphs.

⚠ If the quadratic inequality has terms on both sides, you must first collect everything on one side, as you would do when solving a quadratic equation.

EXAMPLE 4.20 Solve $2x + x^2 > 3$.

SOLUTION

$$2x + x^2 > 3 \implies x^2 + 2x - 3 > 0$$
$$\implies (x - 1)(x + 3) > 0$$

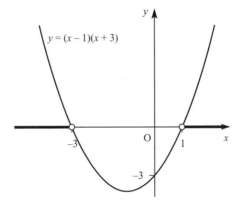

Figure 4.10

From figure 4.10 the solution is $x < -3$ or $x > 1$.

EXERCISE 4E

1 Solve the following inequalities.

(i) $x^2 - 6x + 5 > 0$ (ii) $a^2 + 3a - 4 \leqslant 0$

(iii) $2y^2 + y - 3 < 0$ (iv) $4 - y^2 \geqslant 0$

(v) $x^2 - 4x + 4 > 0$ (vi) $p^2 - 3p \leqslant -2$

(vii) $(a + 2)(a - 1) > 4$ (viii) $8 - 2a \geqslant a^2$

(ix) $3y^2 + 2y - 1 > 0$ (x) $y^2 \geqslant 4y + 5$

2 The square and rectangle have dimensions in centimetres.

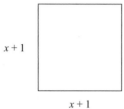 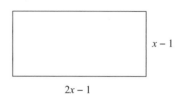

The area of the square is less than the area of the rectangle.

Work out an inequality for x.

3 The triangle and parallelogram have dimensions in metres.

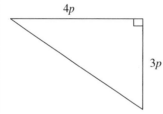 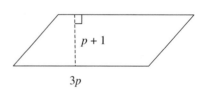

The area of the triangle is greater than the area of the parallelogram.

Work out an inequality for p.

Index laws

Index laws for positive integers have already been used in Chapter 2. The three index laws are summarised below.

$$a^m \times a^n = a^{m+n}$$
$$a^m \div a^n = a^{m-n}$$
$$(a^m)^n = a^{m \times n}$$

These laws apply for **all** values of m and n.

ACTIVITY 4.1

Use the law $a^m \times a^n = a^{m+n}$ to answer these.

(i) Write $a^3 \times a^0$ as a single power of a.
Hence state the value of a^0.

(ii) Write $a^2 \times a^{-2}$ as a single power of a.
Hence write a^{-2} in the form $\dfrac{1}{a^p}$ where p is a positive integer.

(iii) Write $a^{\frac{1}{2}} \times a^{\frac{1}{2}}$ as a single power of a.

Hence copy and complete the statement $\qquad$ $a^{\frac{1}{2}}$ is the .... root of a.

(iv) Write $a^{\frac{1}{3}} \times a^{\frac{1}{3}} \times a^{\frac{1}{3}}$ as a single power of a.

Hence copy and complete the statement $\qquad$ $a^{\frac{1}{3}}$ is the .... root of a.

The following facts should be known.

$$a^0 = 1$$

$$a^{-m} = \frac{1}{a^m}$$

$$a^{\frac{1}{n}} = \sqrt[n]{a}$$

EXAMPLE 4.21

Express as single powers of x.

(i) $\dfrac{x^3 \times x^2}{x^9}$

(ii) $\sqrt[3]{x^5 \div x^3}$

(iii) $\sqrt{\dfrac{x^{\frac{3}{2}} \times x^{\frac{1}{2}}}{\left(x^3\right)^2}}$

SOLUTION

(i) $\dfrac{x^3 \times x^2}{x^9} = \dfrac{x^{3+2}}{x^9}$

$= \dfrac{x^5}{x^9}$

$= x^{5-9}$

$= x^{-4}$

(ii) $\sqrt[3]{x^5 \div x^3} = \sqrt[3]{x^{5-3}}$

$= \sqrt[3]{x^2}$

$= \left(x^2\right)^{\frac{1}{3}}$

$= x^{2 \times \frac{1}{3}}$

$= x^{\frac{2}{3}}$

(iii) $\sqrt{\dfrac{x^{\frac{3}{2}} \times x^{\frac{1}{2}}}{\left(x^3\right)^2}} = \sqrt{\dfrac{x^{\frac{3}{2}+\frac{1}{2}}}{x^{3 \times 2}}}$

$= \sqrt{\dfrac{x^2}{x^6}}$

$= \sqrt{x^{2-6}}$

$= \sqrt{x^{-4}}$

$= \left(x^{-4}\right)^{\frac{1}{2}}$

$= x^{-4 \times \frac{1}{2}}$

$= x^{-2}$

NOTE For fractional powers >1, improper fractions are used. Write $a^{\frac{5}{2}}$ not $a^{2\frac{1}{2}}$.

EXAMPLE 4.22

Solve $\qquad$ **(i)** $x^{\frac{3}{2}} = 8$ $\qquad$ **(ii)** $x^{-\frac{1}{3}} = 10$.

SOLUTION

(i) Method 1

Square both sides $\qquad \left(x^{\frac{3}{2}}\right)^2 = 8^2$

$\qquad\qquad\qquad\qquad x^3 = 64$

Cube root both sides $\qquad x = \sqrt[3]{64}$

$\qquad\qquad\qquad\qquad x = 4$

Method 2

Take power $\dfrac{2}{3}$ of both sides

$$\left(x^{\frac{3}{2}}\right)^{\frac{2}{3}} = 8^{\frac{2}{3}}$$

$$x = \left(8^2\right)^{\frac{1}{3}}$$

$$x = 64^{\frac{1}{3}}$$

$$x = \sqrt[3]{64}$$

$$x = 4$$

(ii) Method 1

Take the reciprocal of both sides

$$\left(x^{-\frac{1}{3}}\right)^{-1} = 10^{-1}$$

> The reciprocal of a^{-m} is a^m.

$$x^{\frac{1}{3}} = \dfrac{1}{10}$$

Cube both sides

$$x = \left(\dfrac{1}{10}\right)^3$$

$$x = \dfrac{1}{1000}$$

Method 2

Cube both sides

$$\left(x^{-\frac{1}{3}}\right) = 10^3$$

$$x^{-1} = 1000$$

Take the reciprocal of both sides

$$x = 1000^{-1}$$

> The reciprocal of x^{-1} is $a^1 = a$.

$$x = \dfrac{1}{1000}$$

EXERCISE 4F

1 Write as single powers of x.

(i) $\dfrac{x \times x^6}{x^3}$

(ii) $x^2 \times x^3 \div x^8$

(iii) $\sqrt{x^7 \div x^2}$

(iv) $x^{\frac{1}{2}} \times x^{\frac{3}{2}} \times x^4$

(v) $\left(x^{\frac{1}{3}}\right)^{12}$

(vi) $\sqrt[3]{x^7 \times x^{-1}}$

(vii) $\sqrt{\dfrac{x^{\frac{5}{2}} \times x^{\frac{1}{2}}}{x^5}}$

(viii) $\left(\sqrt{x}\right)^{10} \div x^{-5}$

(ix) $\sqrt[4]{\dfrac{x^5 \times x^8}{x^3 \times x^2}}$

2 Solve, giving solutions as exact values.

(i) $x^{\frac{1}{2}} = 3$

(ii) $x^{\frac{1}{3}} = -2$

(iii) $x^{\frac{1}{2}} = \dfrac{1}{3}$

(iv) $x^{-\frac{1}{2}} = 2$

(v) $x^{-\frac{1}{3}} = 4$

(vi) $x^{-3} = 2$

(vii) $x^{\frac{2}{3}} = 4$

(viii) $x^{-\frac{1}{2}} = \frac{1}{3}$

(ix) $x^{-2} = \frac{9}{25}$

(x) $x^{\frac{3}{2}} = 27$

(xi) $x^{-\frac{1}{3}} = \frac{2}{3}$

(xii) $x^{-4} = 10\ 000$

3 Expand.

(i) $x^{\frac{1}{2}}\left(x^{\frac{3}{2}} + x^{\frac{1}{2}}\right)$

(ii) $x^{-2}(x^3 - x^2)$

(iii) $x^{\frac{2}{3}}\left(x^{\frac{1}{3}} - x^{\frac{7}{3}}\right)$

(iv) $x^{-3}(x^{-2} + x^{-1})$

(v) $x^{-\frac{1}{2}}\left(x^{\frac{3}{2}} + x^{\frac{7}{2}}\right)$

(vi) $x^{\frac{1}{3}}\left(x^{\frac{8}{3}} - x^{-\frac{1}{3}}\right)$

Algebraic proof

Any of the algebraic skills covered in previous sections may be needed in proofs.

NOTE You should not assume the result you are being asked to prove is true.

EXAMPLE 4.23 Prove that $2a^3 - a^2(2a - 9)$ is a square number when a is a positive integer.

SOLUTION

Expand and simplify
$$2a^3 - a^2(2a - 9) = 2a^3 - 2a^3 + 9a^2$$
$$= 9a^2$$
$$= (3a)^2$$

As a is a positive integer then $3a$ is also a positive integer.

The final line ensures that the solution is complete.

EXAMPLE 4.24 (i) Express $x^2 - 8x + 18$ in the form $(x - a)^2 + b$ where a and b are integers.
(ii) Hence, prove that $x^2 - 8x + 18$ is always positive.

SOLUTION

(i) $$x^2 - 8x + 18 \equiv (x - a)^2 + b$$
$$x^2 - 8x + 18 \equiv x^2 - 2ax + a^2 + b$$

Completing the square.

Equate coefficients of x
$$-8 = -2a$$
$$4 = a$$

Equate constants
$$18 = a^2 + b$$
$$18 = 16 + b$$
$$2 = b$$

$$x^2 - 8x + 18 \equiv (x - 4)^2 + 2$$

(ii) $(x - 4)^2$ is always positive or zero.

Adding 2 means that $(x - 4)^2 + 2$ will always be positive.

EXAMPLE 4.25

c and d are positive integers such that $c > d$.

$$f(x) = \frac{2c + cx}{2d + dx} \qquad x \neq -2$$

Prove that $f(x) > 1$.

SOLUTION

Factorise the numerator and denominator $\qquad f(x) = \dfrac{c(2 + x)}{d(2 + x)}$

Divide numerator and denominator by $(2 + x)$ $\qquad = \dfrac{c}{d}$

As $c > d$ and d is positive, $\dfrac{c}{d} > 1$.

EXERCISE 4G

1 Prove that $2(m + 7) - 2(5 + m)$ is always a positive integer.

2 Prove that $5(c - 3) + 3(c + 7)$ is always even when c is a positive integer.

3 Prove that $(y + 6)(y + 3) - y^2$ is a multiple of 9 when y is a positive integer.

4 $f(n) = n^2$ for all positive integer values of n.
   (i) Show that $f(n + 1) = n^2 + 2n + 1$.
   (ii) Prove that $f(n + 1) + f(n - 1)$ is always even.
   (iii) Prove that $f(n + 1) - f(n - 1)$ is always a multiple of 4.

5 **(i)** Express $x^2 + 2x + 5$ in the form $(x + a)^2 + b$ where a and b are integers.
   (ii) Hence, prove that $x^2 + 2x + 5$ is always positive.

6 Prove that $y^2 - 10y + 26 > 0$ for all values of y.

7 Prove that $9m^2(3m - 1) + (3m)^2$ is a cube number when m is a positive integer.

8 Prove that $\dfrac{6p - 18}{2p - 6}$ is always a positive integer.

9 a is a positive number, b is a negative number.

   $a \neq -b$

   Prove that $\dfrac{a^2 + ab}{ab + b^2}$ is negative.

10 $f(x) = x^2 + 2x$

   Prove that $f(4x) = kx(2x + 1)$ where k is an integer.

Sequences

Here are the first few terms of some sequences.

$$4 \quad 10 \quad 16 \quad 22 \quad 26 \quad \ldots$$

The first term is 4. Each subsequent term can be obtained by adding 6 to the previous term.

$$1 \quad 4 \quad 9 \quad 16 \quad 25 \quad \ldots$$

This is the set of square numbers.

*n*th terms

The *n*th term of a sequence is an expression in terms of *n*.
To find a particular term, a value for *n* is substituted into the expression.

Linear sequences

The *n*th term will be an expression in the form $an + b$ where a and b are constants.

EXAMPLE 4.26 | Work out the *n*th term of the linear sequence   3   12   21   30   39   ...

SOLUTION

Method 1

$$n\text{th term} = an + b$$

When $n = 1$ the term is 3

$3 = a(1) + b$
$3 = a + b$ ①

When $n = 2$ the term is 12

$12 = a(2) + b$
$12 = 2a + b$ ②

Subtracting ① from ②
Substituting in ①

$9 = a$
$3 = 9 + b$
$-6 = b$

$n\text{th term} = 9n - 6$

Method 2

$$n\text{th term} = an + b$$

The common difference between the terms is $12 - 3 = 9$
This will be the coefficient of n

$$a = 9$$

Similarly, $21 - 12 = 9$ and $30 - 21 = 9$ etc.

When $n = 1$ the term is 3

$$3 = 9(1) + b$$
$$3 = 9 + b$$
$$-6 = b$$

$$n\text{th term} = 9n - 6$$

NOTE For the linear sequence   15   13   11   9   ...,   the common difference is $13 - 15 = -2$.

EXERCISE 4H

1 Work out an expression for the nth term for each of the following linear sequences.

(i)   10   14   18   22   26   ...
(ii)   2   9   16   23   ...
(iii)   −5   −3   −1   1   3   ...
(iv)   0   25   50   75   ...
(v)   −11   −3   5   13   ...
(vi)   3   3.5   4   4.5   5   ...
(vii)   40   30   20   10   0   −10   ...
(viii)   7   4   1   −2   −5   ...
(ix)   1 $\frac{1}{2}$ 0 $-\frac{1}{2}$ $-\frac{3}{2}$ ...
(x)   −4   −5.5   −7   −8.5   −10   ...

2 (i)   Work out the 100th term of the linear sequence   −5   1   7   13   ...
  (ii)   Work out the 50th term of the linear sequence   35   28   21   14   ...
  (iii)   Work out the 200th term of the linear sequence   −1   −10   −19   −28   ...

3 Here is a linear sequence.

    3   5.5   8   10.5   13   ...

Work out the value of the first term of the sequence that is greater than 250.

4 Here are two linear sequences.

Sequence A   7   5   3   1   −1   ...

Sequence B   3   0   −3   −6   ...

Prove that the sum of the nth terms of the two sequences is $15 - 5n$.

5 Here is a linear sequence.

    p $p + 2q$ $p + 4q$ $p + 6q$ ...

The third term of the sequence is 20.
The fourth term of the sequence is 56.

(i)   Work out the values of p and q.

(ii)   Work out an expression for the nth term of the sequence.

Quadratic sequences

The nth term will be an expression in the form $an^2 + bn + c$ where a, b and c are constants.

EXAMPLE 4.27

Work out the nth term of the quadratic sequence   3   6   13   24   39   ...

SOLUTION

Method 1

nth term $= an^2 + bn + c$

When $n = 1$ the term is 3

$3 = a(1^2) + b(1) + c$

$3 = a + b + c$ ①

When $n = 2$ the term is 6

$6 = a(2^2) + b(2) + c$

$6 = 4a + 2b + c$ ②

When $n = 3$ the term is 13

$13 = a(3^2) + b(3) + c$

$13 = 9a + 3b + c$ ③

Subtracting ① from ②

$3 = 3a + b$ ④

Subtracting ② from ③

$7 = 5a + b$ ⑤

Subtracting ④ from ⑤

$4 = 2a$

$2 = a$

Substituting in ④

$3 = 6 + b$

$-3 = b$

Substituting in ①

$3 = 2 + -3 + c$

$3 = -1 + c$

$4 = c$

nth term $= 2n^2 - 3n + 4$

Method 2

nth term $= an^2 + bn + c$

Work out up to the second differences

$$\begin{array}{ccccccccc}
3 & & 6 & & 13 & & 24 & & 39 \\
& 3 & & 7 & & 11 & & 15 & \\
& & 4 & & 4 & & 4 & &
\end{array}$$

For a quadratic sequence, all the second differences will be the same value.

Divide the second difference by 2 $4 \div 2 = 2$

This will be the coefficient of n^2 $a = 2$

Subtract $2n^2$ from the sequence

$3 - 2(1)^2$	$6 - 2(2)^2$	$13 - 2(3)^2$	$24 - 2(4)^2$	$39 - 2(5)^2$
1	-2	-5	-8	-11

The nth term of this linear sequence is $-3n + 4$.

nth term $= 2n^2 - 3n + 4$

EXERCISE 41

1 Work out the nth term for each of the following quadratic sequences.

(i)   4   9   16   25   36   .....

(ii)   0   6   14   24   36   .....

(iii)   4   13   24   37   52   .....

(iv)   8   21   40   65   96   .....

(v)   4   13   26   43   64   .....

(vi) -4 -4 0   8   20   .....

(vii)   11   10   7   2 -5 ......

(viii) 98   92   82   68   50   .....

2 (i) Work out the nth term of the linear sequence

1   5   9   13   17   ...

(ii) Hence, work out the nth term of the quadratic sequence

1   25   81   169   289   ...

Give your answer in the form $an^2 + bn + c$.

3 (i) Show that the nth term of the quadratic sequence

2   7   14   23   34   ...

is $n^2 + 2n - 1$.

(ii) Hence, work out the nth term of the quadratic sequence

5   10   17   26   37   ...

Give your answer in the form $an^2 + bn + c$.

4 (i) Show that the nth term of the quadratic sequence

-5 -6 -5 -2 3   ...

is $n^2 - 4n - 2$.

(ii) Hence, work out the nth term of the quadratic sequence

-15 -18 -15 -6 9   ...

Give your answer in the form $an^2 + bn + c$.

(iii) Hence, work out the nth term of the quadratic sequence

0   -3 0   9   24   ...

Give your answer in the form $an^2 + bn + c$.

Other sequences

Some sequences have nth terms that are neither linear nor quadratic expressions.

EXAMPLE 4.28   The nth term of a sequence is $\dfrac{3n+2}{n+4}$.

(i)   Work out the first three terms of the sequence.

(ii)   Work out the position of the term that has value 2.8.

SOLUTION

(i) $n=1$ 1st term $= \dfrac{3(1)+2}{1+4}$

$= \dfrac{5}{5}$

$= 1$

$n=2$ 2nd term $= \dfrac{3(2)+2}{2+4}$

$= \dfrac{8}{6}$

$= \dfrac{4}{3}$

$n=3$ 3rd term $= \dfrac{3(3)+2}{3+4}$

$= \dfrac{11}{7}$

The first three terms are $1, \dfrac{4}{3}, \dfrac{11}{7}$.

(ii)   Set up an equation $\dfrac{3n+2}{n+4} = 2.8$

Multiply both sides by $n+4$ $3n+2 = 2.8(n+4)$

$3n+2 = 2.8n+11.2$

$3n-2.8n = 11.2-2$

$0.2n = 9.2$

$n = \dfrac{9.2}{0.2}$

$n = 46$

The 46th term has the value 2.8.

ACTIVITY 4.2   A sequence has nth term $= \dfrac{3n}{n+1}$.

(i)   Work out the first 15 terms of the sequence.
Write down the value of each term to 3 decimal places.

(ii)   Work out the 1st, 20th, 30th, 40th, 50th, 100th, 200th and 500th terms of the sequence.
Write down the value of each term to 3 decimal places.

(iii)   Explain what is happening to the terms in the sequence as n increases.

Limiting value of a sequence

To find the limiting value, consider the nth term as $n \to \infty$ (n becomes very large).

EXAMPLE 4.29

The nth term of a sequence is $\dfrac{2n - 1}{3n + 2}$.

Prove that the limiting value of the sequence as $n \to \infty$ is $\dfrac{2}{3}$.

SOLUTION

Divide numerator and denominator by n

$$\dfrac{\dfrac{2n}{n} - \dfrac{1}{n}}{\dfrac{3n}{n} + \dfrac{2}{n}}$$

$$= \dfrac{2 - \dfrac{1}{n}}{3 + \dfrac{2}{n}}$$

As $n \to \infty$ $\quad \dfrac{1}{n} \to 0$ and $\dfrac{2}{n} \to 0$

$$\dfrac{2 - \dfrac{1}{n}}{3 + \dfrac{2}{n}} \to \dfrac{2}{3}$$

Limiting value is $\dfrac{2}{3}$.

EXERCISE 4J

1 The nth term of a sequence is $\dfrac{n + 1}{2n + 1}$.

(i) Work out the first 3 terms of the sequence.
(ii) Work out the position of the term that has value 0.52.

2 The nth term of a sequence is $\dfrac{4n - 1}{2n - 5}$.

(i) Work out the position of the term that has value 2.36.
(ii) Show that 1 is not a term in the sequence.

3 The nth terms of sequences are shown.
Work out the limiting value of each sequence as $n \to \infty$.

(i) $\dfrac{2n}{n + 1}$ (ii) $\dfrac{n + 2}{n + 3}$ (iii) $\dfrac{n}{3n - 1}$ (iv) $\dfrac{2n - 1}{4n + 1}$

(v) $\dfrac{3n}{4n + 1}$ (vi) $\dfrac{1 - n}{n + 4}$ (vii) $\dfrac{2n}{3 - 4n}$ (viii) $\dfrac{2 - 6n}{5 - 2n}$

4 The nth term of a sequence is $\dfrac{5n + 1}{2n - 1}$.

Prove that the limiting value of the sequence as $n \to \infty$ is $\dfrac{5}{2}$.

5 The nth term of a sequence is $\dfrac{10 - 6n}{8n - 3}$.

Prove that the limiting value of the sequence as $n \to \infty$ is -0.75.

KEY POINTS

1 Quadratic equations can be solved by
   - factorising
   - completing the square
   - using the quadratic formula
   - drawing graphs.

2 Simultaneous equations can be solved by
   - elimination
   - substitution
   - drawing graphs.

3 Linear inequalities are dealt with like equations *but* if you multiply or divide by a negative number you must reverse the inequality sign.

4 When solving a quadratic inequality it is advisable to sketch the graph.

5 The factor theorem states that if $(x - a)$ is a factor of a polynomial $f(x)$, then $f(a) = 0$ and $x = a$ is a root of the equation $f(x) = 0$. Conversely if $f(a) = 0$, then $(x - a)$ is a factor of $f(x)$.

6 $a^m \times a^n = a^{m+n}$

$a^m \div a^n = a^{m-n}$

$(a^m)^n = a^{m \times n}$

$a^0 = 1$

$a^{-m} = \dfrac{1}{a^m}$

$a^{\frac{1}{n}} = \sqrt[n]{a}$

7 In an algebraic proof, show all your working.

8 A linear sequence has nth term $an + b$ where a and b are constants.

A quadratic sequence has nth term $an^2 + bn + c$ where a, b and c are constants.

GEOMETRY

Co-ordinate geometry

Most of the fundamental ideas of science are essentially simple, and may, as a rule, be expressed in a language comprehensible to everyone.

Albert Einstein

Parallel and perpendicular lines

In Chapter 3 we used this fact.

The line joining (x_1, y_1) to (x_2, y_2) has gradient m, where $m = \dfrac{y_2 - y_1}{x_2 - x_1}$.

If you know the gradients m_1 and m_2 of two lines, you can tell at once if they are parallel or perpendicular.

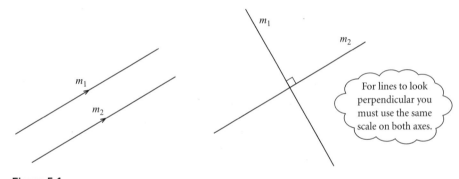

For lines to look perpendicular you must use the same scale on both axes.

Figure 5.1

Parallel lines: $m_1 = m_2$ Perpendicular lines: $m_1 m_2 = -1$

? How would you explain the result for parallel lines?

To illustrate the result for perpendicular lines try activity 5.1 on squared paper.

ACTIVITY 5.1

(i) Draw two congruent right-angled triangles in the positions shown in figure 5.2. p and q can take any value.

(ii) Explain why $\angle ABC = 90°$.

(iii) Calculate the gradient of AB (m_1) and the gradient of BC (m_2).

(iv) Show that $m_1 m_2 = -1$.

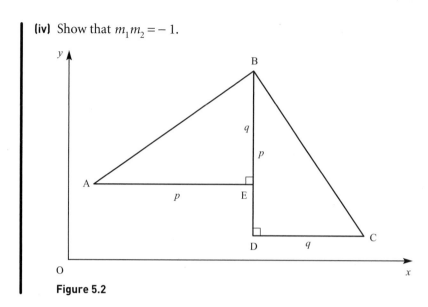

Figure 5.2

The distance between two points

You can use Pythagoras' theorem to find the distance between two points if you know their co-ordinates. Look at figure 5.3. P is $(3, 1)$ and $Q = (6, 5)$.

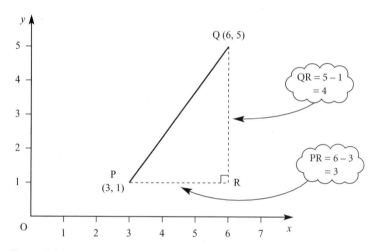

Figure 5.3

$$PQ = \sqrt{3^2 + 4^2} = \sqrt{25} = 5$$

This can be generalised. If P has co-ordinates (x_1, y_1) and Q has co-ordinates (x_2, y_2), then

$$\text{length } PQ = \sqrt{(x_2 - x_1)^2 + (y_2 - y_1)^2}.$$

The midpoint of a line joining two points

Look at the line joining the points $P(1, 2)$ and $Q(7, 4)$ in figure 5.4. The point M is the midpoint of PQ.

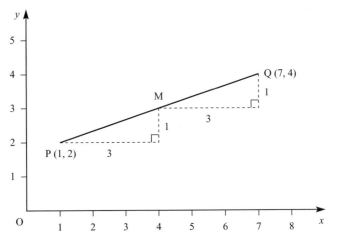

Figure 5.4

The co-ordinates of M are the means of the co-ordinates of P and Q.

$$\frac{1}{2}(1+7) = 4 \quad \text{and} \quad \frac{1}{2}(2+4) = 3$$

M is $(4, 3)$.

Again, if P has co-ordinates (x_1, y_1) and Q has co-ordinates (x_2, y_2), then the co-ordinates of the midpoint of PQ are given by

$$\text{midpoint} = \left(\frac{x_1 + x_2}{2}, \frac{y_1 + y_2}{2} \right).$$

EXAMPLE 5.1

A and B are the points $(-4, 2)$ and $(2, 5)$. Find

(i) the gradient of AB
(ii) the gradient of the line perpendicular to AB
(iii) the length of AB
(iv) the co-ordinates of the midpoint of AB.

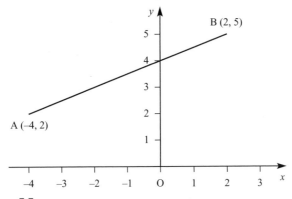

Figure 5.5

SOLUTION

(i) Taking $(-4, 2)$ as (x_1, y_1) and $(2, 5)$ as (x_2, y_2)

$$\text{gradient} = \frac{5 - 2}{2 - (-4)} = \frac{3}{6} = \frac{1}{2}.$$

(ii) $m_1 = \dfrac{1}{2}$ and $m_1 m_2 = -1$

$\Rightarrow \qquad\qquad \dfrac{1}{2} m_2 = -1$

$\Rightarrow \qquad\qquad m_2 = -2$

The line perpendicular to AB has gradient -2.

(iii) $\text{length} = \sqrt{(2 - (-4))^2 + (5 - 2)^2}$

$\qquad\quad = \sqrt{36 + 9}$

$\qquad\quad = \sqrt{45}$

$\qquad\quad = 6.71 \ (3 \text{ s.f.})$

(iv) $\text{midpoint} = \left(\dfrac{-4 + 2}{2}, \dfrac{2 + 5}{2} \right)$

$\qquad\qquad\quad = (-1, 3.5)$

EXAMPLE 5.2

P is the point (a, b) and Q is the point $(3a, 5b)$.

Find, in terms of a and b,
(i)   the gradient of PQ
(ii) the length of PQ
(iii) the midpoint of PQ.

SOLUTION

Taking (a, b) as (x_1, y_1) and $(3a, 5b)$ as (x_2, y_2)

(i) $\text{gradient} = \dfrac{5b - b}{3a - a}$

$\qquad\qquad\quad = \dfrac{4b}{2a} = \dfrac{2b}{a}$

(ii) $\text{length} = \sqrt{(3a - a)^2 + (5b - b)^2}$

$\qquad\qquad = \sqrt{4a^2 + 16b^2}$

? How can this result be simplified further?

(iii) $\text{midpoint} = \left(\dfrac{a + 3a}{2}, \dfrac{b + 5b}{2} \right)$

$\qquad\qquad\quad = (2a, 3b)$

EXAMPLE 5.3

A, B and C are the points $(1, 2)$, $(5, b)$ and $(6, 2)$. $\angle ABC = 90°$.

(i) Find two possible values of b.

(ii) Show all four points on a sketch and describe the shape of the figure you have drawn.

SOLUTION

(i) Gradient of AB $= \dfrac{b-2}{5-1} = \dfrac{b-2}{4}$

Gradient of BC $= \dfrac{2-b}{6-5} = 2 - b$

$\angle ABC = 90° \Rightarrow$ AB and BC are perpendicular.

$\Rightarrow \dfrac{(b-2)}{4} \times (2 - b) = -1$

$\Rightarrow (b-2)(2-b) = -4$

$\Rightarrow 2b - b^2 - 4 + 2b = -4$

$\Rightarrow 4b - b^2 = 0$

$\Rightarrow b(4 - b) = 0$

So $b = 0$ or $b = 4$.

(ii) See figure 5.6.

AB_1CB_2 is a quadrilateral with diagonals that are perpendicular, since AC is parallel to the x axis and B_1B_2 is parallel to the y axis.

This makes AB_1CB_2 a kite.

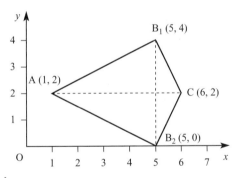

Figure 5.6

EXERCISE 5A

1 For each of the following pairs of points A and B, calculate

(a) the gradient of the line perpendicular to AB

(b) the length of AB

(c) the co-ordinates of the midpoint of AB.

(i)	A(4, 3)	B(8, 11)	**(ii)**	A(3, 4)	B(0, 13)
(iii)	A(5, 3)	B(10, −8)	**(iv)**	A(−6, −14)	B(1, 7)
(v)	A(6, 0)	B(8, 15)	**(vi)**	A(−2, −4)	B(3, 9)
(vii)	A(−3, −6)	B(2, −7)	**(viii)**	A(4, 7)	B(7, −4)

2 A(0, 5), B(4, 1) and C(2, 7) are the vertices of a triangle. Show that the triangle is right-angled
 (i) by finding the gradients of the sides
 (ii) by finding the lengths of the sides.

3 A(3, 6), B(7, 4) and C(1, 2) are the vertices of a triangle. Show that ABC is a right-angled isosceles triangle.

4 A(3, 5), B(3, 11) and C(6, 2) are vertices of a triangle.
 (i) Find the perimeter of the triangle.
 (ii) Using AB as the base, find the area of the triangle.

5 A quadrilateral PQRS has vertices at P(−2, −5), Q(11, − 7), R(9, 6) and S(−4, 8).
 (i) Find the lengths of the four sides of PQRS.
 (ii) Find the midpoints of the diagonals PR and QS.
 (iii) Without drawing a diagram, show why PQRS cannot be a square. What is it?

6 The points A, B and C have co-ordinates (2, 3), (6, 12) and (11, 7).
 (i) Draw the triangle ABC.
 (ii) Show by calculation that the triangle is isosceles and name the two equal sides.
 (iii) Find the midpoint of the third side.
 (iv) By calculating appropriate lengths, find the area of triangle ABC.

7 A parallelogram WXYZ has three of its vertices at W(2, 1), X(−1, 5) and Y(−3, 3).
 (i) Find the midpoint of WY.
 (ii) Use this information to find the co-ordinates of Z.

8 A triangle ABC has vertices at A(3, 2), B(4, 0) and C(8, 2).
 (i) Show that the triangle is right-angled.
 (ii) Find the co-ordinates of the point D such that ABCD is a rectangle.

9 The three points P(−2, 3), Q(1, q) and R(7, 0) are collinear (i.e. they lie on the same straight line).
 (i) Find the value of q.
 (ii) Find the ratio of the lengths PQ : QR.

10 A quadrilateral has vertices A(−2, 8), B(−5, 5), C(5, 3) and D(3, 7).
 (i) Draw the quadrilateral.
 (ii) Show by calculation that it is a trapezium.
 (iii) Find the co-ordinates of E when ABCE is a parallelogram.

Equation of a straight line

In Chapter 3 we used these three facts.

- The equation of the line with gradient m cutting the y-axis at the point $(0, c)$ is
$y = mx + c$.
- The equation of the line with gradient m passing through (x_1, y_1) is
$y - y_1 = m(x - x_1)$.
- The equation of the line passing through (x_1, y_1) and (x_2, y_2) is $\dfrac{y - y_1}{x - x_1} = \dfrac{y_2 - y_1}{x_2 - x_1}$.

EXAMPLE 5.4

An isosceles triangle with AB = AC has vertices at A(2, 3), B(8, 5) and C(4, 9). Find the equation of the line of symmetry.

SOLUTION

Figure 5.7 shows the triangle ABC with the line of symmetry joining A to the midpoint of BC.

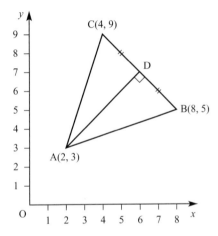

Figure 5.7

The co-ordinates of D are $\left(\dfrac{8 + 4}{2}, \dfrac{5 + 9}{2} \right) = (6, 7)$.

Let (x_1, y_1) be $(2, 3)$ and (x_2, y_2) be $(6, 7)$.

$$\frac{y - y_1}{y_2 - y_1} = \frac{x - x_1}{x_2 - x_1}$$

$$\Rightarrow \quad \frac{y - 3}{7 - 3} = \frac{x - 2}{6 - 2}$$

$$\Rightarrow \quad \frac{y - 3}{4} = \frac{x - 2}{4}$$

$$\Rightarrow \quad y = x + 1$$

EXAMPLE 5.5

The straight line with equation $5x - 4y = 40$ intersects the x axis at P and the y axis at Q.

(i) Work out the area of triangle OPQ where O is the origin.

(ii) Work out the equation of the line that passes through Q and is perpendicular to PQ.

SOLUTION

(i) Find the co-ordinates of P and Q.

Substitute $y = 0$ in equation of line $5x - 0 = 40$

$x = 8$ P $(8, 0)$

Substitute $x = 0$ in equation of line $0 - 4y = 40$

$y = -10$ Q $(0, -10)$

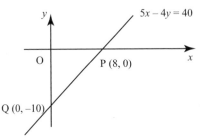

A sketch graph will often be useful.

Figure 5.8

Distance OP = 8 and distance OQ = 10.

Area of triangle $= \frac{1}{2} \times$ base $\times$ height

$$= \frac{1}{2} \times 8 \times 10$$

$$= 40 \text{ units}^2$$

(ii) Work out the gradient of PQ

$$\frac{0 - (-10)}{8 - 0}$$

$$= \frac{10}{8}$$

$$= \frac{5}{4}$$

Gradient of line perpendicular to PQ $= -\dfrac{4}{5}$

Line passes through $(0, -10)$ $y = -\dfrac{4}{5}x - 10$

EXERCISE 5B

1 By calculating the gradients of the following pairs of lines, state whether they are parallel, perpendicular or neither.

(i)	$x = 2$	**(ii)**	$y = 2x$	**(iii)**	$x + 2y = 1$		
	$y = -2$		$y = -2x$		$2x - y = 1$		
(iv)	$y = x - 3$	**(v)**	$y = 3 - 4x$	**(vi)**	$x + y = 5$		
	$x - y + 4 = 0$		$y = 4 - 3x$		$x - y = 5$		
(vii)	$x - 2y = 3$	**(viii)**	$x + 3y - 4 = 0$	**(ix)**	$2y = x$		
	$y = \frac{1}{2}x - 1$		$y = 3x + 4$		$2x + y = 4$		
(x)	$2x + 3y - 4 = 0$	**(xi)**	$x + 3y = 1$	**(xii)**	$2x = 5y$		
	$2x + 3y - 6 = 0$		$y + 3x = 1$		$5x + 2y = 0$		

2 Find the equations of these lines.
- (i)   Parallel to $y = 3x$ and passing through $(3, -1)$.
- (ii) Parallel to $y = 2x + 3$ and passing through $(0, 7)$.
- (iii) Parallel to $y = 3x - 4$ and passing through $(3, -7)$.
- (iv) Parallel to $4x - y + 2 = 0$ and passing through $(5, 0)$.
- (v)   Parallel to $3x + 2y - 1 = 0$ and passing through $(3, -2)$.
- (vi) Parallel to $2x + 4y - 5 = 0$ and passing through $(0, 5)$.

3 Find the equations of these lines.
- (i)   Perpendicular to $y = 2x$ and passing through $(0, 0)$.
- (ii) Perpendicular to $y = 3x - 1$ and passing through $(0, 4)$.
- (iii) Perpendicular to $y + x = 2$ and passing through $(3, -1)$.
- (iv) Perpendicular to $2x - y + 4 = 0$ and passing through $(1, -1)$.
- (v)   Perpendicular to $3x + 2y + 4 = 0$ and passing through $(3, 0)$.
- (vi) Perpendicular to $2x + y - 1 = 0$ and passing through $(4, 1)$.

4 Points P and Q have co-ordinates $P(3, -1)$ and $Q(5, 7)$.
- (i)   Find the gradient of PQ.
- (ii) Find the co-ordinates of the midpoint of PQ.
- (iii) Find the equation of the perpendicular bisector of PQ.

5 A triangle has vertices $P(2, 5)$, $Q(-2, -2)$ and $R(6, 0)$.
- (i)   Sketch the triangle.
- (ii) Find the co-ordinates of L, M and N, which are the midpoints of PQ, QR and RP respectively.
- (iii) Find the equations of the lines LR, MP and NQ (these are the medians of the triangle).
- (iv) Show that the point $(2, 1)$ lies on all three of these lines. (This shows that the medians of a triangle are concurrent.)

6 The straight line with equation $2x + 3y - 12 = 0$ cuts the x axis at A and the y axis at B.
- (i)   Sketch the line.
- (ii) Find the co-ordinates of A and B.
- (iii) Find the area of triangle OAB where O is the origin.
- (iv) Find the equation of the line which passes through O and is perpendicular to AB.
- (v)   Find the length of AB and, using the result in (iii), calculate the shortest distance from O to AB.

7 A quadrilateral has vertices at the points $A(-7, 0)$, $B(2, 3)$, $C(5, 0)$ and $D(-1, -6)$.
- (i)   Sketch the quadrilateral.
- (ii) Find the gradient of each side.
- (iii) Find the equation of each side.
- (iv) Find the length of each side.
- (v)   Find the area of the quadrilateral.

The intersection of two lines

You can find the point of intersection of any two lines (or curves) by solving their equations simultaneously.

EXAMPLE 5.6

(i) Sketch the lines $x + 3y - 6 = 0$ and $y = 2x - 5$ on the same axes.

(ii) Find the co-ordinates of the point where they intersect.

SOLUTION

(i) The line $x + 3y - 6 = 0$ passes through $(0, 2)$ and $(6, 0)$.

The line $y = 2x - 5$ passes through $(0, -5)$ and has a gradient of 2.

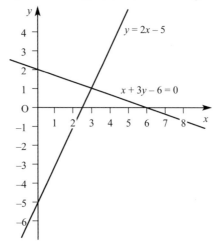

Figure 5.9

(ii)
$$x + 3y - 6 = 0 \quad \Rightarrow \quad 2x + 6y - 12 = 0 \quad \text{(multiplying by 2)} \quad \text{①}$$
$$y = 2x - 5 \quad \Rightarrow \quad 2x - y - 5 = 0 \quad \text{②}$$
$$\text{① - ②} \quad \Rightarrow \quad 7y - 7 = 0$$
$$\Rightarrow \quad y = 1$$

Substituting $y = 1$ in ① gives $2x + 6 - 12 = 0$
$$\Rightarrow \quad x = 3$$

The co-ordinates of the point of intersection are therefore $(3, 1)$.

An alternative method for solving these equations simultaneously would be to plot both lines on graph paper and read off the co-ordinates of the point of intersection.

? Graphical methods such as this will have limited accuracy. What factors would affect the accuracy of your solution in this case?

EXAMPLE 5.7

(i) Plot the lines $x + y - 2 = 0$ and $4y - x = 4$ on the same set of axes, for $-4 \leqslant x \leqslant 4$, using 1 cm to represent 1 unit on both axes.

(ii) Read off the solution to the simultaneous equations
$$x + y - 2 = 0$$
$$4y - x = 4$$

SOLUTION

(i) For each line choose three values of x and calculate the corresponding values of y. Then plot the lines and read off the co-ordinates of the point of intersection.

$x + y - 2 = 0$ $4y - x = 4$

x	-2	0	2
y	4	2	0

x	-4	0	4
y	0	1	2

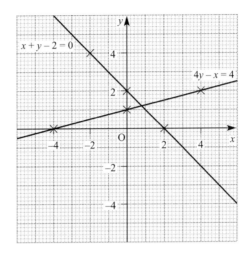

Figure 5.10

(ii) The point of intersection is $(0.8, 1.2)$, so the solution to the simultaneous equations is

$$x = 0.8, y = 1.2.$$

? Why should you plot three points for each line?

? Two lines may not intersect. When is this the case?

EXERCISE 5C

You will need graph paper for this exercise.

1 Solve these pairs of simultaneous equations by plotting their graphs. In each case you are given a suitable range of values of x.

   (i) $x = 3y + 1$ $0 \leqslant x \leqslant 3$
            $y = x - 1$

   (ii) $3x + 2y = 5$ $-2 \leqslant x \leqslant 2$
            $x + y = 3$

   (iii) $y = 2x - 4$ $0 \leqslant x \leqslant 6$
            $3x + 4y = 17$

   (iv) $6x + y = 1$ $0 \leqslant x \leqslant 2$
            $4x - y = 4$

2 (i)   Plot the lines $x = 4$, $y = x + 4$ and $4x + 3y = 12$ on the same axes for $-1 \leqslant x \leqslant 5$.

(ii) State the co-ordinates of the three points of intersection, and for each point give the pair of simultaneous equations that are satisfied there.

(iii) Find the area of the triangle enclosed by the three lines.

3 (i) Using the same scale for both axes, plot the lines $2y + x = 4$ and $2y + x = 10$ on the same axes, for $0 \leqslant x \leqslant 6$, and say what you notice about them. Why is this the case?

(ii) Add the line $y = 2x$ to your graph. What do you notice now? Can you justify what you see?

(iii) State the co-ordinates of the two points of intersection, and for each point give the pair of simultaneous equations that are satisfied there.

Dividing of a line in a given ratio

You can use similar triangles to work out the co-ordinates of a point that divides a line in a given ratio if you know the co-ordinates of the end points of the line.

Look at figure 5.11. A is $(4, 7)$ and B is $(19, 27)$.
C divides line AB in the ratio $2:3$, i.e. $AC:CB = 2:3$.

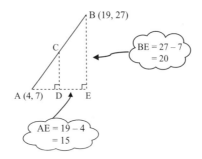

Figure 5.11

$$AC = \tfrac{2}{5} AB \qquad \text{so} \qquad AD = \tfrac{2}{5} AE$$
$$= \tfrac{2}{5} (15)$$
$$= 6$$
$$\text{Also} \qquad CD = \tfrac{2}{5} BE$$
$$= \tfrac{2}{5} (20)$$
$$= 8$$

The x co-ordinate of C is x co-ordinate of A + AD   i.e. $4 + 6 = 10$.
The y co-ordinate of C is y co-ordinate of A + CD   i.e. $7 + 8 = 15$.
Point C is $(10, 15)$.

This result can be generalised.

If C divides line AB in the ratio $p:q$ where A is (x_1, y_1) and B is (x_2, y_2) then

$$C \text{ is } \left(\frac{qx_1 + px_2}{p + q}, \frac{qy_1 + py_2}{p + q} \right)$$

Show that the above result is true.

Use figure 5.12. A is (x_1, y_1) and B is (x_2, y_2). C divides line AB in the ratio $p:q$.

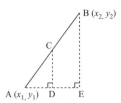

Figure 5.12

EXAMPLE 5.8 AB is a straight line. A is $(-3, 2)$ and B is $(4, -19)$.

C is a point on AB such that AC:CB is $4:3$.

Work out the co-ordinates of C.

SOLUTION

Taking $(-3, 2)$ as (x_1, y_1) and $(4, -19)$ as (x_2, y_2) and $p:q$ as $4:3$

$$x \text{ co-ordinate of C is } \frac{3(-3) + 4(4)}{3 + 4} = \frac{-9 + 16}{7}$$

$$= 1$$

$$y \text{ co-ordinate of C is } \frac{3(2) + 4(-19)}{3 + 4} = \frac{6 - 76}{7}$$

$$= -10$$

C is $(1, -10)$.

EXAMPLE 5.9 In figure 5.13, PQR is a straight line and PQ:QR is $2:5$.

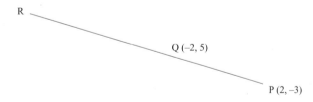

Figure 5.13

Work out the co-ordinates of R.

SOLUTION

Take $(2, -3)$ as (x_1, y_1) and R as (x_2, y_2). To find the x co-ordinate

$$-2 = \frac{5(2) + 2(x_2)}{2 + 5}$$

$$-2 = \frac{10 + 2x_2}{7} \qquad \text{(multiplying by 7)}$$

$$-14 = 10 + 2x_2 \qquad \text{(subtracting 10)}$$
$$-24 = 2x_2$$
$$-12 = x_2$$

To find the y co-ordinate

$$5 = \frac{5(-3) + 2(y_2)}{2 + 5}$$

$$5 = \frac{-15 + 2y_2}{7} \qquad \text{(multiplying by 7)}$$

$$35 = -15 + 2y_2 \qquad \text{(adding 15)}$$

$$50 = 2y_2$$

$$25 = y_2$$

R is $(-12, 25)$.

EXERCISE 5D

1 In each part, AB is a straight line and C is a point on AB. Work out the co-ordinates of C.

(i)	A is $(8, 3)$	B is $(3, 18)$	AC:CB is $3:2$
(ii)	A is $(12, -1)$	B is $(3, 5)$	AC:CB is $1:2$
(iii)	A is $(-2, 4)$	B is $(14, -4)$	AC:CB is $3:5$
(iv)	A is $(11, 9)$	B is $(-1, 19)$	AC:CB is $4:1$
(v)	A is $(0, -6)$	B is $(-18, -15)$	AC:CB is $5:4$

2 In each part, DEF is a straight line.

(i)	D is $(4, 3)$	E is $(8, 5)$	DE:EF is $2:3$	Find the co-ordinates of F.
(ii)	D is $(19, -5)$	E is $(7, 3)$	DE:EF is $4:3$	Find the co-ordinates of F.
(iii)	E is $(4, 9)$	F is $(16, 33)$	DE:EF is $1:4$	Find the co-ordinates of D.
(iv)	E is $(2, -8)$	F is $(7, -19)$	DE:EF is $3:5$	Find the co-ordinates of D.
(v)	D is $(-15, -8)$	E is $(-3, -2)$	DE:EF is $6:5$	Find the co-ordinates of F.

3 ABC is a straight line. AB is 25% longer than BC.

(i)   Work out the ratio AB:BC in its simplest form.

(ii) Work out the co-ordinates of C.

4 PRQ is a straight line.

PQ = 4PR

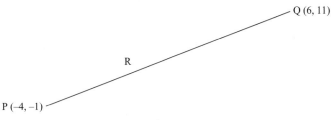

Work out the co-ordinates of R.

5 ABC is a straight line.

AC : BC = 8 : 5

Work out the co-ordinates of B.

Equation of a circle

When you draw a circle, you open your compasses to a fixed distance (the radius) and choose a position (the centre) for the point of your compasses. These facts are used to derive the *equation* of the circle.

Circles with centre (0, 0)

Figure 5.14 shows a circle with centre O (0, 0) and radius 4. P (*x*, *y*) is a general point on the circle.

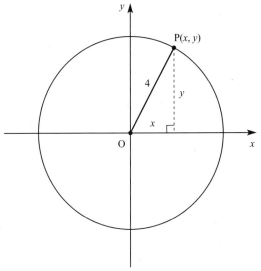

Figure 5.14

$$OP = \sqrt{(x - 0)^2 + (y - 0)^2} = 4$$

This simplifies to $x^2 + y^2 = 16$, which is the equation of the circle.

This can be generalised. A circle with centre $(0, 0)$, radius r has equation

$$x^2 + y^2 = r^2.$$

Circles with centre (a, b)

Figure 5.15 shows a circle with centre C $(4, 5)$ and radius 3. P (x, y) is a general point on the circle.

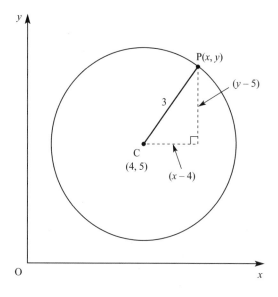

Figure 5.15

$$CP = \sqrt{(x - 4)^2 + (y - 5)^2} = 3$$

This simplifies to $(x - 4)^2 + (y - 5)^2 = 9$, which is the equation of the circle.

This can be generalised. A circle with centre (a, b), radius r has equation

$$(x - a)^2 + (y - b)^2 = r^2.$$

NOTE Multiplying out this equation gives

$$x^2 - 2ax + a^2 + y^2 - 2by + b^2 = r^2.$$

This rearranges to

$$x^2 + y^2 - 2ax - 2by + (a^2 + b^2 - r^2) = 0.$$

This form of the equation highlights some of the important characteristics of the equation of a circle. In particular

- the coefficients of x^2 and y^2 are equal

- there is no xy term.

EXAMPLE 5.10

Find the centre and radius of the circle

$$x^2 + (y+3)^2 = 25.$$

SOLUTION

Comparing with the general equation for a circle with radius r and centre (a, b),

$$(x - a)^2 + (y - b)^2 = r^2$$

gives $a = 0$, $b = -3$ and $r = 5$

$\Rightarrow$ the centre is $(0, -3)$, the radius is 5.

EXAMPLE 5.11

Figure 5.16 shows a circle with centre $(1, -2)$, which passes through the point $(4, 2)$.

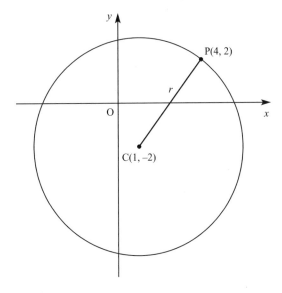

Figure 5.16

(i) Find the radius of the circle.
(ii) Find the equation of the circle.

SOLUTION

(i) Use the two points you are given to find the radius of the circle.

$$r^2 = (4 - 1)^2 + (2 - (-2))^2$$

$$= 25$$

$\Rightarrow$ radius $= 5$

(ii) Now using $(x - a)^2 + (y - b)^2 = r^2$

$\Rightarrow$ $(x - 1)^2 + (y + 2)^2 = 25$

is the equation of the circle.

EXAMPLE 5.12 Show that the equation $x^2 + y^2 + 4x - 6y - 3 = 0$ represents a circle.

Hence give the co-ordinates of the centre and the radius of the circle.

SOLUTION

Using completing the square

$$x^2 + 4x + y^2 - 6y = 3$$
$$x^2 + 4x + 4 + y^2 - 6y + 9 = 3 + 4$$
$$(x + 2)^2 + (y - 3)^2 = 3 + 4 + 9$$
$$\Rightarrow \qquad (x + 2)^2 + (y - 3)^2 = 16$$

This represents a circle with centre $(-2, 3)$, radius 4.

EXERCISE 5E

1 Find the equations of these circles.

    (i)   centre $(1, 2)$, radius 3
    (ii)   centre $(4, -3)$, radius 4
    (iii) centre $(1, 0)$, radius 5
    (iv) centre $(-2, -2)$, radius 2
    (v)   centre $(-4, 3)$, radius 1

2 For each of the circles given below

    (a) state the co-ordinates of the centre
    (b) state the radius
    (c) sketch the circle, paying particular attention to its position in relation to the origin and the co-ordinate axes.
        (i) $x^2 + y^2 = 25$
        (ii) $(x - 3)^2 + y^2 = 9$
        (iii) $(x + 4)^2 + (y - 3)^2 = 25$
        (iv) $(x + 1)^2 + (y + 6)^2 = 36$
        (v) $(x - 4)^2 + (y - 4)^2 = 16$

3 Find the equation of the circle with centre $(2, -3)$ which passes through $(1, -1)$.

4 A and B are $(4, -4)$ and $(2, 6)$ respectively. Find
    (i)   the midpoint C of AB
    (ii) the distance AC
    (iii) the equation of the circle that has AB as its diameter.

5 Show that the equation $x^2 + y^2 - 4x - 8y + 4 = 0$ represents a circle. Hence give the co-ordinates of the centre and the radius of the circle, and sketch the circle.

Circle geometry facts

Questions may use some of the circle geometry facts listed below.

The angle in a semi-circle is 90°

AB is a diameter.

P is a point on the circumference.

Angle APB = 90°

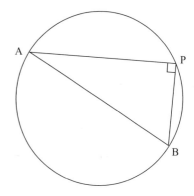

Figure 5.17

The perpendicular from the centre to a chord bisects the chord

C is the centre.

RS is a chord.

M is the midpoint of *RS*.

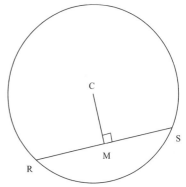

Figure 5.18

The angle between tangent and radius is 90°

C is the centre.

TQ is a tangent, touching the circle at Q.

QC is a radius.

Angle TQC = 90°

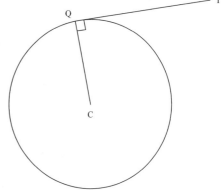

Figure 5.19

EXAMPLE 5.13

The circle in figure 5.20 has centre C.

PT is a tangent that touches the circle at P.

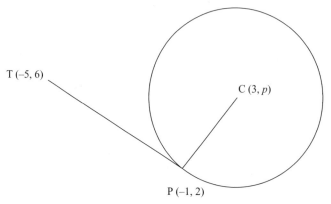

Figure 5.20

Work out the value of p.

SOLUTION

Work out gradient of PT.

Gradient of PT is

$$\frac{2 - 6}{-1 - (-5)} = \frac{-4}{-1 + 5}$$

$$= \frac{-4}{4}$$

$$= -1$$

Lines PT and PC are perpendicular since the angle between tangent and radius is 90°, so gradient of PC is 1.

$$\frac{p - 2}{3 - (-1)} = 1$$

$$\frac{p - 2}{4} = 1$$

$$p - 2 = 4$$

$$p = 6$$

EXAMPLE 5.14

A circle has centre C and passes through A $(-2, 1)$ and B $(4, 2)$.

Work out the equation of the line that is perpendicular to AB and passes through C. Give your answer in the form $ax + by = c$.

SOLUTION

Sketch the circle.

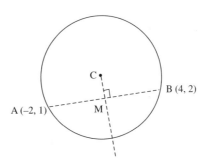

Figure 5.21

The perpendicular from the centre to a chord bisects the chord, so the required line will pass through the midpoint M of the chord AB.

Co-ordinates of M are $\left(\dfrac{-2 + 4}{2}, \dfrac{1 + 2}{2} \right) = \left(1, \dfrac{3}{2} \right)$

Gradient of AB is $\qquad \dfrac{2 - 1}{4 - (-2)} = \dfrac{1}{6}$

Lines CM and AB are perpendicular.

Gradient of perpendicular $= \dfrac{1}{m}$

Gradient of required line is -6.

Using $\qquad y - y_1 = m(x - x_1)$

$y - \dfrac{3}{2} = -6(x - 1)$

$y - \dfrac{3}{2} = -6x + 6$

$2y - 3 = -12x + 12$

$12x + 2y = 15$

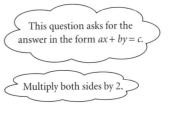

This question asks for the answer in the form $ax + by = c$.

Multiply both sides by 2.

EXERCISE 5F

If a diagram is not given, drawing a sketch may help.

1   AB is a diameter of a circle. P is a point on the circumference of the circle.
    A is $(2, 8)$ and P is $(4, -2)$.
    Work out the gradient of BP.

2   A circle has centre C.
    RS is a chord of the circle and R is $(-1, 6)$.
    Y $(2, 3)$ is a point on RS such that angle CYR $= 90°$.
    Work out the co-ordinates of S.

3 AB is a diameter of the circle.
A is $(k, 5)$, P is $(3, 8)$ and B is $(7, 2)$.

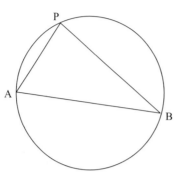

Work out the value of k.

4 AB is a chord of a circle, centre C.
D is a point on AB such that angle ADC is 90°.

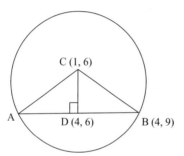

Work out the equation of the line that passes through A and C.

5 T $(3, -4)$ is a point on the circumference of the circle $x^2 + y^2 = 25$.

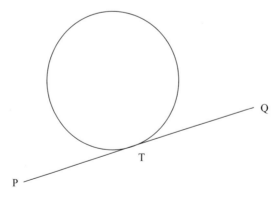

Work out the equation of the tangent PTQ.
Give your answer in the form $y = mx + c$.

6 The diagram shows a circle that intersects the x axis at $(-2, 0)$ and $(6, 0)$. The centre of the circle is $(a, 3)$.

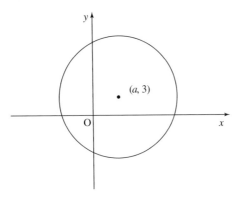

Work out the equation of the circle.

KEY POINTS

1 Two lines are parallel when their gradients are equal.

2 Two lines are perpendicular when the product of their gradients is -1.

3 When the points A and B have co-ordinates (x_1, y_1) and (x_2, y_2) respectively then

$$\text{distance AB} = \sqrt{(x_2 - x_1)^2 + (y_2 - y_1)^2}$$

$$\text{midpoint of AB is} \left(\frac{x_1 + x_2}{2}, \frac{y_1 + y_2}{2} \right).$$

4 The co-ordinates of the point of intersection of two lines are found by solving their equations simultaneously.

5 If C divides line AB in the ratio $p:q$ where A is (x_1, y_1) and B is (x_2, y_2) then

$$\text{C is} \left(\frac{qx_1 + px_2}{p + q}, \frac{qy_1 + py_2}{p + q} \right).$$

6 The equation of a circle with centre (h, k) and radius r is

$$(x - h)^2 + (y - k)^2 = r^2.$$

When the centre is at the origin $(0, 0)$ this simplifies to

$$x^2 + y^2 = r^2.$$

Geometry I

The difficulty lies, not in the new ideas, but in escaping the old ones, which ramify, for those brought up as most of us have been, into every corner of our minds.

John Maynard Keynes

Knowledge of geometry topics will be needed within many sections of the specification.

This section provides a summary of the main facts that are required.

Mensuration

You need to recall these formulae.

Area of triangle $= \frac{1}{2} \times$ base $\times$ height

Area of parallelogram $=$ base $\times$ height

Circumference of circle $= \pi d$ Area of circle $= \pi r^2$

Volume of prism $=$ area of cross section $\times$ length

Volume of pyramid $= \frac{1}{3} \times$ base area $\times$ height

These formulae are given on the formula sheet.

Volume of cone $= \frac{1}{3}\pi r^2 h$ Curved surface area of cone $= \pi r l$

Volume of sphere $= \frac{4}{3}\pi r^3$ Surface area of sphere $= 4\pi r^2$

Pythagoras' theorem

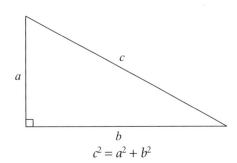

Figure 6.1

$$c^2 = a^2 + b^2$$

Write down the square of all the integers from 1 to 25 inclusive.

Check that $5^2 = 3^2 + 4^2$.

Write down as many other examples of $c^2 = a^2 + b^2$ as you can find.

How is each set of a, b and c linked to a right-angled triangle?

Pythagorean triples

These are all Pythagorean triples as each set of three numbers satisfies $c^2 = a^2 + b^2$.

3, 4, 5   5, 12, 13   8, 15, 17   7, 24, 25

By similar triangles, any multiple or fraction of each set will also be a Pythagorean triple.

For example,   9, 12, 15   2.5, 6, 6.5   16, 30, 34   1.4, 4.8, 5

Angle facts

Angle properties of parallel and intersecting lines should be known.

Angle properties of triangles, quadrilaterals and polygons should be known.

Circle theorems

The following angle properties should be known.

Angles in the same segment are equal

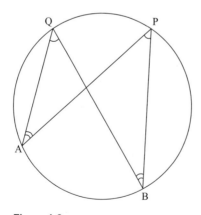

> Can also be referred to as **Angles subtended by the same arc are equal.**

Figure 6.2

A, B, P and Q are points on the circumference.

Angle APB = angle AQB

Also,   angle QAP = angle QBP

Angle at the centre is double the angle at the circumference

C is the centre.

A, B and D are points on the circumference.

> Both angles must be subtended from the same arc.

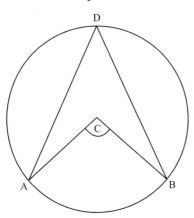

Figure 6.3

Angle ACB = 2 × angle ADB

S is the centre.

P, Q and R are points on the circumference.

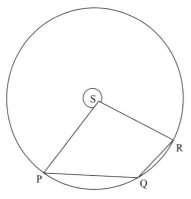

Figure 6.4

Reflex angle PSR = 2 × angle PQR

Opposite angles of a cyclic quadrilateral add up to 180°

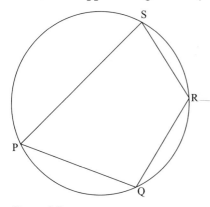

> A cyclic quadrilateral has all four vertices on the circumference.

P, Q, R and S are points on the circumference.

Angle PQR + angle RSP = 180°

Also,　angle SPQ + angle QRS = 180°

Figure 6.5

Alternate segment theorem

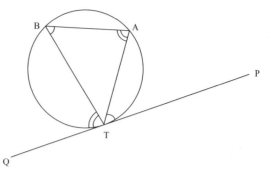

PTQ is a tangent, touching the circle at T. A and B are points on the circumference.

Figure 6.6

Angle ATP = angle TBA

> The angle between the tangent PT and the chord TA is equal to the angle in the other segment.

Also, angle QTB = angle BAT

> The angle between the tangent QT and the chord TB is equal to the angle in the other segment.

Circle theorems and other angle facts will be needed in the Geometric proof section (page 124).

Circle theorems and other angle facts will be needed in the Geometric proof section (page 124).

EXERCISE 6A

1 Work out angle *x* and/or angle *y* in each of the following. C is the centre of the circle.

(i)

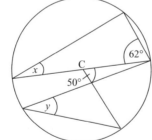

(ii)

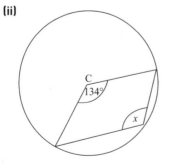

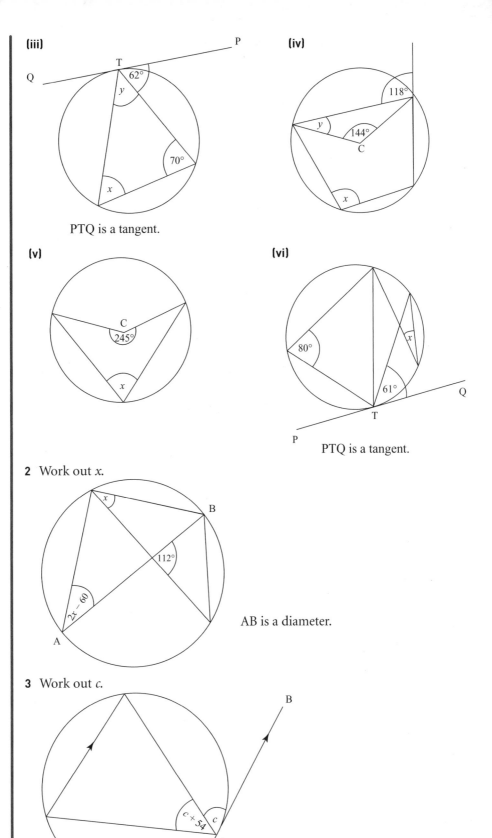

(iii)

PTQ is a tangent.

(iv)

(v)

(vi)

PTQ is a tangent.

2 Work out x.

AB is a diameter.

3 Work out c.

AB is a tangent.

4 Work out x and y.

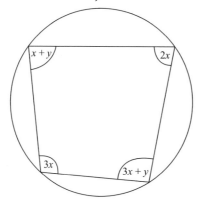

Geometric proof

In this section you will need to construct formal proofs.

Geometrical properties used must be stated using correct notation and vocabulary.

EXAMPLE 6.1

In triangle BCD, BC = BD.

ABC is a straight line.

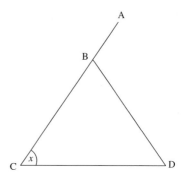

Figure 6.7

Prove that angle ABD = $2x$.

SOLUTION

Method 1

angle CDB = x	(base angles of isosceles triangle)
angle CBD = $180 - 2x$	(angle sum of triangle)
angle ABD = $2x$	(adjacent angles on a straight line)

Abbreviations may be used but the reasons must be unambiguous.

Method 2

angle CDB = x	(base angles of isosceles triangle)
angle ABD = $2x$	(exterior angle of triangle = sum of interior opposite angles)

There will often be more than one method in a geometric proof. You only need to provide one.

EXAMPLE 6.2

AP is a tangent that touches the circle at P.

AP is parallel to QR.

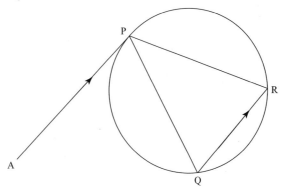

Figure 6.8

Prove that triangle PQR is isosceles.

SOLUTION

Method 1

angle APQ = angle PQR   (alternate angles)

angle APQ = angle PRQ   (alternate segment theorem)

Therefore,   angle PQR = angle PRQ

Triangle with two equal angles is isosceles.

Method 2

Let angle APQ = x

angle PQR = x (alternate angles)

angle PRQ = x (alternate segment theorem)

Therefore,   angle PQR = angle PRQ

Triangle with two equal angles is isosceles.

> This is very similar to **method 1** but starts by introducing a lower case letter.

EXAMPLE 6.3

PQRS is a cyclic quadrilateral.

C is the centre.

Angle QPS = y Angle QCR = $2x$ Angle SQR = 40°

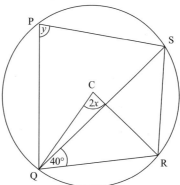

Figure 6.9

Prove that $y = x + 40$.

SOLUTION

angle QSR $= x$ (angle at circumference is half angle at centre)

angle SRQ $= 180 - y$ (opposite angles of cyclic quadrilateral)

In triangle QRS, $x + 180 - y + 40 = 180$ (angle sum of triangle)

Rearranging $x + 40 = y$

NOTE The use of congruent triangles will not be required.

The examples show the recommended way to present a proof.

EXERCISE 6B

1 AC is a diameter. B is a point on the circumference.

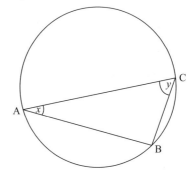

Prove that $x = 90 - y$.

2 ABCD is parallel to EFG.

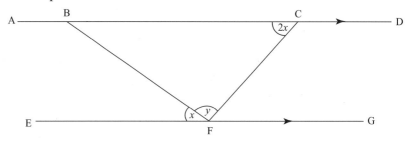

Prove that $3x + y = 180$.

3 AB is a diameter. X and Y are points on the circumference.

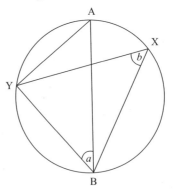

Prove that $a + b = 90$.

4 CBE and DBF are straight lines.

CD is parallel to AB.

BC = BD

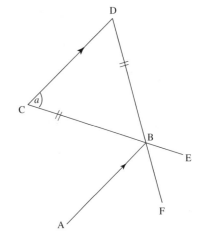

Prove that angle ABC = angle ABF.

5 PT is a tangent, touching the circle at T. C is the centre.

M and N are points on the circumference.

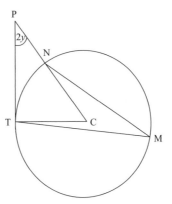

Prove that angle TMN = $45 - y$.

6 AB is a tangent, touching the circle at B.

ADC is a straight line.

AB = BC

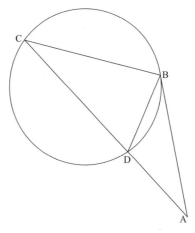

Prove that triangle ABD is isosceles.

7 DEFG is a cyclic quadrilateral.

C is the centre.

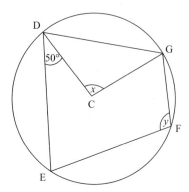

Prove that $x = 2y - 80$.

8 C is the centre.

P, Q and R are points on the circumference.

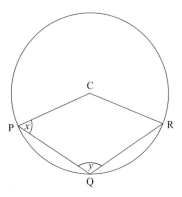

Prove that $y = 2x$.

Trigonometry in two dimensions

You have met definitions of the three trigonometrical functions, sin, cos and tan, using the sides of a right-angled triangle.

sin is an abbreviation of sine, cos of cosine and tan of tangent.

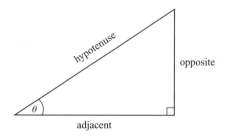

Figure 6.10

In figure 6.10

$$\sin\theta = \frac{\text{opposite}}{\text{hypotenuse}} \qquad \cos\theta = \frac{\text{adjacent}}{\text{hypotenuse}} \qquad \tan\theta = \frac{\text{opposite}}{\text{adjacent}}$$

? Do these definitions work for angles of any size?

EXAMPLE 6.4

Find the length of the side marked a in the triangle in figure 6.11.

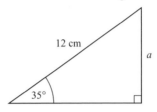

Figure 6.11

SOLUTION

Side a is *opposite* the angle of 35°, and the *hypotenuse* is 12 cm, so we use sin 35°.

$$\sin 35° = \frac{\text{opposite}}{\text{hypotenuse}}$$

$$= \frac{a}{12}$$

$$\Rightarrow \qquad a = 12 \sin 35°$$
$$\Rightarrow \qquad a = 6.9\,\text{cm} \;(1\text{ d.p.})$$

EXAMPLE 6.5

The diagram represents a ladder leaning against a wall.

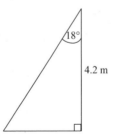

Figure 6.12

Work out the length of the ladder.

Give your answer to 3 significant figures.

SOLUTION

The side of length 4.2 m is *adjacent* to the angle of 18°, and we want the *hypotenuse* so use cos 18°.

$$\cos 18° = \frac{\text{adjacent}}{\text{hypotenuse}}$$

$$= \frac{4.2}{\text{hypotenuse}}$$

$$\text{hypotenuse} = \frac{4.2}{\cos 18°}$$

$$= 4.42 \text{ m (3 s.f.)}$$

EXAMPLE 6.6

Find the size of the angle marked θ in the triangle in figure 6.13.

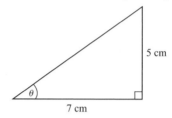

Figure 6.13

SOLUTION

The sides whose lengths are known are those *opposite* and *adjacent* to θ so we use $\tan \theta$.

$$\tan \theta = \frac{\text{opposite}}{\text{adjacent}} = \frac{5}{7} = 0.714\,285\,714$$

$$\Rightarrow \qquad \theta = 35.5° \text{ (1 d.p.)}$$

? The full calculator value for $\frac{5}{7}$ has been used to find the value of θ. What is the least number of decimal places that you could use to give the same value for the angle (to 1 d.p.) in this example?

EXAMPLE 6.7

A bird flies straight from the top of a 15 m tall tree, at an angle of depression of 27°, to catch a worm on the ground.

(i) How far does the bird fly?

(ii) How far was the worm from the bottom of the tree?

SOLUTION

First draw a sketch, labelling the information given and using letters to mark what you want to find.

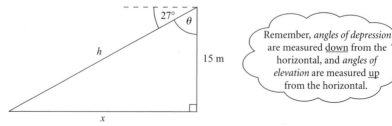

Remember, *angles of depression* are measured <u>down</u> from the horizontal, and *angles of elevation* are measured <u>up</u> from the horizontal.

Figure 6.14

(i) $\theta + 27° = 90°$

$\Rightarrow \quad \theta = 63°$

$$\cos 63° = \frac{15}{h}$$

$\Rightarrow \quad h = \dfrac{15}{\cos 63°} = 33.040\,338\,97$

The bird flies 33 m.

(ii)   Using Pythagoras' theorem

$$h^2 = x^2 + 15^2$$

$\Rightarrow \quad x^2 = 33.040\,338\,97^2 - 15^2 = 866.663\,999$

$\Rightarrow \quad x = 29.439\,157\,58$

The worm is 29.4 m from the bottom of the tree.

?   If you used trigonometry for part **(ii)** of this question, which would be the best function to use? Why?

NOTE   Examination questions involving right-angled triangles will involve applying trigonometry in a context. Examples and exercises include some questions without a context to provide practice at the skills needed in applications questions.

Historical note   The word for trigonometry is derived from three Greek words.

Tria: *three*   gonia: *angle*   metron *measure*
(τρια)   (γονια)   (μετρον)

This shows how trigonometry developed from studying angles, often in connection with astronomy, although the subject was probably discovered independently by a number of people. Hipparchus (150 BC) is believed to have produced the first trigonometrical tables which gave lengths of chords of a circle of unit radius. His work was further developed by Ptolemy in AD 100.

EXERCISE 6C

1   Find the length marked *x* in each of these triangles. Give your answers correct to 1 decimal place.

(i)
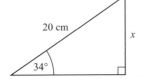

(ii)
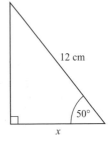

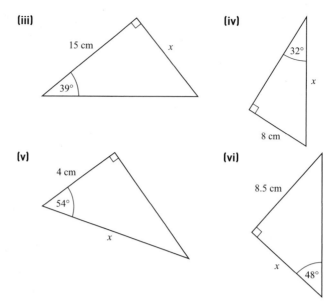

(iii) 15 cm 39° x

(iv) 32° x 8 cm

(v) 4 cm 54° x

(vi) 8.5 cm x 48°

2 Find the angle marked θ in each of these triangles. Give your answers correct to 1 decimal place.

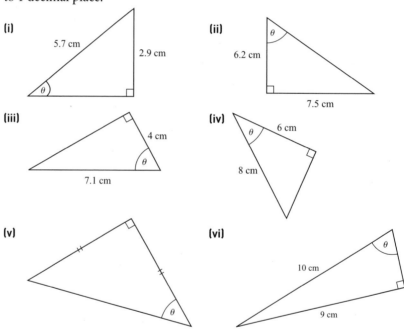

(i) 5.7 cm 2.9 cm θ

(ii) θ 6.2 cm 7.5 cm

(iii) 4 cm θ 7.1 cm

(iv) θ 6 cm 8 cm

(v) θ

(vi) θ 10 cm 9 cm

3 In an isosceles triangle, the line of symmetry bisects the base of the triangle. Use this fact to find the angle θ and the lengths x and y in these diagrams.

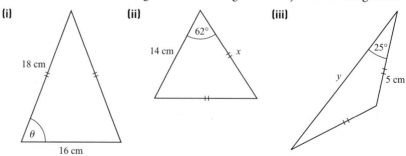

(i) 18 cm θ 16 cm

(ii) 62° 14 cm x

(iii) 25° y 5 cm

4 A ladder 5 m long rests against a wall. The foot of the ladder makes an angle of 65° with the ground.
How far up the wall does the ladder reach?

5 From the top of a vertical cliff 30 m high, the angle of depression of a boat at sea is 21°.
How far is the boat from the bottom of the cliff?

6 From a point 120 m from the base of an office block, the angle of elevation of the top of the block is 67°.
How tall is the block?

7 A rectangle has sides of length 12 cm and 8 cm.
What angle does the diagonal make with the longest side?

8 The diagram shows the positions of three airports: E (East Midlands), M (Manchester) and L (Leeds).
The distance from M to L is 65 km on a bearing of 060°.
Angle LME = 90° and ME = 100 km.
  (i) Calculate, correct to three significant figures, the distance LE.
  (ii) Calculate, correct to the nearest degree, the size of angle MEL.
  (iii) An aircraft leaves M at 10.45 am and flies direct to E, arriving at 11.03 am. Calculate, correct to three significant figures, the average speed of the aircraft in kilometres per hour.

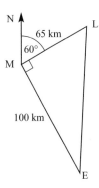

Angles of 45°, 30° and 60°

The sine, cosine and tangent of these angles have exact values.

When working without a calculator, the exact values should be known or derived.

Consider an isosceles right-angled triangle with AB = BC = 1 unit.

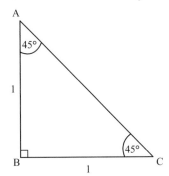

Figure 6.15

Using Pythagoras' theorem
$$AC^2 = 1^2 + 1^2$$
$$AC = \sqrt{2}$$

$$\sin 45° = \frac{\text{opp}}{\text{hyp}}$$

$$\sin 45° = \frac{1}{\sqrt{2}} \qquad \cos 45° = \frac{1}{\sqrt{2}} \qquad \tan 45° = 1$$

? What would the results be if you used AB = BC = 2 units?

Consider an equilateral triangle of side length 2 (Figure 6.16**(a)**).

By adding an angle bisector we get two congruent triangles (Figure 6.16**(b)**).

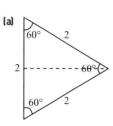

Figure 6.16

Using Pythagoras' theorem

$$QR^2 = 2^2 - 1^2$$
$$QR = \sqrt{3}$$

Using the trig ratios this gives us

$$\sin 30° = \frac{1}{2} \qquad \cos 30° = \frac{\sqrt{3}}{2} \qquad \tan 30° = \frac{1}{\sqrt{3}}$$

$$\sin 60° = \frac{\sqrt{3}}{2} \qquad \cos 60° = \frac{1}{2} \qquad \tan 60° = \sqrt{3}$$

EXAMPLE 6.8

Do not use a calculator for this question.

Work out the exact value of *y*.

Give your answer in the form $p + q\sqrt{3}$ where *p* and *q* are integers.

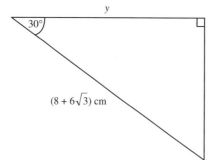

Figure 6.17

SOLUTION

$$\cos 30° = \frac{y}{8 + 6\sqrt{3}}$$

$$\Rightarrow \qquad \frac{\sqrt{3}}{2} = \frac{y}{8 + 6\sqrt{3}}$$

$$\Rightarrow \frac{\sqrt{3}}{2} \times (8 + 6\sqrt{3}) = y$$

$$\Rightarrow \qquad 4\sqrt{3} + 9 = y$$

$$y = 9 + 4\sqrt{3}$$

EXERCISE 6D

Use of a calculator is not allowed.

1 Work out the exact value of *x* in each of the following.
 Give answers in their simplest form.

(i)

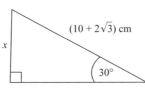

(ii)

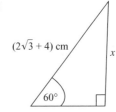

(iii)

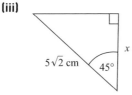

(iv)

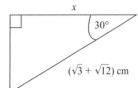

2 Show that *y* is an integer.

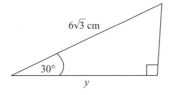

3 Show that *p* is an integer.

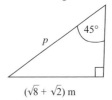

4

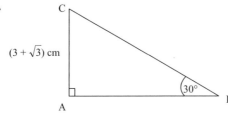

Work out the area of triangle ABC.

Give your answer in the form $p + q\sqrt{3}$ where *p* and *q* are integers.

5 Work out the exact value of CD.

Give your answer in the form $k\sqrt{6}$ where k is an integer.

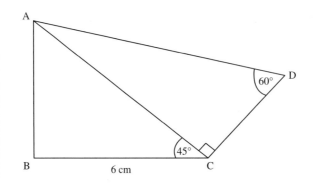

Problems in three dimensions

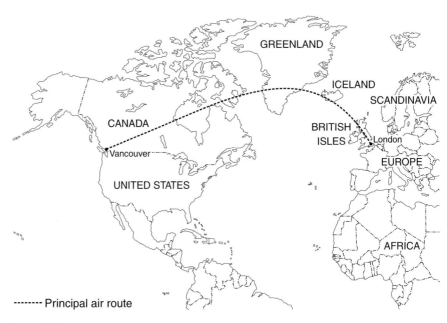

-------- Principal air route

Figure 6.18

? An aircraft flying between two places at the same latitude doesn't usually follow a route along the line of latitude. Why?

When you are solving three-dimensional problems it is extremely important to draw good diagrams. There are two types:

- representations of three-dimensional objects
- true shape diagrams of two-dimensional sections within a three-dimensional object.

Representations of three-dimensional objects

Figures 6.19 and 6.20 illustrate ways in which you can draw a clear diagram.

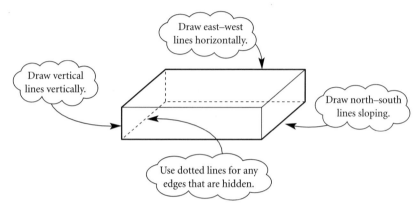

Figure 6.19

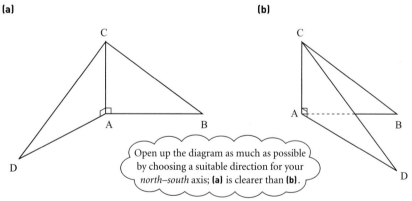

Figure 6.20

True shape diagrams

In a two-dimensional representation of a three-dimensional object, right angles do not always appear to be 90°, so draw as many true shape diagrams as necessary.

For example, if you need to do calculations on the triangular cross-section BCD in figure 6.21**(a)**, you should draw the triangle so that the right angle really does look 90° as in figure 6.21**(b)**.

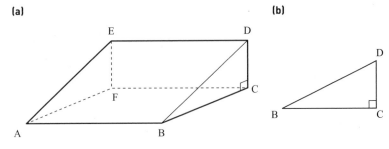

(a)   (b)

Figure 6.21

Lines and planes in three dimensions

A *plane* is a flat surface (not necessarily horizontal).

A *line of greatest slope* of a sloping plane is a line of greatest gradient, i.e. the line that a ball would follow if allowed to roll down it. This is shown in figure 6.22.

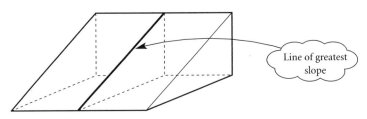

Figure 6.22

? Give an example of a sloping plane from everyday life.

In three-dimensional problems you need to be aware of the relationships between lines and planes.

Two lines

In two dimensions, two lines either meet (when extended if necessary), or they are parallel.

In three dimensions, there is a third option: they are *skew*, as in figure 6.23.

The road under the bridge and the road over the bridge are skew lines.

Figure 6.23

A line and a plane

In three dimensions there are three options.

1 The line and the plane are *parallel*. A curtain rail is *parallel* to the floor.

2 The line meets the plane at a *single point*. When you are writing, your pen meets the paper at a *single point*.

3 The line *lies in* the plane. When you put your pen down, your pen *lies in* the plane of the paper.

(a)   **(b)**   **(c)**

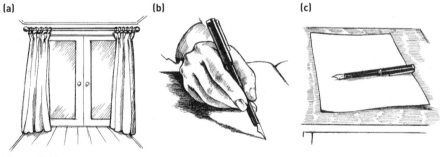

Figure 6.24

Angle between a line and a plane

Draw a perpendicular from the line to the plane.

Line PQ meets the plane ABCD at Q.

PR is perpendicular to the plane.

QR is in the plane.

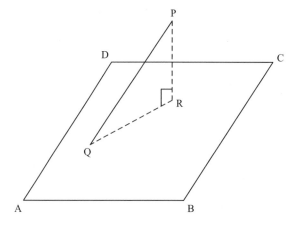

Figure 6.25

Angle between line and plane is angle PQR.

Two planes

In three dimensions there are two options.

1 The two planes are *parallel*. Opposite walls of a room are *parallel*.

2 The two planes meet *in a line*. The ceiling meets each wall of a room *in a line*. An open gate and a wall meet *in a line*.

(a)   (b)

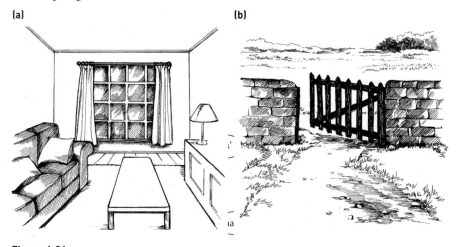

Figure 6.26

? Give other examples of these cases.

Angle between two planes

Find the line where the planes meet.

Draw a line in each plane that is perpendicular to the line where the planes meet.

The angle between these two lines is the angle between the planes.

Planes ABCD and APQD meet along AD.

The dashed lines are each perpendicular to AD.

x is the angle between the planes.

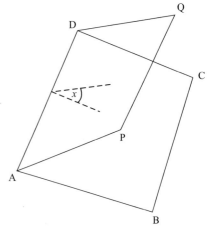

Figure 6.27

EXAMPLE 6.9

Figure 6.28 shows a wedge ABCDEF with AB = 8 cm, BC = 6 cm and CD = 2 cm. The angle BCD is 90°.

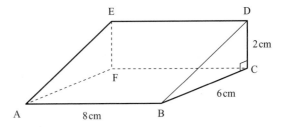

Figure 6.28

Find

(i) AC **(ii)** AD **(iii)** the angle between DA and ABCF
(iv) the angle between ABDE and ABCF

SOLUTION

(i) From figure 6.29**(a)**
$$AC^2 = 8^2 + 6^2 \qquad \text{(Pythagoras)}$$
$$\Rightarrow \quad AC = 10 \, \text{cm}$$

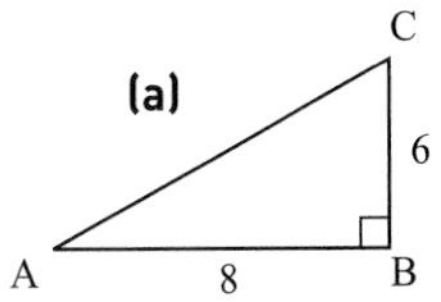

(a)

(ii) From figure 6.29**(b)**
$$AD^2 = AC^2 + 2^2$$
(Pythagoras)
$$\Rightarrow \quad AD = 10.2 \, \text{cm} \quad \text{(1 d.p.)}$$

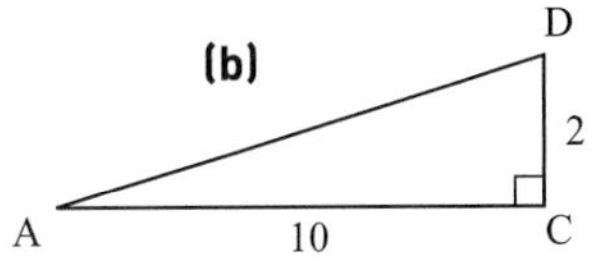

(b)

DA and ABCF meet at A. DC is perpendicular to ABCF.

Figure 6.29

(iii) From figure 6.29**(b)**, the angle between DA and ABCF is $\angle DAC$

$$\tan \angle DAC = \frac{2}{10}$$

$\Rightarrow \quad \angle DAC = 11.3° \qquad (1 \text{ d.p.})$

(iv) From figure 6.29**(c)**, the angle between ABDE and ABCF is $\angle DBC$

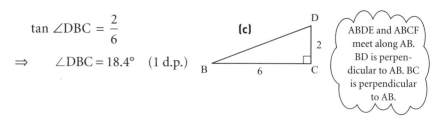

$$\tan \angle DBC = \frac{2}{6}$$

$\Rightarrow \quad \angle DBC = 18.4° \quad (1 \text{ d.p.})$

ABDE and ABCF meet along AB. BD is perpendicular to AB. BC is perpendicular to AB.

EXAMPLE 6.10

Figure 6.30 shows a straight level road AB, 400 m long. A vertical radio mast XY stands some distance from the road and the bottom of the mast, X, is on the same level as the road. The angle of elevation of Y from A is 30°, $\angle XAB = 25°$ and $\angle AXB = 90°$. Calculate

(i) the distance AX

(ii) the height of the mast

(iii) the distance of X from the road.

Give your answers to 3 significant figures.

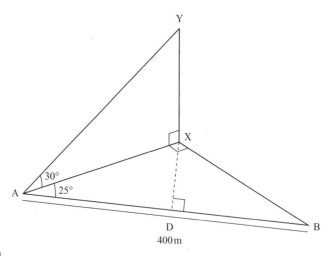

Figure 6.30

SOLUTION

(i) From figure 6.31**(a)**

$$\frac{AX}{400} = \cos 25°$$

$\Rightarrow \quad AX = 362.523\ldots$

$\Rightarrow \quad$ The distance $AX = 363$ m.

(ii) From figure 6.31**(b)**

$$\frac{XY}{362.523\ldots} = \tan 30°$$

$\Rightarrow \quad XY = 209.302\ldots$

$\Rightarrow \quad$ The height of the mast $XY = 209$ m.

(iii) From figure 6.31**(c)**

$$\frac{DX}{362.523\ldots} = \sin 25°$$

$\Rightarrow \quad DX = 153.208\ldots$

$\Rightarrow \quad$ The distance of X from the road $= 153$ m.

(a)

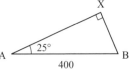

(b)

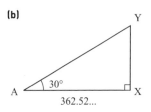

(c)

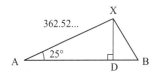

Figure 6.31

EXAMPLE 6.11

The right pyramid VABCD has square base ABCD.

The vertex, V, is directly above the centre, X, of the base.

M is the midpoint of BC.

AB = 8 metres and VX = 15 metres.

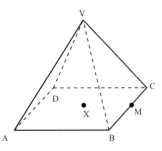

Figure 6.32

Work out the angle between the planes ABCD and VBC.

SOLUTION

The planes meet along BC.

MX and VM are both perpendicular to BC.

Angle VXM is 90°.

$XM = 8 \div 2$

$\quad = 4$ m

$\tan VMX = \dfrac{15}{4}$

angle $VMX = 75.1°$ (1 d.p.)

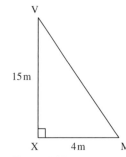

Figure 6.33

1   The cube ABCDEFGH shown in the
diagram has sides of length 10 cm.

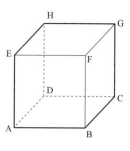

Find

(i)   the length AC
(ii)   the length AG
(iii) the angle GAC

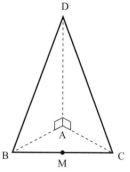

2   The diagram represents a pyramid ABCD.
ABC is an isosceles triangle with AB = AC = 5 cm
and BC = 8 cm.
BCD is an isosceles triangle with BD = CD = 13 cm.
D is vertically above A and ∠BAD = ∠CAD = 90°.
M is the midpoint of BC.
Calculate

(i)   the length AM
(ii)   the angle BCD
(iii) the angle between the planes BCA and BCD.

3   The diagram shows a wedge ABCDEF which has been made to hold a door open.
AB = 5 cm, BC = 12 cm and FC = 4 cm.
Find

(i)   the angle FBC
(ii)   the length AC
(iii) the angle between the line
       FA and the plane ABCD.

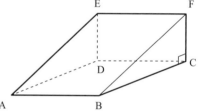

There is a gap of 2 cm between the door and the floor.

(iv)   How far along BF will the base of the door meet the wedge?

4   A, B and C are points on a horizontal plane.
A is 75 m from C on a bearing of 210° and the bearing of B from C is 120°. The
bearing of B from A is 075°.
From A the angle of elevation of the top T of a vertical tower at C is 42°.
Find

(i)   the distance BC
(ii)   the height of the tower
(iii) the angle of elevation of T from B.

5   C is the foot of a vertical tower CT 28 m high.
A and B are points in the same horizontal plane as C and CA = CB.
P is the point on AB that is nearest to C.
The angle of elevation of the top of the tower from P is 40° and ∠ACB = 120°.
Calculate

(i)   the length CP
(ii)   the length CB
(iii) the length AB
(iv)   the angle of elevation of the top of the tower from B.

6 The waste-paper basket shown in the diagram has a top ABCD that is a square of side 30 cm and a base PQRS that is a square of side 20 cm.
The line joining the centres of the top and base is perpendicular to both and is 40 cm long.

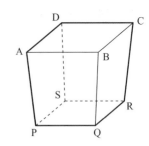

Find

(i) the length PR

(ii) the length AC

(iii) the length AP.

7 In Egypt, pyramids were used as burial chambers for the Pharaohs.
The largest of these, shown in the diagram and built about 2500BC for Cheops, is 146 m high and has a square base of side 231 m.
E is the centre of the base and VE = 146 m.

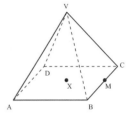

Find

(i) the angle between VA and ABCD

(ii) the length VA

(iii) the length VM where M is the midpoint of AB

(iv) the angle between VAB and ABCD.

8 The tent shown in the diagram has a base that is 2.2 m wide and 3.6 m long.
The ends are isosceles triangles, inclined at an angle of 80° to the base.
∠AEB = ∠DFC = 70° and M is the midpoint of AB.

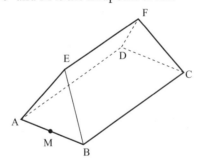

Find

(i) the length of EM

(ii) the height of EF above the base

(iii) the length of EF.

9 The right pyramid VABCD has rectangular base ABCD.
The vertex, V, is directly above the centre, X, of the base.
M is the midpoint of BC.
AB = 12 metres, BC = 9 metres and VA = 18 metres.

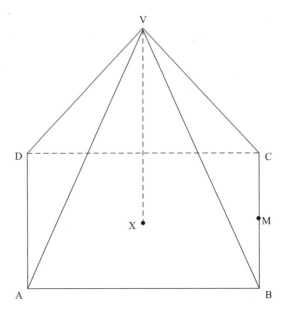

Work out

(i) AC   **(ii)** VX   **(iii)** angle between VA and ABCD

(iv) angle between VBC and ABCD.

10 A new perfume is to be packaged in a box that is in the shape of a regular tetrahedron VABC of side 6 cm standing on a triangular prism ABCDEF as shown in the diagram.

The height of the prism is 12 cm.

M is the midpoint of BC.

Find

(i) the length AM

(ii) the length VM

(iii) the angle VAM

(iv) the total height of the box.

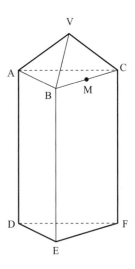

KEY POINTS

1 In a right-angled triangle

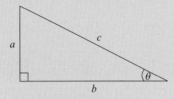

$$c^2 = a^2 + b^2$$

$$\sin\theta = \frac{a}{c} \qquad \cos\theta = \frac{b}{c} \qquad \tan\theta = \frac{a}{b}$$

2 $\sin 45° = \dfrac{1}{\sqrt{2}} \qquad \cos 45° = \dfrac{1}{\sqrt{2}} \qquad \tan 45° = 1$

$\sin 30° = \dfrac{1}{2} \qquad \cos 30° = \dfrac{\sqrt{3}}{2} \qquad \tan 30° = \dfrac{1}{\sqrt{3}}$

$\sin 60° = \dfrac{\sqrt{3}}{2} \qquad \cos 60° = \dfrac{1}{2} \qquad \tan 60° = \sqrt{3}$

3 In a geometrical proof, show all your working and give unambiguous reasons for each stage.

4 When solving three-dimensional problems always draw a clear diagram where:

- vertical lines are drawn vertically
- east–west lines are drawn horizontally
- north–south lines are drawn sloping
- edges that are hidden are drawn as dotted lines.

Geometry II

7

What is it that breathes fire into the equations and makes a universe for them to describe?

Stephen W Hawking

Trigonometrical functions for angles of any size

Note that the specification only requires knowledge for angles between 0° and 360°.

However, negative angles may be obtained when using a calculator during the solution of a trigonometric equation. Also, the cyclic nature of the trigonometric graphs should be known.

Positive and negative angles

By convention, angles are measured from the positive x axis (figure 7.1). Anticlockwise is taken to be positive and clockwise to be negative.

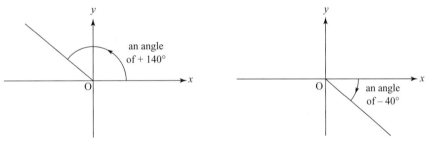

Figure 7.1

The only exception is for compass bearings, which are measured clockwise from the north.

? Is it possible to extend the definitions of trigonometrical functions to angles greater than 90°, like sin 156°, cos 202° or tan 320°?

It is not difficult to extend these definitions, as follows.

First look at the right-angled triangle in figure 7.2 which has a hypotenuse of unit length.

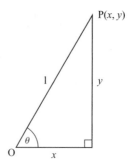

Figure 7.2

This gives the definitions:

$$\sin\theta = \frac{y}{1} = y \qquad \cos\theta = \frac{x}{1} = x \qquad \tan\theta = \frac{y}{x}$$

Now imagine the angle θ situated at the origin, as in figure 7.3, and allow θ to take any value. The vertex marked P has co-ordinates ($\cos\theta$, $\sin\theta$) and can now be anywhere on the unit circle.

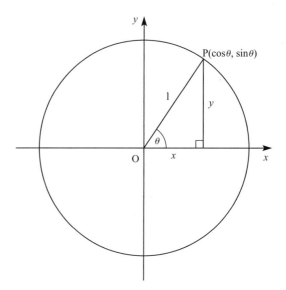

Figure 7.3

You can now see that these definitions can be applied to *any* angle θ, whether it is positive or negative, and whether it is less than or greater than 90°.

$$\sin\theta = y \qquad \cos\theta = x \qquad \tan\theta = \frac{y}{x}$$

For some angles, x or y (or both) will take a negative value, so the signs of $\sin\theta$, $\cos\theta$ and $\tan\theta$ will vary accordingly.

The sine and cosine graphs

Look at figure 7.4. There is a unit circle and angles have been drawn at intervals of 30°. The resulting y co-ordinates are plotted relative to the axes on the right.

They have been joined with a continuous curve to give the graph of $\sin\theta$ for $0 \leqslant \theta \leqslant 360°$.

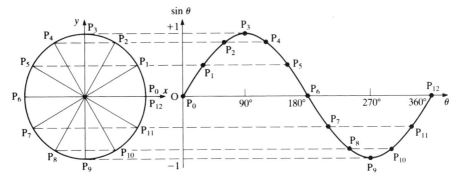

Figure 7.4

Continue this process for angles 390°, 420°, ... and angles −30°, −60°, ...

What do you notice?

Since the curve repeats itself every 360°, as shown in figure 7.5, the sine function is described as *periodic* with *period* 360°.

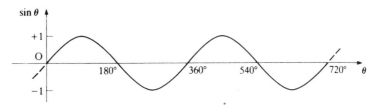

Figure 7.5

In a similar way you can transfer the x co-ordinates onto a set of axes to obtain the graph of $\cos\theta$. This is most easily illustrated if you first rotate the circle through 90° anticlockwise.

Figure 7.6 shows this new orientation, together with the resulting graph.

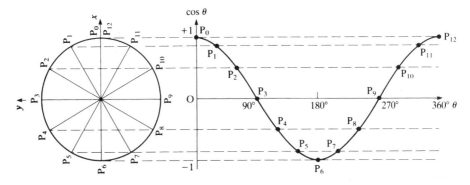

Figure 7.6

For angles in the interval $360° \leqslant \theta \leqslant 720°$, the cosine curve will repeat itself. You can see that the cosine function is also periodic with a period of 360°.

Notice that the graphs of sin θ and cos θ have exactly the same shape. The cosine graph can be obtained by translating the sine graph 90° to the left, as shown in figure 7.7.

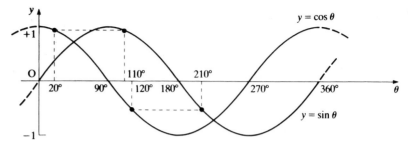

Figure 7.7

The tangent graph

The value of tan θ can be worked out from the definition $\tan \theta = \dfrac{y}{x}$ or by using

$$\tan \theta = \frac{\sin \theta}{\cos \theta}$$

? The function tan θ is undefined for θ = 90°. What does *undefined* mean?
How can you tell that tan 90° is undefined?
For which other values of θ is tan θ undefined?

The graph of tanθ is shown in figure 7.8. The dotted lines θ = ± 90° and θ = 270° are *asymptotes*; they are not actually part of the curve.

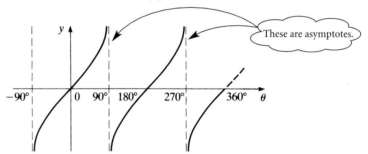

Figure 7.8

? How would you describe an asymptote to a friend?

? The graph of tan θ is periodic, like those for sin θ and cos θ. What is the period of this graph?

Show how the part of the curve for 0° ≤ θ < 90° can be used to generate the rest of the curve using rotations and translations.

ACTIVITY 7.2 Draw the graphs of $y = \sin\theta$, $y = \cos\theta$ and $y = \tan\theta$ for values of θ between $-180°$ and $360°$.

These graphs will be useful for solving trigonometrical equations, so keep them handy. It is also a good idea to learn them at this stage.

The area of a triangle

You are familiar with the use of capital letters to label the vertices of a triangle. In a similar way you can use lower case letters to name the sides. To do this you would use a to denote the length of the side opposite angle A, b to denote the length of the side opposite angle B, etc. as in figure 7.9.

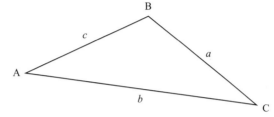

Figure 7.9

Using this notation, for any triangle ABC the area is given by the formula

$$\text{area} = \frac{1}{2}bc\sin A.$$

Proof

Figure 7.10 shows a triangle ABC. The perpendicular CD is the height h corresponding to AB as base.

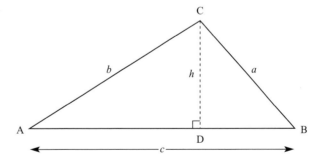

Figure 7.10

Using area of a triangle equals half its base times its height,

$$\text{area} = \frac{1}{2}ch \qquad \qquad ①$$

In triangle ACD

$$\sin A = \frac{h}{b}$$

$$\Rightarrow \qquad h = b\sin A.$$

Substituting in ① gives

$$\text{area} = \frac{1}{2}bc\sin A.$$

NOTE Taking the other two points in turn as the top of the triangle gives equivalent results:

$$\text{area} = \frac{1}{2}ca\sin B$$

and

$$\text{area} = \frac{1}{2}ab\sin C.$$

This can be remembered as half the product of two sides times the sine of the angle between them.

EXAMPLE 7.1 Figure 7.11 shows a regular pentagon, PQRST, inscribed in a circle, centre C, radius 8 cm. Calculate the area of

(i) triangle CPQ
(ii) the pentagon.

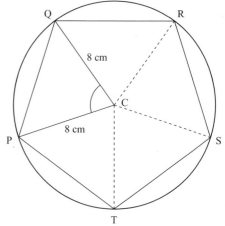

Figure 7.11

SOLUTION

(i) angle PCQ $= 360° \div 5$

$$= 72°$$

$$\text{area PCQ} = \frac{1}{2} \times 8 \times 8 \times \sin 72°$$

$$= 30.4338 \ldots$$

$\Rightarrow$ area PCQ $= 30.4\,\text{cm}^2$ (1 d.p.)

(ii) area PQRST $= 5 \times 30.4338 \ldots$

$$= 152.169\ldots$$

$\Rightarrow$ area PQRST $= 152.2\,\text{cm}^2$ (1 d.p.)

EXAMPLE 7.2

Figure 7.12 shows an isosceles triangle with an area of $24\,\text{cm}^2$ and one angle of $40°$.

Calculate the lengths of the two equal sides.

SOLUTION

Let the equal sides be of length x cm.

This gives

$$24 = \frac{1}{2} \times x \times x \times \sin 40°$$

$$\Rightarrow \quad x^2 = \frac{48}{\sin 40°}$$

$$\Rightarrow \quad x = 8.64\,\text{cm} \; (3\text{ s.f.})$$

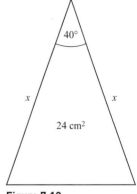

Figure 7.12

EXERCISE 7A

1 Find the area of each of the following triangles.

(i)

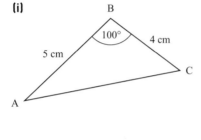

(ii)

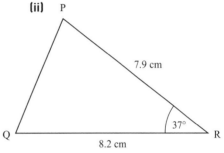

(iii)

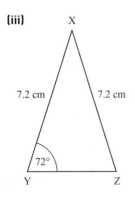

(iv)

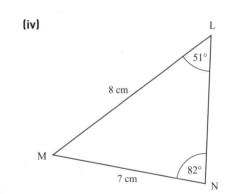

2 A regular hexagon is made up of six equilateral triangles. Find the area of a regular hexagon of side 7 cm.

3 A pyramid on a square base has four identical triangular faces which are isosceles triangles with equal sides 9 cm and equal angles 72°.
   (i)   Find the area of a triangular face.
   (ii)   Find the length of a side of the base.
   (iii) Hence find the total surface area of the pyramid.

4 A tiler wishes to estimate the
number of triangular tiles needed
to tile an area of 10 m². The
dimensions of each tile are shown in
the diagram.

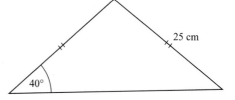

(i)   Find the area of a tile.

The tiler then divides 10 m² by this area and rounds to the next whole number.

(ii)   What result would this give?

(iii) Explain what is wrong with this estimate.

5 A regular tetrahedron has four sides, each of which is an equilateral triangle of
side 10 cm. Find the total surface area of the tetrahedron.

You can use trigonometry to find sides and angles in non-right-angled triangles.
This involves two important rules, the sine rule and the cosine rule.

The sine rule

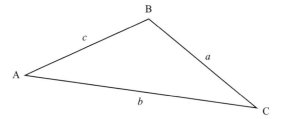

Figure 7.13

You have already seen that for any triangle ABC

$$\text{area} = \tfrac{1}{2}bc\sin A = \tfrac{1}{2}ca\sin B = \tfrac{1}{2}ab\sin C$$

$$\Rightarrow \quad \frac{bc\sin A}{abc} = \frac{ca\sin B}{abc} = \frac{ab\sin C}{abc}$$

$$\Rightarrow \quad \frac{\sin A}{a} = \frac{\sin B}{b} = \frac{\sin C}{c}$$

This is one form of the *sine rule* and is the version that is easier to use if you want
to find an angle.

Inverting this gives

$$\frac{a}{\sin A} = \frac{b}{\sin B} = \frac{c}{\sin C}$$

which is better when you need to find a side.

? Why is the inverted form of the sine rule better when you want to find a side?

EXAMPLE 7.3

Find the side BC in the triangle shown in figure 7.14.

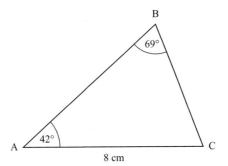

Figure 7.14

SOLUTION

Using the sine rule

$$\frac{a}{\sin A} = \frac{b}{\sin B} = \frac{c}{\sin C}$$

$$\Rightarrow \quad \frac{a}{\sin 42°} = \frac{8}{\sin 69°}$$

$$\Rightarrow \quad a = \frac{8 \sin 42°}{\sin 69°}$$

$$= 5.733887...$$

$$\Rightarrow \quad \text{side BC} = 5.7 \, \text{cm} \ (1 \, \text{d.p.}).$$

> Do the calculation entirely on your calculator, and round only the final answer.

⚠ When using the sine rule to find an angle, you need to be careful because sometimes there are two possible answers, as in the next example.

EXAMPLE 7.4

Find the angle P in the triangle PQR, given that R = 32°, $r = 4$ cm and $p = 7$ cm.

SOLUTION

The sine rule for △ PQR is

$$\frac{\sin P}{p} = \frac{\sin Q}{q} = \frac{\sin R}{r}$$

$$\Rightarrow \quad \frac{\sin P}{7} = \frac{\sin 32°}{4}$$

$$\Rightarrow \quad \sin P = 0.927358712$$

$$\Rightarrow \quad P = 68.0° \ (1 \, \text{d.p.}) \text{ or } P = (180° - 68.0°) = 112° \ (1 \, \text{d.p.}).$$

Both solutions are possible as indicated in figure 7.15.

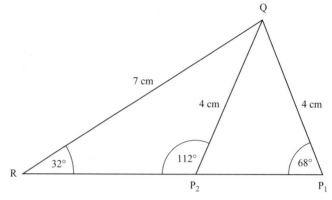

Figure 7.15

⚠ You should always check to see if there is a second solution, but sometimes only one solution is possible since the second would give an angle sum greater than 180°.

❓ Figure 7.16 shows triangle XYZ with XY = 6 cm, XZ = 8 cm and ∠XYZ = 78°. What happens when you use the sine rule to calculate the remaining angles?

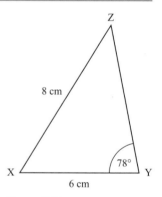

Figure 7.16

EXERCISE 7B

1 Find the length *x* in each of these triangles.

(i) (ii) (iii)

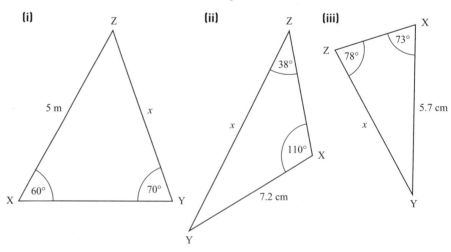

2 Find the angle θ in each of these triangles.

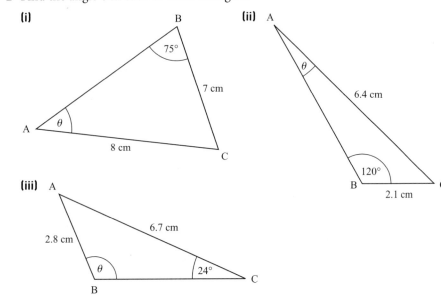

(i)

(ii)

(iii)

The cosine rule

Sometimes it is not possible to use the sine rule with the information you have about a triangle. For example, you know all three sides but none of the angles.

Like the sine rule, the cosine rule can be applied to any triangle, and again there are equivalent versions.

$$a^2 = b^2 + c^2 - 2bc\cos A$$

When you want to find a side.

$$\cos A = \frac{b^2 + c^2 - a^2}{2bc}$$

When you want to find an angle.

Proof

For the $\triangle ABC$, CD is the perpendicular from C to AB as shown in figure 7.17.

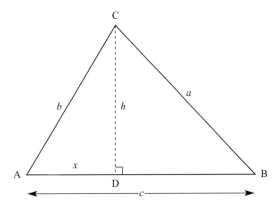

Figure 7.17

In △ ACD

$$b^2 = x^2 + h^2$$ ← Pythagoras' theorem ①

$$\cos A = \frac{x}{b}, \text{ so } x = b\cos A.$$ ②

In △BCD

$$a^2 = (c - x)^2 + h^2$$ ← Pythagoras' theorem

$$\Rightarrow \quad a^2 = c^2 - 2cx + x^2 + h^2$$

$$\Rightarrow \quad a^2 = c^2 - 2cx + b^2 \qquad \text{using ①}$$

$$\Rightarrow \quad a^2 = c^2 - 2cb\cos A + b^2 \qquad \text{using ②}$$

$$\Rightarrow \quad a^2 = b^2 + c^2 - 2bc\cos A \qquad \text{as required.}$$

Rearranging this gives

$$2bc\cos A = b^2 + c^2 - a^2$$

$$\Rightarrow \quad \cos A = \frac{b^2 + c^2 - a^2}{2bc}$$

which is the second form of the cosine rule.

NOTE Starting with a perpendicular from a different vertex would give the following similar results.

$$b^2 = a^2 + c^2 - 2ac\cos B$$

$$\cos B = \frac{a^2 + c^2 - b^2}{2ac}$$

$$c^2 = a^2 + b^2 - 2ab\cos C$$

$$\cos C = \frac{a^2 + b^2 - c^2}{2ab}$$

EXAMPLE 7.5 Find the side AB in the triangle shown in figure 7.18.

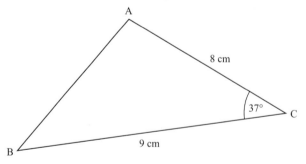

Figure 7.18

SOLUTION

$$c^2 = a^2 + b^2 - 2ab\cos C$$

$$= 9^2 + 8^2 - 2 \times 9 \times 8\cos 37°$$

$$AB = 5.5\,\text{cm} \ (1 \text{ d.p.})$$

EXAMPLE 7.6   Find the angle P in the triangle shown in figure 7.19.

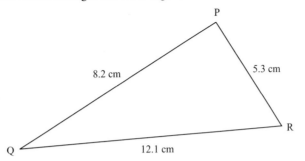

Figure 7.19

SOLUTION

The cosine rule for this triangle can be written as

$$\cos P = \frac{q^2 + r^2 - p^2}{2qr}$$

$$= \frac{5.3^2 + 8.2^2 - 12.1^2}{2 \times 5.3 \times 8.2}$$

$$P = 126.0°\,(1\ \text{d.p.})$$

EXERCISE 7C   **1** Find the length x in each of these triangles.

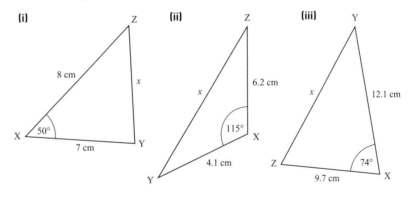

2 Find the angle θ in each of the following triangles.

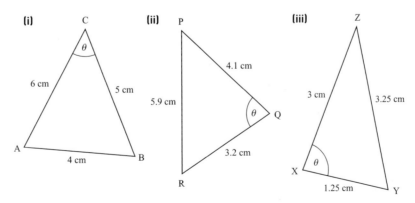

3 The diagonals of a parallelogram have lengths of 12 cm and 18 cm and the angle between them is 72°. Find the lengths of the sides of the parallelogram.

4 The diagram shows a quadrilateral ABCD with AB = 8 cm, BC = 6 cm, CD = 7 cm, DA = 5 cm and ∠ABC = 90°. Calculate

(i) AC

(ii) ∠ADC.

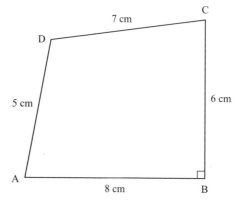

5 The diagram shows two circles. One has centre A and a radius of 8 cm. The other has centre B and a radius of 10 cm. AB = 12 cm and the circles intersect at P and Q. Calculate ∠PAB.

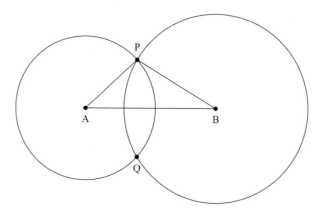

Using the sine and cosine rules together

Sometimes you need to use both the sine and cosine rules in the same problem, as in the next example.

EXAMPLE 7.7   Figure 7.20 shows the positions of three towns, Aldbury, Bentham and Chorton. Bentham is 8 km from Aldbury on a bearing of 037° and Chorton is 9 km from Bentham on a bearing of 150°. Find

(i)   the angle ABC

(ii) the distance of Chorton from Aldbury (to 0.1 km)

(iii) the bearing of Chorton from Aldbury (to 1°).

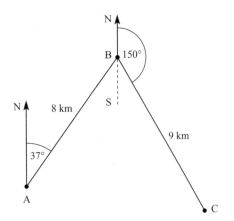

Figure 7.20

SOLUTION

(i)   ∠ABS = 37° (alternate angles)

and ∠SBC = 30° (adjacent angles)

so ∠ABC = 67°

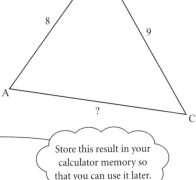

(ii) Using the cosine rule

$$b^2 = a^2 + c^2 - 2ac\cos B$$

$$= 9^2 + 8^2 - 2 \times 9 \times 8 \cos 67$$

$$= 88.7347...$$

$$b = 9.4199...$$

Store this result in your calculator memory so that you can use it later.

Chorton is 9.4 km from Aldbury (1 d.p.).

(iii) Using the sine rule

$$\frac{\sin A}{a} = \frac{\sin B}{b}$$

$$\frac{\sin A}{9} = \frac{\sin 67°}{9.4199...}$$

$$\sin A = 0.87947...$$

$$A = 61.57...°$$

The bearing of Chorton from Aldbury is 099°.

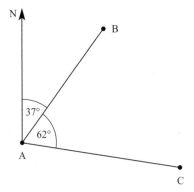

Figure 7.21

? The other value of A that gives sin A = 0.879 47... is 118.42...°
Why does this not give an alternative solution to this problem?

EXAMPLE 7.8

A triangular plot of land has sides of length 70 m, 80 m and 95 m.
Find its area in hectares. (1 hectare (ha) is 10 000 m²)

SOLUTION

First draw a sketch and label the sides.

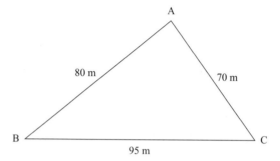

Figure 7.22

You can now see that the first step is to find one of the angles, and this will need
the cosine rule.

? How do you decide that it is the cosine rule you want to use?

Using $\cos A = \dfrac{b^2 + c^2 - a^2}{2bc}$

gives $\cos A = \dfrac{70^2 + 80^2 - 95^2}{2 \times 70 \times 80} = 0.2031\ldots$

$\Rightarrow \qquad A = 78.28\ldots°.$

Now using area $= \dfrac{1}{2} bc \sin A$

$\Rightarrow \qquad$ area $= \dfrac{1}{2} \times 70 \times 80 \sin 78.28\ldots°$

$\qquad\qquad = 2741.625\ldots \text{m}^2$

$\Rightarrow \qquad$ area $= 0.27 \text{ ha (2 d.p.)}.$

EXERCISE 7D

1 The hands of a clock have lengths 6 cm and 8 cm.
Find the distance between the tips of the hands at 8 pm.

2 From a lighthouse L, a ship A is 4 km away on a bearing of 340° and a ship B is
5 km away on a bearing of 065°.
Find the distance AB.

3 When I am at a point X, the angle of elevation of the top of a tree T is 27°, but if I walk 20 m towards the tree, to point Y, the angle of elevation is then 47°.
  (i) Find the distance TY.
  (ii) Find the height of the tree.

4 Two adjacent sides of a parallelogram are of lengths 9.3 cm and 7.2 cm, and the shorter diagonal is of length 8.1 cm.
  (i) Find the angles of the parallelogram.
  (ii) Find the length of the other diagonal of the parallelogram.

5 A yacht sets off from A and sails for 5 km on a bearing of 067° to a point B so that it can clear the headland before it turns onto a bearing of 146°. It then stays on that course for 8 km until it reaches a point C.
  (i) Find the distance AC.
  (ii) Find the bearing of C from A.

6 Two ships leave the docks, D, at the same time. *Princess Pearl*, P, sails on a bearing of 160° at a speed of 18 km/h, and *Regal Rose*, R, sails on a bearing of 105°. After two hours the angle DRP is 80°.
  (i) Find the distance between the ships at this time.
  (ii) Find the speed of the *Regal Rose*.

7 The diagram represents a simplified drawing of the timber cross-section of a roof. Find the lengths of the struts BD and EG.

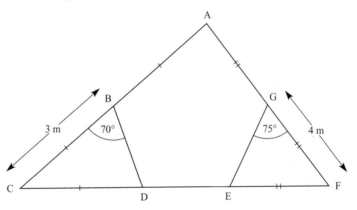

8 Sam and Aziz cycle home from school.
Sam cycles due east for 4 km, and Aziz cycles due south for 3 km and then for 2 km on a bearing of 125°.
How far apart are their homes?

Solution of trigonometrical equations

Suppose that you want to solve the equation

$\sin \theta = 0.5.$

You start by pressing the calculator keys

and the answer comes up as 30°.

NOTE The $\sin^{-1}$ key may also be labelled invsin or arcsin.

However, look at the graph of $y = \sin \theta$ (figure 7.23). You can see that there are other roots as well.

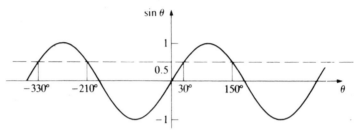

Figure 7.23

? How many roots does the equation have?

The root 30° is called the *principal value*.

Other roots can be found by looking at the graph. The roots for $\sin \theta = 0.5$ are seen (figure 7.11) to be:

$\theta = \ldots, -330°, -210°, 30°, 150°, \ldots.$

Note that on this specification, you will only be asked to find solutions between 0° and 360° inclusive.

NOTE A calculator always gives the principal value of the solution. These values are in the range

$0° \leqslant \theta \leqslant 180°$ (cos)
$-90° \leqslant \theta \leqslant 90°$ (sin)
$-90° < \theta < 90°$ (tan)

EXAMPLE 7.9 Find values of θ in the interval $0° \leqslant \theta \leqslant 360°$ for which $\cos \theta = 0.4$.

SOLUTION

$\cos \theta = 0.4 \quad \Rightarrow \quad \theta = 66.4°$ (principal value).

Figure 7.24 shows the graph of $y = \cos \theta$.

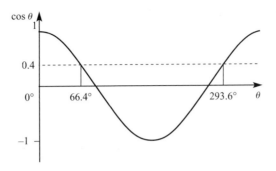

Figure 7.24

The values of θ for which $\cos \theta = 0.4$ are

66.4°, 293.6°.

Here all values are given rounded to 1 decimal place.

? How do you arrive at 293.6°?

EXAMPLE 7.10 Find values of θ in the interval $0° \le \theta \le 360°$ for which $\tan \theta = -0.7$.

SOLUTION

$$\tan \theta = -0.7 \quad \Rightarrow \quad \theta = -35.0° \text{ (principal value).}$$

Figure 7.25 shows the graph of $y = \tan \theta$.

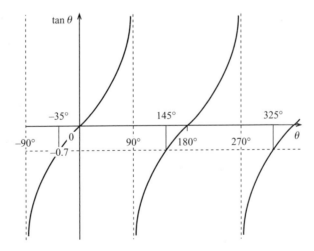

Figure 7.25

The values of θ for which $\tan \theta = -0.7$ are

145.0°, 325.0°.

1 Solve the following equations for $0° \leqslant \theta \leqslant 360°$. Give answers to 1 decimal place where necessary.

(i) $\cos \theta = 0.5$
(ii) $\tan \theta = 1$
(iii) $\sin \theta = \frac{\sqrt{3}}{2}$

(iv) $\sin \theta = -0.5$
(v) $\cos \theta = 0$
(vi) $\tan \theta = -5$

(vii) $\tan \theta = 0$
(viii) $\cos \theta = -0.54$
(ix) $\sin \theta = 1$

2 Solve the following equations for $0° \leqslant \theta \leqslant 360°$. Give your answers to 1 decimal place where necessary.

(i) $3\cos \theta = 2$
(ii) $7\sin \theta = 5$
(iii) $3\tan \theta = 8$

(iv) $6\sin \theta + 5 = 0$
(v) $5\cos \theta + 2 = 0$
(vi) $5 - 9\tan \theta = 10$

3 Solve the following equations for $0° \leqslant \theta \leqslant 360°$.

(i) $\sin^2 \theta = 0.75$
(ii) $\cos^2 \theta = 0.5$
(iii) $\tan^2 \theta = 1$

4 (i) Factorise $2x^2 + x - 1$.

(ii) Hence solve $2x^2 + x - 1 = 0$.

(iii) Use your results to solve these equations for $0° \leqslant \theta \leqslant 360°$.

(a) $2\sin^2 \theta + \sin \theta - 1 = 0$

(b) $2\cos^2 \theta + \cos \theta - 1 = 0$

(c) $2\tan^2 \theta + \tan \theta - 1 = 0$

5 Solve the following equations for $0 \leqslant x \leqslant 360°$.

(i) $\tan^2 x - 3 \tan x = 0$
(ii) $1 - 2\sin^2 x = 0$

(iii) $3\cos^2 x + 2\cos x - 1 = 0$
(iv) $2\sin^2 x = \sin x + 1$

6 *Use of a calculator is not allowed in this question.*

Solve the following equations for $0 \leqslant x \leqslant 360°$.

(i) $\tan x = \sqrt{3}$
(ii) $2\sin x = 1$

(iii) $\sqrt{2} \cos x - 1 = 0$
(iv) $2\sin x = \sqrt{3}$

(v) $\tan^2 x - \tan x = 0$
(iv) $4\cos x = \sqrt{12}$

Trigonometrical identities

Remember the earlier definitions for trigonometrical functions of angles of any magnitude

$$\sin \theta = y \qquad \cos \theta = x \qquad \tan \theta = \frac{y}{x}$$

where the angle θ was defined by a point $P(x, y)$ on a circle of unit radius (figure 7.26).

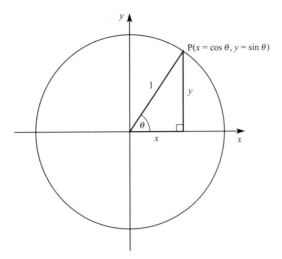

Figure 7.26

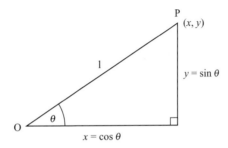

Figure 7.27

EXAMPLE 7.11   Solve the equation $2\cos^2\theta - \sin\theta - 1 = 0$ for values of θ in the range $0°$ to $360°$.

SOLUTION

$$2\cos^2\theta - \sin\theta - 1 = 0$$
$$\Rightarrow \quad 2(1 - \sin^2\theta) - \sin\theta - 1 = 0$$
$$\Rightarrow \quad 2 - 2\sin^2\theta - \sin\theta - 1 = 0$$
$$\Rightarrow \quad 0 = 2\sin^2\theta + \sin\theta - 1$$

> This is now a quadratic in $\sin\theta$.

Factorising

$$\Rightarrow \quad (\sin\theta + 1)(2\sin\theta - 1) = 0$$
$$\Rightarrow \quad \sin\theta = -1 \text{ or } \sin\theta = 0.5$$

$$\sin\theta = -1 \Rightarrow \theta = -90° \text{ or } \theta = 270°$$

$\theta = -90°$ is the principal value but it is outside the required range. $\theta = 270°$ is inside the required range.

$$\sin\theta = 0.5 \Rightarrow \theta = 30° \text{ (principal value) or } \theta = 150°$$

$\theta = 30°$ and $\theta = 150°$ are both inside the required range. The next value, $390°$, is too big.

The solution of the equation is therefore $\theta = 30°$, $150°$ or $270°$.

Using trigonometrical identities to solve equations

The identity

$$\sin^2\theta + \cos^2\theta = 1$$

is particularly useful when solving equations which contain both $\sin\theta$ and $\cos\theta$ with one of the functions squared. You can rearrange it to get

$$\sin^2\theta = 1 - \cos^2\theta \quad \text{or} \quad \cos^2\theta = 1 - \sin^2\theta.$$

Other uses

Identities can also be used to simplify expressions and to prove other identities.

EXAMPLE 7.12

Show that $\dfrac{\tan x \cos x}{\sqrt{1 - \cos^2 x}}$ simplifies to 1.

SOLUTION

$$\frac{\tan x \cos x}{\sqrt{1 - \cos^2 x}} = \frac{\dfrac{\sin x}{\cos x}\cos x}{\sqrt{\sin^2 x}}$$

$$= \frac{\sin x}{\sin x}$$

$$= 1$$

EXAMPLE 7.13

(i) Prove that $\cos^2 x - \sin^2 x \equiv 2\cos^2 x - 1$.

(ii) Hence, solve $\cos^2 x - \sin^2 x = 0.5$ for $0° \leqslant x \leqslant 180°$.

SOLUTION

(i) Start with the left hand side
$$\cos^2 x - \sin^2 x \equiv \cos^2 x - (1 - \cos^2 x)$$
$$\equiv \cos^2 x - 1 + \cos^2 x$$
$$\equiv 2\cos^2 x - 1$$

(ii) Using part (i)

$$2\cos^2 x - 1 = 0.5$$

$$2\cos^2 x = 1.5$$

$$\cos^2 x = 0.75$$

$$\cos x = \pm\sqrt{0.75}$$

$$\cos x = \sqrt{0.75} \text{ so } x = 30° \text{ (principal value)}$$

$$\cos x = -\sqrt{0.75} \text{ so } x = 150° \text{ (principal value)}$$

The values of x for which $\cos^2 x - \sin^2 x = 0.5$ are 30° and 150°.

EXERCISE 7F

1 For each of the equations (i)–(v):

    (a) use the identity $\sin^2\theta + \cos^2\theta \equiv 1$ to rewrite the equation in a form involving only one trigonometrical function

    (b) factorise, and hence solve, the resulting equation for $0° \leqslant \theta \leqslant 360°$.

        (i) $2\cos^2\theta + \sin\theta - 1 = 0$

        (ii) $\sin^2\theta + \cos\theta + 1 = 0$

        (iii) $2\sin^2\theta - \cos\theta - 1 = 0$

        (iv) $\cos^2\theta + \sin\theta = 1$

        (v) $1 + \sin\theta - 2\cos^2\theta = 0$

2 For each of the equations (i)–(iii):

    (a) use the identity $\sin^2\theta + \cos^2\theta \equiv 1$ to rewrite the equation in a form involving only one trigonometrical function

    (b) use the quadratic formula to solve the resulting equation for $0° \leqslant \theta \leqslant 180°$.

        (i) $\sin^2\theta - 2\cos\theta + 1 = 0$

        (ii) $\cos^2\theta - \sin\theta = 0$

        (iii) $\sin^2\theta - 3\cos\theta = 0$

3 (i) Use the identity

$$\tan\theta \equiv \frac{\sin\theta}{\cos\theta}$$

    to rewrite the equation $\sin\theta = 2\cos\theta$ in terms of $\tan\theta$.

  (ii) Hence solve the equation $\sin\theta = 2\cos\theta$ for $0° \leqslant \theta \leqslant 180°$.

4 Use the identity

$$\tan\theta \equiv \frac{\sin\theta}{\cos\theta}$$

to solve the following equations for $0 \leqslant \theta \leqslant 360°$.

    (i) $2\sin\theta + \cos\theta = 0$

    (ii) $\sqrt{3}\tan\theta = 2\sin\theta$

    (iii) $4\cos\theta\tan\theta = 1$

5 Write the following in terms of $\sin x$.

    (i) $\cos^2 x \tan^2 x$ **(ii)** $\tan x \cos^3 x$ **(iii)** $\cos x\,(2\cos x - 3\tan x)$

6 Show that $3\sin x\,(\sin x + 2) - 3(2\sin x - \cos^2 x)$ simplifies to an integer.

7 Prove the following identities.

(i) $\quad \tan x \sqrt{1 - \sin^2 x} \equiv \sin x$

(ii) $\quad \dfrac{1 - \cos^2 x}{1 - \sin^2 x} \equiv \tan^2 x$

(iii) $\quad (1 + \sin x)(1 - \sin x) \equiv \cos^2 x$

(iv) $\quad \dfrac{2 \sin x \cos x}{\tan x} \equiv 2 - 2 \sin^2 x$

KEY POINTS

1 For an angle θ in a right-angled triangle

$$\sin \theta = \frac{\text{opposite}}{\text{hypotenuse}} \qquad \cos \theta = \frac{\text{adjacent}}{\text{hypotenuse}} \qquad \tan \theta = \frac{\text{opposite}}{\text{adjacent}}$$

2 The point (x, y) at angle θ on the unit circle with centre $(0, 0)$ has co-ordinates $(\cos \theta, \sin \theta)$ for all θ, i.e. $\cos \theta = x$ and $\sin \theta = y$.

This also gives $\tan \theta = \dfrac{y}{x}$.

3 The graphs of $\sin \theta$, $\cos \theta$ and $\tan \theta$ are as shown below.

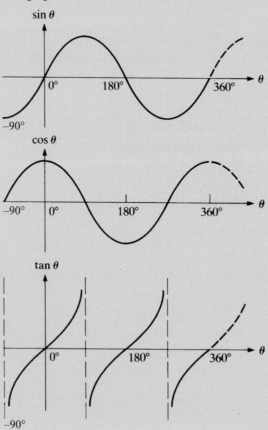

4 $\tan\theta \equiv \dfrac{\sin\theta}{\cos\theta}$

5 $\sin^2\theta + \cos^2\theta \equiv 1$

6 For a triangle ABC

$$\text{area} = \frac{1}{2}bc\sin A$$

$$\left.\begin{aligned} \frac{a}{\sin A} &= \frac{b}{\sin B} = \frac{c}{\sin C} \\[4pt] \frac{\sin A}{a} &= \frac{\sin B}{b} = \frac{\sin C}{c} \end{aligned}\right\} \quad \text{the sine rule}$$

$$\left.\begin{aligned} a^2 &= b^2 + c^2 - 2bc\cos A \\[4pt] \cos A &= \frac{b^2 + c^2 - a^2}{2bc} \end{aligned}\right\} \quad \text{the cosine rule}$$

CALCULUS

8

Calculus

I do not know what I may appear to the world; but to myself I seem to have been only like a boy playing on the seashore, and diverting myself in now and then finding a smoother pebble or a prettier shell than ordinary, whilst the great ocean of truth lay all undiscovered before me.

Isaac Newton (1642–1727)

The gradient of a curve

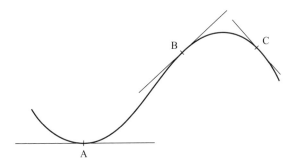

Figure 8.1

In figure 8.1 the curve has a zero gradient at A, a positive gradient at B and a negative gradient at C.

One way of finding these gradients is to draw the tangents and use two points on each one to calculate its gradient. This is time-consuming and the results depend on the accuracy of your drawing and measuring. If you know the equation of the curve, then *differentiation* provides another method of calculating the gradient.

Differentiation

Instead of trying to draw an accurate tangent, this method starts by calculating the gradients of chords PQ_1, PQ_2, ... As the different positions of Q get closer to P, the values of the gradient of PQ get closer to the gradient of the tangent at P. The first few positions of Q are shown in figure 8.2.

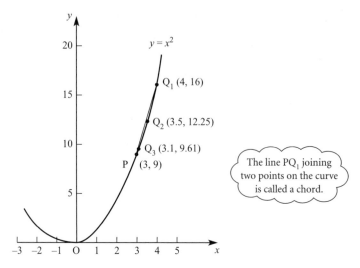

Figure 8.2

The line PQ_1 joining two points on the curve is called a chord.

For P at $(3, 9)$

chord	co-ordinate of Q	gradient of PQ
PQ_1	$(4, 16)$	$\dfrac{16 - 9}{4 - 3} = 7$
PQ_2	$(3.5, 12.25)$	$\dfrac{12.25 - 9}{3.5 - 3} = 6.5$
PQ_3	$(3.1, 9.61)$	$\dfrac{9.61 - 9}{3.1 - 3} = 6.1$
PQ_4	$(3.01, 9.0601)$	$\dfrac{9.0601 - 9}{3.01 - 3} = 6.01$
PQ_5	$(3.001, 9.006001)$	$\dfrac{9.006001 - 9}{3.001 - 3} = 6.001$

In this process the gradient of the chord PQ gets closer and closer to that of the tangent, and hence the gradient of the curve at $(3, 9)$.
Look at the sequence formed by the gradients of the chords.

$$7, 6.5, 6.1, 6.01, 6.001, \ldots$$

It looks as though this sequence is converging to 6.

? Do you think the limit will still be 6 if the points Q are positioned on the other side of P?

ACTIVITY 8.1

Take points R_1 to R_5 on the curve $y = x^2$ with x co-ordinates 2, 2.5, 2.9, 2.99, and 2.999 respectively and find the gradients of the chords joining each of these points to P(3, 9).

The calculations above show that the gradient of the curve $y = x^2$ at (3, 9) seems to be 6 or about 6 but do not provide conclusive proof of its value. To do that you need to apply the method in more general terms.

Take the point P(3, 9) and another point Q close to (3, 9) on the curve $y = x^2$. Let the x co-ordinate of Q be $(3 + h)$ where h is small. Since $y = x^2$ at all points on the curve, the y co-ordinate of Q will be $(3 + h)^2$.

⚠ Figure 8.3 shows Q in a position where h is positive. Negative values of h would put Q to the left of P.

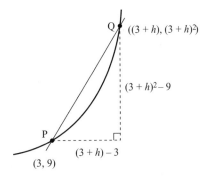

Figure 8.3

From figure 8.3, the gradient of PQ is $\dfrac{(3 + h)^2 - 9}{h}$

$$= \frac{9 + 6h + h^2 - 9}{h}$$

$$= \frac{6h + h^2}{h}$$

$$= \frac{h(6 + h)}{h}$$

$$= 6 + h.$$

For example, when $h = 0.001$, the gradient of PQ is 6.001 and when $h = -0.001$, the gradient of PQ is 5.999. The gradient of the tangent at P is between these two values. Similarly the gradient of the tangent at P would be between $6 - h$ and $6 + h$ for all small non-zero values of h.

For this to be true, the gradient of the tangent at (3, 9) must be *exactly* 6.

In this case, 6 was the *limit* of the gradient values, whether you approached P from the right or the left.

ACTIVITY 8.2

Using a similar method, find the gradient of the tangent to the curve at

(i) $(2, 4)$

(ii) $(-1, 1)$

(iii) $(-3, 9)$.

What do you notice?

The gradient function

The work so far has involved finding the gradient of the curve $y = x^2$ at just one particular point. It would be very tedious if you had to do this every time and so instead you can consider a general point (x, y) and then substitute the value(s) of x and/or y corresponding to the point(s) of interest.

EXAMPLE 8.1

Find the gradient of the curve $y = x^3$ at the general point (x, y).

SOLUTION

Let P have the general value x as its x co-ordinate, so P is the point (x, x^3) (since it is on the curve $y = x^3$).

Let the x co-ordinate of Q be $(x + h)$ so Q is the point $((x + h), (x + h)^3)$.

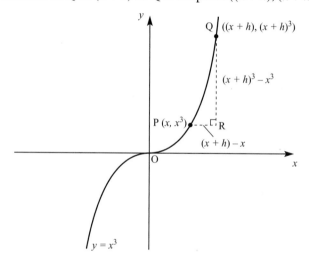

Figure 8.4

The gradient of the chord PQ is given by

$$\frac{QR}{PR} = \frac{(x + h)^3 - x^3}{(x + h) - x}$$

$$= \frac{x^3 + 3x^2h + 3xh^2 + h^3 - x^3}{h}$$

$$= \frac{3x^2h + 3xh^2 + h^3}{h}$$

$$= \frac{h(3x^2 + 3xh + h^2)}{h}$$

$$= 3x^2 + 3xh + h^2$$

As Q gets closer to P, h takes smaller and smaller values and the gradient approaches the value of $3x^2$, which is the gradient of the tangent at P.

The gradient of the curve $y = x^3$ at the point (x, y) is equal to $3x^2$.

EXERCISE 8A

1 (i) For the curve $y = x^4$ estimate the gradient at the point P(2, 16) by taking different positions of Q with x co-ordinates 2.1, 2.01 and 2.001 respectively.

(ii) Use a similar method to estimate the gradient at the points (3, 81) and (−1, 1).

2 Use the method in Example 8.1 to prove that the gradient of the curve $y = x^2$ at the point (x, y) is equal to $2x$.

An alternative notation

So far, h has been used to denote the difference between the x co-ordinates of our points P and Q, where Q is close to P.

h is sometimes replaced by δx. The Greek letter δ(delta) is shorthand for 'a small change in' and so δx represents a small change in x, δy a small change in y and so on.

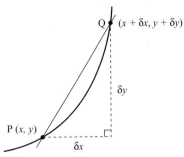

Figure 8.5

In figure 8.5 the gradient of the chord PQ is $\dfrac{\delta y}{\delta x}$.

In the limit as δx tends towards 0, δx and δy both become infinitesimally small and the value obtained for $\dfrac{\delta y}{\delta x}$ approaches the gradient of the tangent at P.

> Read this as 'the limit as δx tends towards 0'.

$\underset{\delta x \to 0}{\text{Lim}}\, \dfrac{\delta y}{\delta x}$ is written as $\dfrac{dy}{dx}$.

Using this notation, you have a rule for differentiation.

$$y = x^n \implies \frac{dy}{dx} = nx^{n-1}$$

The gradient function, $\dfrac{dy}{dx}$, is sometimes called the *derivative* of y with respect to x and when you find it you have *differentiated* y with respect to x.

Because of the connection with gradient, $\dfrac{dy}{dx}$ is also referred to as the **rate of change of y with respect to x.**

ACTIVITY 8.3

(i) Plot the curve with equation $y = x^2 + 2$ for values of x from -2 to $+2$.

(ii) On the same axes and for the same range of values of x, plot the curves $y = x^2 - 2$, $y = x^2$ and $y = x^2 + 5$.

(iii) What do you notice about the gradients of this family of curves when $x = 0$? What about when $x = 1$ and $x = -1$?

(iv) Differentiate the equation $y = x^2 + c$, where c is a constant. How does this result help you to explain your finding in (iii)?

Differentiation using standard results

Finding the gradient from first principles establishes a formal basis for differentiation but in practice you would use the differentiation rule. This also includes the results obtained by differentiating (i.e. finding the gradient of) equations which represent straight lines.

The gradient of the line $y = x$ is 1.
The gradient of the line $y = c$ is 0   where c is a constant, since this line is parallel to the x axis.

The rule can be extended further to include functions of the type $y = kx^n$ for any constant k, to give

$$y = kx^n \quad \Rightarrow \quad \frac{dy}{dx} = nkx^{n-1}.$$

You may find it helpful to remember the rule as multiply by the power of x and reduce the power by 1.

EXAMPLE 8.2

Find the gradient function for each of the following functions.

(i) $y = x^7$ (ii) $y = 4x^3$ (iii) $y = 5x^2$

SOLUTION

(i) $\dfrac{dy}{dx} = 7x^6$ (ii) $\dfrac{dy}{dx} = 12x^2$ (iii) $\dfrac{dy}{dx} = 10x$

Sums and differences of functions

Many of the functions you will meet are sums or differences of simpler ones. For example, the function $(4x^3 + 3x)$ is the sum of the functions $4x^3$ and $3x$. To differentiate a function such as this you differentiate each part separately and then add the results together.

EXAMPLE 8.3

Differentiate $y = 4x^3 + 3x$.

SOLUTION

$$\frac{dy}{dx} = 12x^2 + 3$$

EXAMPLE 8.4

Given that $y = 2x^3 - 3x + 4$, find

(i) $\dfrac{dy}{dx}$

(ii) the gradient of the curve at the point (2, 14)

(iii) the rate of change of y with respect to x when $x = -3$.

SOLUTION

(i) $\dfrac{dy}{dx} = 6x^2 - 3$

(ii) At (2, 14), $x = 2$.

Substituting $x = 2$ in the expression for $\dfrac{dy}{dx}$ gives

$$\frac{dy}{dx} = 6 \times (2)^2 - 3 = 21.$$

(iii) $\dfrac{dy}{dx}$ is the rate of change of y with respect to x.

Substituting $x = -3$ in the expression for $\dfrac{dy}{dx}$ gives

$$\frac{dy}{dx} = 6 \times (-3)^2 - 3$$

$$= 51.$$

EXERCISE 8B

1 Differentiate the following functions.

(i) $y = x^4$

(ii) $y = 2x^3$

(iii) $y = 5x^2$

(iv) $y = 7x^9$

(v) $y = -3x^6$

(vi) $y = 5$

(vii) $y = 10x$

(viii) $y = 2x^5 + 4x^2$

(ix) $y = 3x^4 + 8x$

(x) $y = x^3 + 4$

(xi) $y = x - 5x^3$

(xii) $y = 3x^5 + 4x^4 - 3x^2 + 2$

(xiii) $y = 4x^3 + 2x$

(xiv) $y = 2x + 6$

(xv) $y = x^5 + 12x^3 + 3x$

(xvi) $y = 3x^5 + 2$

(xvii) $y = \frac{1}{4}x^3$

(xviii) $y = x^3 + 42x^2 - 5x + 24$

(xix) $y = 2\pi x$

(xx) $y = \pi x^2$

2 A rectangle has length $6x$ and width $3x$.

$3x$

$6x$

The area of the rectangle is y.

(i) Write down y in terms of x.

(ii) Work out $\dfrac{dy}{dx}$.

3 An expanding sphere has radius $2x$.

(i) Show that the volume, y, of the sphere is given by the formula
$$y = \frac{32}{3}\pi x^3.$$

(ii) Work out the rate of change of y with respect to x when $x = 2$.

Products and quotients of functions

If a function is a product or quotient of simpler ones, you must manipulate them into a sum or difference before differentiating.

EXAMPLE 8.5

Work out $\dfrac{dy}{dx}$.

(i) $y = x^3(x^2 - 4)$

(ii) $y = \dfrac{x^5 + x^2}{x}$

SOLUTION

(i) Expand $\quad y = x^5 - 4x^3$
$$\frac{dy}{dx} = 5x^4 - 12x^2$$

(ii) Make into two fractions $\quad y = \dfrac{x^5}{x} + \dfrac{x^2}{x}$
$$y = x^4 + x$$
$$\frac{dy}{dx} = 4x^3 + 1$$

EXERCISE 8C

1 Work out the gradient function for each of the following functions.

(i) $y = x(x^2 + 2)$ (ii) $y = 2x^2(3x - 4)$ (iii) $y = (x + 3)(x + 2)$

(iv) $y = (x + 5)(x + 2)$ (v) $y = x^3(4 + x - x^2)$ (vi) $y = \dfrac{x^5 + x^3}{4}$

2 Work out an expression for the rate of change of y with respect to x for each of the following.

(i) $y = (x + 2)(x - 5)$ (ii) $y = \dfrac{x^7 + x^3}{x^2}$ (iii) $y = \dfrac{4x^6 - 2x^2}{x^2}$

(iv) $y = (3x + 1)(x - 2)$ (v) $y = x^{\frac{1}{2}}(x^{\frac{3}{2}} + x^{\frac{1}{2}})$ (vi) $y = x^{\frac{1}{2}}(x^{\frac{7}{2}} + x^{-\frac{1}{2}})$

3 Work out the gradient of the curve $y = x^3(x - 2)$ at the point $(3, 27)$.

4 Work out the rate of change of y with respect to x for $y = \dfrac{6x^4 + 2x^5}{2x^3}$ when $x = -1$.

5 Work out the rate of change of y with respect to x for $y = x^{\frac{1}{3}}(x^{\frac{5}{3}} - x^{\frac{2}{3}})$ when $x = -3$.

6 Work out the gradient of the curve $y = \dfrac{3x^4 + x^2 - 5x}{x}$ at the point $(1, -1)$.

Tangents and normals

Now that you know how to find the gradient of a curve at any point you can use this to find the equation of the tangent at any particular point on the curve.

(i) Find the equation of the tangent to the curve $y = 3x^2 - 5x - 2$ at the point $(1, -4)$.

(ii) Sketch the curve and show the tangent on your sketch.

SOLUTION

(i) First find the gradient function $\dfrac{dy}{dx}$

$$\frac{dy}{dx} = 6x - 5$$

Substitute $x = 1$ into this gradient function to find the gradient, m, of the tangent at $(1, -4)$

$$m = 6 \times 1 - 5$$
$$= 1$$

The equation of the tangent is given by

$$y - y_1 = m(x - x_1)$$
$$y - (-4) = 1(x - 1)$$
$$\Rightarrow \qquad y = x - 5.$$

$x_1 = 1, y_1 = -4$ and $m = 1$.

(ii) $y = 3x^2 - 5x - 2$ is a $\cup$-shaped quadratic curve.

It crosses the x axis when $3x^2 - 5x - 2 = 0$.

$$\Rightarrow \qquad (3x + 1)(x - 2) = 0$$
$$\Rightarrow \qquad x = -\frac{1}{3} \text{ or } x = 2$$

It crosses the y axis when $y = -2$.

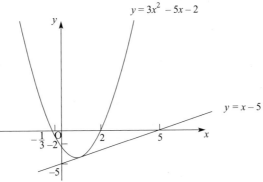

Figure 8.6

The *normal* to a curve at a particular point is the straight line that is at right angles to the tangent at that point (see figure 8.7). Remember that for perpendicular lines $m_1 m_2 = -1$.

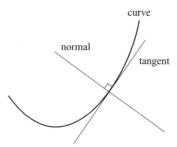

Figure 8.7

EXAMPLE 8.7

Figure 8.8 is a sketch of the curve $y = x^3 - 3x^2 + 2x$ and the point P(3, 6). Find the equation of the normal to the curve $y = x^3 - 3x^2 + 2x$ at P.

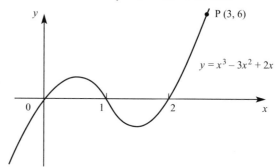

Figure 8.8

SOLUTION

$$y = x^3 - 3x^2 + 2x \quad \Rightarrow \quad \frac{dy}{dx} = 3x^2 - 6x + 2$$

Substitute $x = 3$ to find the gradient, m_1, of the tangent at the point (3, 6)

$$m_1 = 3 \times (3)^2 - 6 \times 3 + 2 = 11$$

The gradient, m_2, of the normal to the curve at this point is given by

$$m_2 = -\frac{1}{m_1} = -\frac{1}{11}. \qquad \boxed{m_1 m_2 = -1}$$

The equation of the normal is given by

$$y - y_1 = m_2(x - x_1) \qquad \boxed{(x_1, y_1) \text{ is } (3, 6).}$$

$$\Rightarrow \quad y - 6 = -\frac{1}{11}(x - 3)$$

$$\Rightarrow \quad 11y - 66 = -x + 3 \qquad \boxed{\begin{array}{c}\text{Multiply by 11} \\ \text{to eliminate the} \\ \text{fraction.}\end{array}}$$

$$\Rightarrow \quad x + 11y - 69 = 0$$

1 The sketch shows the graph of $y = 5x - x^2$.

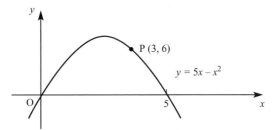

The marked point, P, has co-ordinates $(3, 6)$. Find

(i) the gradient function $\dfrac{dy}{dx}$

(ii) the gradient of the curve at P

(iii) the equation of the tangent at P

(iv) the equation of the normal at P.

2 The sketch shows the graph of $y = 3x^2 - x^3$.

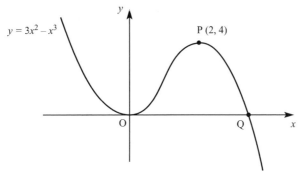

(i) The marked point, P, has co-ordinates $(2, 4)$. Find

(a) the gradient function $\dfrac{dy}{dx}$

(b) the gradient of the curve at P

(c) the equation of the tangent at P

(d) the equation of the normal at P.

(ii) The graph touches the x axis at the origin O and crosses it at the point Q. Find

(a) the co-ordinates of Q

(b) the gradient of the curve at Q

(c) the equation of the tangent at Q.

(iii) Without further calculation, state the equation of the tangent to the curve at O.

3 The sketch shows the graph of $y = x^5 - x^3$.

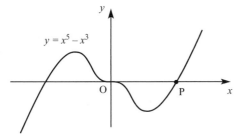

(i) Find the co-ordinates of the point P where the curve crosses the positive *x* axis.

(ii) Find the equation of the tangent at P.

(iii) Find the equation of the normal at P.

The tangent at P meets the *y* axis at Q and the normal meets the *y* axis at R.

(iv) Find the co-ordinates of Q and R and hence find the area of triangle PQR.

4 (i) Given that $y = x^3 - 3x^2 + 4x + 1$, find $\dfrac{dy}{dx}$.

(ii) The point P is on the curve $y = x^3 - 3x^2 + 4x + 1$ and its *x* co-ordinate is 2.

(a) Calculate the *y* co-ordinate of P.

(b) Find the equation of the tangent at P.

(c) Find the equation of the normal at P.

(iii) Find the values of *x* for which the curve has a gradient of 13.

5 The sketch shows the graph of $y = x^3 - 9x^2 + 23x - 15$.

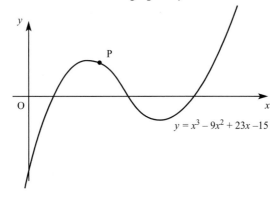

The point P marked on the curve has its *x* co-ordinate equal to 2. Find

(i) the gradient function $\dfrac{dy}{dx}$

(ii) the gradient of the curve at P

(iii) the equation of the tangent at P

(iv) the co-ordinates of another point, Q, on the curve at which the tangent is parallel to the tangent at P

(v) the equation of the tangent at Q.

6 The point $(2, -8)$ is on the curve $y = x^3 - px + q$.

(i) Use this information to find a relationship between *p* and *q*.

(ii) Find the gradient function $\dfrac{dy}{dx}$.

The tangent to this curve at the point $(2, -8)$ is parallel to the *x* axis.

(iii) Use this information to find the value of *p*.

(iv) Find the co-ordinates of the other point where the tangent is parallel to the *x* axis.

(v)   State the co-ordinates of the point P where the curve crosses the y axis.

(vi)   Find the equation of the normal to the curve at the point P.

7 The sketch shows the graph of $y = x^2 - x - 1$.

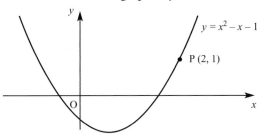

(i)   Find the equation of the tangent at the point.

The normal at a point Q on the curve is parallel to the tangent at P.

(ii)   State the gradient of the tangent at Q.

(iii)   Find the co-ordinates of the point Q.

8 A curve has the equation $y = (x - 3)(7 - x)$.

(i)   Find the gradient function $\dfrac{dy}{dx}$.

(ii)   Find the equation of the tangent at the point $(6, 3)$.

(iii)   Find the equation of the normal at the point $(6, 3)$.

(iv)   Which one of these lines passes through the origin?

9 A curve has the equation $y = 1.5x^3 - 3.5x^2 + 2x$.

(i)   Show that the curve passes through the points $(0, 0)$ and $(1, 0)$.

(ii)   Find the equations of the tangents and normals at each of these points.

(iii)   Prove that the four lines in (ii) form a rectangle.

Increasing and decreasing functions

A function $y = f(x)$ is

    increasing if $\dfrac{dy}{dx} > 0$

    decreasing if $\dfrac{dy}{dx} < 0$.

Some functions are increasing or decreasing over their whole domain.

For example, $y = 3 - 2x$ is a decreasing function for all real values of x because $\dfrac{dy}{dx} = -2$ which is < 0.

Other functions are increasing over parts of their domain.

EXAMPLE 8.8

Work out the value of x for which the function $y = x^2 - 4x + 1$ is an increasing function.

SOLUTION

Work out $\dfrac{dy}{dx}$ $\dfrac{dy}{dx} = 2x - 4$

To be an increasing function $\dfrac{dy}{dx} > 0$

$2x - 4 > 0$

$2x > 4$

$x > 2$

EXERCISE 8E

1 Work out the values of x for which the following functions are increasing.

(i) $y = x^2 + 4$	**(ii)** $y = 2x - 3$	**(iii)** $y = x^2 + 2x - 5$
(iv) $y = x^2 - 3x$	**(v)** $y = 3x^2 + 4x + 7$	**(vi)** $y = (x + 6)(x - 2)$
(vii) $y = \dfrac{1}{3}x^3 - 2x^2$	**(viii)** $y = x^3 + 6x^2 - 15x$	**(ix)** $y = x^3 - 3x^2 - 9x + 1$

2 Work out the values of x for which the following functions are decreasing.

(i) $y = 4x^2$	**(ii)** $y = x^2 - 6x + 2$	**(iii)** $y = x(x + 2)$
(iv) $y = 3 + 4x - x^2$	**(v)** $y = 12 - x$	**(vi)** $y = (2x + 1)^2$
(vii) $y = \dfrac{1}{3}x^3 + x^2$	**(viii)** $y = 2x^3 - 3x^2 - 72x$	**(ix)** $y = 27x - x^3$

3 Prove that $y = \dfrac{1}{3}x^3 + 2x^2 + 7x + 1$ is an increasing function for all values of x.

4 Prove that $y = x^3 - 6x^2 + 27x - 4$ is an increasing function for all values of x.

5 Prove that $y = 12 - 2x - x^3$ is a decreasing function for all values of x.

Stationary points

ACTIVITY 8.4

(i) Plot the graph of $y = x^4 - 3x^3 - x^2 + 3x$, taking values of x from -1.5 to $+3.5$ in steps of 0.5.
You will need your y axis to go from -10 to $+20$.

(ii) How many turning points are there on the graph?

(iii) What is the gradient at each of these turning points?

(iv) One of the turning points is a maximum and the others are minima. Which are of each type?

(v) Is the maximum the highest point of the graph?

(vi) Do the two minima occur exactly at the points you plotted?

(vii) Estimate the lowest value that y takes.

A *stationary point* on a curve is one where the gradient is zero. This means that the tangents to the curve at these points are horizontal. Figure 8.9 shows a curve with four stationary points A, B, C and D.

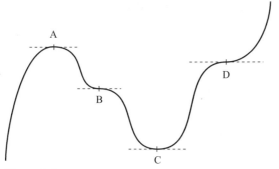

Figure 8.9

As the curve passes through the points A and C it changes direction completely. At A the gradient changes from positive to negative and at C from negative to positive. A is called a *maximum* point and C is a *minimum* point.

NOTE Maximum and minimum points are turning points. Questions on this specification will not use the term 'turning points'.

At B the curve does not turn. The gradient is negative both to the left and to the right of the point. B is a *point of inflection*.

? What can you say about the gradient to the left and to the right of D?

NOTE Points where a curve just 'twists', but doesn't have a zero gradient are also called points of inflection, but only *stationary* points of inflection, ones where the gradient is zero, are included in this section. The tangent at a point of inflection both touches and intersects the curve.

ACTIVITY 8.5

Figure 8.10 shows the graph of $y = \cos x$.

Describe the gradient of the curve, using the words 'positive', 'negative', 'zero', 'increasing' and 'decreasing', as x increases from 0° to 360°.

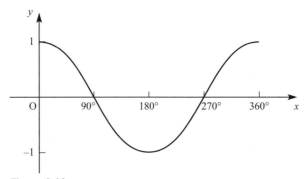

Figure 8.10

Maximum and minimum points

Figure 8.11 shows the graph of $y = 4x - x^2$. It has a *maximum* point at $(2, 4)$.

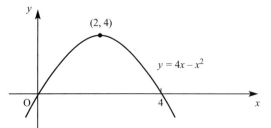

Figure 8.11

You can see that

- at the maximum point the gradient $\dfrac{dy}{dx}$ is zero
- the gradient is positive to the left of the maximum and negative to the right of it.

This is true for any maximum point (see figure 8.12).

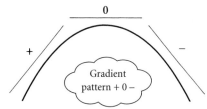

Figure 8.12

In the same way, for any minimum point (see figure 8.13)

- the gradient is zero at the minimum
- the gradient goes from negative to zero to positive.

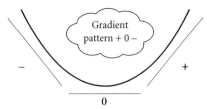

Figure 8.13

Once you have found the position and type of any stationary points, you can use this information to sketch the curve.

EXAMPLE 8.9

For the curve $y = x^3 - 12x + 3$

(i) find $\dfrac{dy}{dx}$ and the values of x for which $\dfrac{dy}{dx} = 0$

(ii) classify the points on the curve with these x values

(iii) find the corresponding y values

(iv) sketch the curve.

SOLUTION

(i) $\dfrac{dy}{dx} = 3x^2 - 12$

When $\dfrac{dy}{dx} = 0$

$$3x^2 - 12 = 0$$
$$\Rightarrow \quad 3(x^2 - 4) = 0$$
$$\Rightarrow \quad 3(x + 2)(x - 2) = 0$$
$$\Rightarrow \quad x = -2 \text{ or } x = 2$$

(ii) For $x = -2$

$$x = -3 \Rightarrow \frac{dy}{dx} = 3(-3)^2 - 12 = +15$$

$$x = -1 \Rightarrow \frac{dy}{dx} = 3(-1)^2 - 12 = -9.$$

Gradient pattern + 0 −
$\Rightarrow$ maximum point when $x = -2$.

For $x = +2$

$$x = 1 \Rightarrow \frac{dy}{dx} = 3(1)^2 - 12 = -9$$

$$x = 3 \Rightarrow \frac{dy}{dx} = 3(3)^2 - 12 = +15.$$

Gradient pattern − 0 +
$\Rightarrow$ minimum point when $x = +2$.

(iii) When $x = -2$, $y = (-2)^3 - 12(-2) + 3 = 19$.
When $x = +2$, $y = (2)^3 - 12(2) + 3 = -13$.
There is a maximum at $(-2, 19)$ and a minimum at $(2, -13)$.

(iv) The only other information you need to sketch the curve is the value of y when $x = 0$. This tells you where the curve crosses the y axis.
When $x = 0$, $y = (0)^3 - 12(0) + 3 = 3$.

The graph of $y = x^3 - 12x + 3$ is shown in figure 8.14.

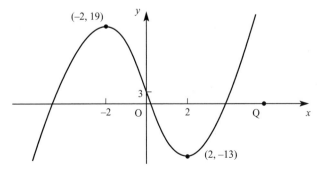

Figure 8.14

? Why can you be confident about continuing the sketch of the curve beyond the x values of the stationary points?

? In Example 8.9 you did not find the co-ordinates of the points where the curve crosses the x axis.

(i) Why was this?

(ii) Under what circumstances would you find these points?

EXAMPLE 8.10 Find all the stationary points on the curve of $y = x^4 - 2x^3 + x^2 - 2$ and sketch the curve.

SOLUTION

$$\frac{dy}{dx} = 4x^3 - 6x^2 + 2x$$

Stationary points occur when $\dfrac{dy}{dx} = 0$.

$\Rightarrow \qquad 2x(2x^2 - 3x + 1) = 0$

$\Rightarrow \qquad 2x(2x - 1)(x - 1) = 0$

$\Rightarrow \quad x = 0$ or $x = 0.5$ or $x = 1$

You may find it helpful to summarise your working in a table. You can find the various signs, + or −, by taking a test point in each interval, for example $x = 0.25$ in the interval $0 < x < 0.5$.

	$x < 0$	0	$0 < x < 0.5$	0.5	$0.5 < x < 1$	1	$x > 1$
sign of $\frac{dy}{dx}$	−	0	+	0	−	0	+
turning point		min		max		min	

When $x = 0$: $y = (0)^4 - 2(0)^3 + (0)^2 - 2 = -2$.
When $x = 0.5$: $y = (0.5)^4 - 2(0.5)^3 + (0.5)^2 - 2 = -1.9375$.
When $x = 1$: $y = (1)^4 - 2(1)^3 + (1)^2 - 2 = -2$.

Therefore $(0.5, -1.9375)$ is a maximum stationary point and $(0, -2)$ and $(1, -2)$ are both minimum stationary points.

The graph of $y = x^4 - 2x^3 + x^2 - 2$ is shown in figure 8.15.

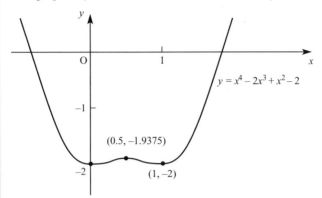

Figure 8.15

If you have access to a graphic calculator you will find it helpful to use it to check your answers.

1 For each of the curves given below

   (a) find $\dfrac{dy}{dx}$ and the value(s) of x for which $\dfrac{dy}{dx} = 0$

   (b) classify the point(s) on the curve with these x values
   (c) find the corresponding y value(s)
   (d) sketch the curve.

   (i) $y = 1 + x - 2x^2$ (ii) $y = 12x + 3x^2 - 2x^3$
   (iii) $y = x^3 - 4x^2 + 9$ (iv) $y = x^2 (x - 1)^2$
   (v) $y = x^4 - 8x^2 + 4$ (vi) $y = x^3 - 48x$
   (vii) $y = x^3 + 6x^2 - 36x + 25$ (viii) $y = 2x^3 - 15x^2 + 24x + 8$

2 The graph of $y = px + qx^2$ passes through the point $(3, -15)$ and its gradient at that point is -14.
   (i)   Find the values of p and q.
   (ii) Calculate the maximum value of y and state the value of x at which it occurs.

3 (i)   Find the stationary points of the function $f(x) = x^2(3x^2 - 2x - 3)$ and distinguish between them.
   (ii) Sketch the curve $y = f(x)$.

Points of inflection

Stationary points of inflection also have their own gradient patterns that you can use to classify them.

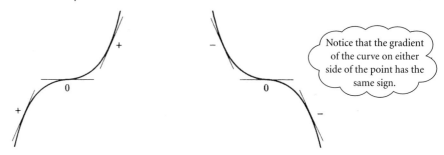

Notice that the gradient of the curve on either side of the point has the same sign.

Figure 8.16

EXAMPLE 8.11

(i) Find the stationary values of the function $y = 4x^3 - x^4$ and distinguish between them.

(ii) Sketch the curve.

SOLUTION

(i) $\dfrac{dy}{dx} = 12x^2 - 4x^3$

Stationary points occur when $12x^2 - 4x^3 = 0$

$\Rightarrow \quad 4x^2(3 - x) = 0$

$\Rightarrow \quad x = 0 \text{ or } x = 3$

For $x = 0$

$$x = -1 \quad \Rightarrow \quad \frac{dy}{dx} = 12(-1)^2 - 4(-1)^3 = +16$$

$$x = 1 \quad \Rightarrow \quad \frac{dy}{dx} = 12(1)^2 - 4(1)^3 = +8$$

Gradient pattern $+ \; 0 \; + \Rightarrow$ point of inflection when $x = 0$.

For $x = 3$

$$x = 2 \quad \Rightarrow \quad \frac{dy}{dx} = 12(2)^2 - 4(2)^3 = +16$$

$$x = 4 \quad \Rightarrow \quad \frac{dy}{dx} = 12(4)^2 - 4(4)^3 = -64$$

Gradient pattern $+ \; 0 \; - \Rightarrow$ maximum point when $x = 3$.

Substituting the x co-ordinates in the equation of the curve gives the *stationary values* of the function.

$x = 0 \Rightarrow y = 0$ and $x = 3 \Rightarrow y = 27$

(ii) The curve crosses the y axis at $(0, 0)$.

The graph of $y = 4x^3 - x^4$ is shown in figure 8.17.

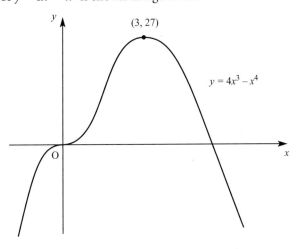

Figure 8.17

If you have access to a graphic calculator you will find it helpful to use it to check your answers.

1 For each of the curves given below

(a) find $\dfrac{dy}{dx}$ and the value(s) of x for which $\dfrac{dy}{dx} = 0$

(b) classify the point(s) that correspond to these x values

(c) find the corresponding y values(s)

(d) sketch the curve.

    (i) $y = x^3 + 6x^2 + 12x + 8$ **(ii)** $y = 3x^4 + 4x^3$

    (iii) $y = 3 + 4x^3 - x^4$ **(iv)** $y = 3x^5 - 5x^3$

    (v) $y = 4x^3 (2 - x)$ **(vi)** $y = x^3 - 3x^2 + 3x + 1$

2 (i) Find the position and nature of any stationary points of the curve
$y = x^3 - 3x^2 + 3x + 2$.

  (ii) sketch the curve.

3 The function $y = px^4 + qx^3$, where p and q are constants, has a stationary point at $(1, -3)$.

  (i) Using the fact that $(1, -3)$ lies on the curve, form an equation involving p and q.

  (ii) Differentiate y and, using the fact that $(1, -3)$ is a stationary point, form another equation involving p and q.

  (iii) Solve these two equations simultaneously to find the values of p and q.

  (iv) Determine the nature of the stationary point at $(1, -3)$.

  (v) Locate and classify the other stationary point on the curve.

1 $y = kx^n \quad \Rightarrow \quad \dfrac{\mathrm{d}y}{\mathrm{d}x} = nkx^{n-1}$

$y = c \quad \Rightarrow \quad \dfrac{\mathrm{d}y}{\mathrm{d}x} = 0$

where n is a positive integer and k and c are constants.

2 $y = \mathrm{f}(x) + \mathrm{g}(x) \quad \Rightarrow \quad \dfrac{\mathrm{d}y}{\mathrm{d}x} = \mathrm{f}'(x) + \mathrm{g}'(x)$

3 For the tangent and normal at (x_1, y_1)

- the gradient of the tangent, m_1 = the value of $\dfrac{\mathrm{d}y}{\mathrm{d}x}$
- the gradient of the normal, $m_2 = -\dfrac{1}{m_1}$
- the equation of the tangent is $y - y_1 = m_1(x - x_1)$
- the equation of the normal is $y - y_1 = m_2(x - x_1)$.

4 A function $y = \mathrm{f}(x)$ is increasing if $\dfrac{\mathrm{d}y}{\mathrm{d}x} > 0$.

A function $y = \mathrm{f}(x)$ is decreasing if $\dfrac{\mathrm{d}y}{\mathrm{d}x} < 0$.

5 At a stationary point, $\dfrac{\mathrm{d}y}{\mathrm{d}x} = 0$.

The nature of the stationary point can be determined by looking at the sign of the gradient just either side of it.

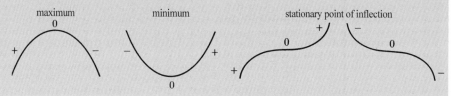

MATRICES

Matrices

Nothing tends so much to the advancement of knowledge as the application of a new instrument.

Sir Humphry Davy

An arrangement of information presented in columns and rows is called a matrix.

The numbers of male and female students in two tutor groups are shown in the following matrix.

$$\begin{array}{cc} & \text{Male} \quad \text{Female} \\ \text{Tutor group A} & \begin{pmatrix} 8 & 7 \\ 6 & 9 \end{pmatrix} \\ \text{Tutor group B} & \end{array}$$

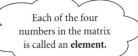

Each of the four numbers in the matrix is called an **element.**

The matrix has 2 rows and 2 columns and is called a 2×2 matrix.

The matrix $\begin{pmatrix} 4 \\ -3 \end{pmatrix}$ has 2 rows and 1 column and is called a 2×1 matrix.

NOTE A 2×1 matrix is also a **vector.**

The term vector will not be used in this specification but vectors will be referred to later when considering transformations (page 204).

Multiplying matrices

Multiplication of a matrix by a scalar

A scalar is a constant value.

All elements are multiplied by the scalar.

EXAMPLE 9.1

$\mathbf{A} = \begin{pmatrix} 2 & -3 \\ -1 & 5 \end{pmatrix}$. Work out 4**A**.

SOLUTION

$$4 \begin{pmatrix} 2 & -3 \\ -1 & 5 \end{pmatrix} = \begin{pmatrix} 8 & -12 \\ -4 & 20 \end{pmatrix}$$

Multiplication of a 2 × 2 matrix by a 2 × 1 matrix

Each row of the 2×2 matrix is multiplied by the column of the 2×1 matrix.

EXAMPLE 9.2

$P = \begin{pmatrix} -3 & -1 \\ 4 & 2 \end{pmatrix}$, $Q = \begin{pmatrix} 3 \\ 2 \end{pmatrix}$. Work out **PQ**. $\boxed{PQ = P \times Q}$

SOLUTION

$\begin{pmatrix} -3 & -1 \\ 4 & 2 \end{pmatrix}\begin{pmatrix} 3 \\ 2 \end{pmatrix} = \begin{pmatrix} (-3) \times 3 + (-1) \times 2 \\ 4 \times 3 + 2 \times 2 \end{pmatrix}$

$= \begin{pmatrix} -11 \\ 16 \end{pmatrix}$

> It is not possible to multiply in the
> order $\begin{pmatrix} 3 \\ 2 \end{pmatrix}\begin{pmatrix} -3 & -1 \\ 4 & 2 \end{pmatrix}$
> because the number of columns
> in the first matrix is different
> to the number of rows in
> the second matrix.

Multiplication of a 2 × 2 matrix by a 2 × 2 matrix

Each row of the first 2 × 2 matrix is multiplied by each column of the second 2 × 2 matrix.

EXAMPLE 9.3

$C = \begin{pmatrix} 0 & -1 \\ -2 & 3 \end{pmatrix}$, $D = \begin{pmatrix} 2 & 4 \\ -3 & 1 \end{pmatrix}$. Work out **CD**.

SOLUTION

$\begin{pmatrix} 0 & -1 \\ -2 & 3 \end{pmatrix}\begin{pmatrix} 2 & 4 \\ -3 & 1 \end{pmatrix} = \begin{pmatrix} 0 \times 2 + (-1) \times (-3) & 0 \times 4 + (-1) \times 1 \\ (-2) \times 2 + 3 \times (-3) & (-2) \times 4 + 3 \times 1 \end{pmatrix}$

$= \begin{pmatrix} 3 & -1 \\ -13 & -5 \end{pmatrix}$

Equating elements

If two matrices are equal, the elements can be equated.
This is used in the following example.

EXAMPLE 9.4

Given that $\begin{pmatrix} 3 & a \\ -2 & 1 \end{pmatrix}\begin{pmatrix} 2 & -2 \\ -3 & b \end{pmatrix} = \begin{pmatrix} 12 & 2 \\ -7 & 0 \end{pmatrix}$

work out the values of a and b.

SOLUTION

Multiply out the left hand side

$\begin{pmatrix} 3 & a \\ -2 & 1 \end{pmatrix}\begin{pmatrix} 2 & -2 \\ -3 & b \end{pmatrix} = \begin{pmatrix} 6 - 3a & -6 + ab \\ -7 & 4 + b \end{pmatrix}$

Put equal to the right hand side

$\begin{pmatrix} 6 - 3a & -6 + ab \\ -7 & 4 + b \end{pmatrix} = \begin{pmatrix} 12 & 2 \\ -7 & 0 \end{pmatrix}$

Equate elements in row 1 column 1

$$6 - 3a = 12$$
$$6 - 12 = 3a$$
$$-6 = 3a$$
$$a = -2$$

Equate elements in row 2 column 2

$$4 + b = 0$$
$$b = -4$$

ACTIVITY 9.1

$$A = \begin{pmatrix} 2 & 4 \\ -3 & 1 \end{pmatrix} \qquad B = \begin{pmatrix} 1 & 2 \\ 3 & -4 \end{pmatrix}$$

Work out **AB** and **BA**.

? Can you find matrix **P** and matrix **Q** for which $PQ = QP$?

EXERCISE 9A

1 $A = \begin{pmatrix} 2 & 3 \\ 1 & 1 \end{pmatrix}$ $\qquad B = \begin{pmatrix} -2 & 0 \\ 3 & 1 \end{pmatrix}$ $\qquad C = \begin{pmatrix} 6 & -2 \\ -3 & -1 \end{pmatrix}$ $\qquad D = \begin{pmatrix} 0 & 0 \\ -3 & -5 \end{pmatrix}$

$E = \begin{pmatrix} 1 \\ 2 \end{pmatrix}$ $\qquad F = \begin{pmatrix} 7 \\ 3 \end{pmatrix}$ $\qquad G = \begin{pmatrix} -3 \\ 4 \end{pmatrix}$ $\qquad H = \begin{pmatrix} -2 \\ -1 \end{pmatrix}$

Work out

(i) 4A $\qquad$ (ii) 2D $\qquad$ (iii) AF $\qquad$ (iv) CE $\qquad$ (v) DH $\qquad$ (vi) BH

(vii) AB $\qquad$ (viii) BA $\qquad$ (ix) BC $\qquad$ (x) CB $\qquad$ (xi) DA $\qquad$ (xii) BD

(xiii) AC $\qquad$ (xiv) DC.

2 Work out the value of p in each of the following.

(i) $\begin{pmatrix} 4 & 2 \\ 1 & -1 \end{pmatrix}\begin{pmatrix} p \\ 3 \end{pmatrix} = \begin{pmatrix} 2 \\ -4 \end{pmatrix}$

(ii) $\begin{pmatrix} 2 & -1 \\ p & 3 \end{pmatrix}\begin{pmatrix} 2 \\ -1 \end{pmatrix} = \begin{pmatrix} 5 \\ 9 \end{pmatrix}$

(iii) $\begin{pmatrix} p & 1 \\ 5 & 4 \end{pmatrix}\begin{pmatrix} 3 \\ p \end{pmatrix} = \begin{pmatrix} 2 \\ 17 \end{pmatrix}$

(iv) $\begin{pmatrix} p & 4p \\ p & -2p \end{pmatrix}\begin{pmatrix} -2 \\ -1 \end{pmatrix} = \begin{pmatrix} -9 \\ 0 \end{pmatrix}$

(v) $\begin{pmatrix} 3 & 0 \\ 1 & 2 \end{pmatrix}\begin{pmatrix} 2 & 1 \\ p & 4 \end{pmatrix} = \begin{pmatrix} 6 & 3 \\ 16 & 9 \end{pmatrix}$

(vi) $\begin{pmatrix} 4 & -1 \\ 0 & 0 \end{pmatrix}\begin{pmatrix} 2 & 2p \\ -1 & p \end{pmatrix} = \begin{pmatrix} 9 & -14 \\ 0 & 0 \end{pmatrix}$

3 Work out the values of x and y in each of the following.

(i) $\begin{pmatrix} 2 & 1 \\ 1 & y \end{pmatrix}\begin{pmatrix} x \\ 3 \end{pmatrix} = \begin{pmatrix} 11 \\ 10 \end{pmatrix}$

(ii) $\begin{pmatrix} 1 & x \\ 2y & 3y \end{pmatrix}\begin{pmatrix} -1 \\ 2 \end{pmatrix} = \begin{pmatrix} -3 \\ -8 \end{pmatrix}$

(iii) $\begin{pmatrix} -3 & 0 \\ 1 & -2 \end{pmatrix}\begin{pmatrix} 2 & 0 \\ x & y \end{pmatrix} = \begin{pmatrix} -6 & 0 \\ -4 & 10 \end{pmatrix}$

(iv) $\begin{pmatrix} x & 1 \\ -1 & 0 \end{pmatrix}\begin{pmatrix} 2 & 4 \\ x & y \end{pmatrix} = \begin{pmatrix} -9 & -5 \\ -2 & -4 \end{pmatrix}$

4 Given that $\begin{pmatrix} 5 & 3 \\ 2 & -1 \end{pmatrix}\begin{pmatrix} x \\ y \end{pmatrix} = \begin{pmatrix} 1 \\ -4 \end{pmatrix}$

(i) show that $5x + 3y = 1$

(ii) work out a different equation in x and y

(iii) work out x and y by solving the pair of simultaneous equations.

5 Work out the values of a and b in each of the following.

(i) $\begin{pmatrix} 3 & -2 \\ 2 & 3 \end{pmatrix}\begin{pmatrix} a \\ b \end{pmatrix} = \begin{pmatrix} -1 \\ 21 \end{pmatrix}$

(ii) $\begin{pmatrix} a & b \\ b & a \end{pmatrix}\begin{pmatrix} 4 \\ -1 \end{pmatrix} = \begin{pmatrix} -12 \\ 18 \end{pmatrix}$

(iii) $\begin{pmatrix} 3 & b \\ 0 & 2 \end{pmatrix}\begin{pmatrix} a & 2a \\ 1 & -1 \end{pmatrix} = \begin{pmatrix} -2 & 11 \\ 2 & -2 \end{pmatrix}$

(iv) $\begin{pmatrix} 5 & 1 \\ 3a & b+1 \end{pmatrix}\begin{pmatrix} 1 & 1 \\ 2 & -1 \end{pmatrix} = \begin{pmatrix} 7 & 4 \\ 12 & 3 \end{pmatrix}$

Transformations

A point P (x, y) can be transformed to an **image** point P' (x', y').

P is mapped to the image P'.

For example,

(i) when $(4, 2)$ is transformed by reflection in the y axis, the image point is $(-4, 2)$. $(4, 2)$ is mapped to $(-4, 2)$.

(ii) when $(3, -1)$ is transformed by rotation through 270°, centre O, the image point is $(-1, 3)$. $(3, -1)$ is mapped to $(-1, 3)$.

Matrix transformations

A transformation can be defined by a matrix. For a transformation that maps

> A line from $(0, 0)$ to $(1, 0)$ is the vector $\begin{pmatrix} 1 \\ 0 \end{pmatrix}$.

$\begin{pmatrix} 1 \\ 0 \end{pmatrix}$ to $\begin{pmatrix} a \\ c \end{pmatrix}$ and $\begin{pmatrix} 0 \\ 1 \end{pmatrix}$ to $\begin{pmatrix} b \\ d \end{pmatrix}$

> A line from $(0, 0)$ to $(0, 1)$ is the vector $\begin{pmatrix} 0 \\ 1 \end{pmatrix}$.

the transformation matrix is $\begin{pmatrix} a & b \\ c & d \end{pmatrix}$.

The point P (x, y) and the image point P' (x', y') are connected by

$\begin{pmatrix} a & b \\ c & d \end{pmatrix}\begin{pmatrix} x \\ y \end{pmatrix} = \begin{pmatrix} x' \\ y' \end{pmatrix}$.

EXAMPLE 9.5

Work out the image of point $(-2, 5)$ for the transformation defined by matrix $\begin{pmatrix} 2 & 3 \\ -2 & 1 \end{pmatrix}$.

SOLUTION

Write the co-ordinates $(-2, 5)$ as a 2×1 matrix.

$$\begin{pmatrix} 2 & 3 \\ -2 & 1 \end{pmatrix} \begin{pmatrix} -2 \\ 5 \end{pmatrix} = \begin{pmatrix} 11 \\ 9 \end{pmatrix}$$

Write the 2×1 matrix as co-ordinates.

The image point is $(11, 9)$.

ACTIVITY 9.2

(i) For the transformation defined by matrix $\begin{pmatrix} 1 & 0 \\ 0 & 1 \end{pmatrix}$, work out the image of each

of the following points.

$(3, 2)$ $(-1, 5)$ $(6, 0)$ $(-3, -4)$ and (x, y)

How would you describe the transformation?

(ii) For the transformation defined by matrix $\begin{pmatrix} 1 & 0 \\ 0 & -1 \end{pmatrix}$, work out the image of
each of the following points.

$(2, 1)$ $(-4, 3)$ $(0, 4)$ $(-5, -1)$ and (x, y)

How would you describe the transformation?

Identity matrix

The matrix $\begin{pmatrix} 1 & 0 \\ 0 & 1 \end{pmatrix}$ is called the identity matrix **I**.

When multiplied by another matrix **A** $\mathbf{AI} = \mathbf{IA} = \mathbf{A}$

When **I** is used as a transformation matrix, no movement occurs.

EXERCISE 9B

1 Work out the image of point $(4, 2)$ for the transformation defined by matrix
$\begin{pmatrix} 3 & 4 \\ 1 & 2 \end{pmatrix}$.

2 Work out the image of point $(1, -3)$ for the transformation represented by
matrix $\begin{pmatrix} 0 & -3 \\ -1 & 5 \end{pmatrix}$.

3 Work out the image of point $(-2, -3)$ for the transformation defined by matrix
$\begin{pmatrix} -2 & -3 \\ 2 & -1 \end{pmatrix}$.

4 The image of point $(4, 3)$ under the transformation matrix $\begin{pmatrix} 2 & 1 \\ c & 3 \end{pmatrix}$ is $(11, 1)$.
Work out the value of c.

5 The image of point $(a, 1)$ under the transformation matrix $\begin{pmatrix} 1 & -2 \\ 2 & -1 \end{pmatrix}$ is $(7, 17)$.
Work out the value of a.

6 The image of point $(3, -2)$ under the transformation matrix $\begin{pmatrix} a & 2a \\ b & 3 \end{pmatrix}$ is (b, b).
Work out the values of a and b.

7 The transformation matrix $\begin{pmatrix} 2c & d \\ c & -d \end{pmatrix}$ maps the point $(2, 5)$ to the point $(-6, 12)$.

Work out the values of c and d.

8 Given that $\mathbf{A} = \begin{pmatrix} 0 & -1 \\ -1 & 0 \end{pmatrix}$, show that $\mathbf{A}^2 = \mathbf{I}$.

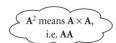
$\mathbf{A}^2$ means $\mathbf{A} \times \mathbf{A}$, i.e. $\mathbf{AA}$

9 Given that $\begin{pmatrix} 5 & -2 \\ -7 & 3 \end{pmatrix}\begin{pmatrix} 3 & 2 \\ 7 & p \end{pmatrix} = \mathbf{I}$, work out the value of p.

Transformations of the unit square

The unit square has vertices O $(0, 0)$, A $(1, 0)$, B $(1, 1)$ and C $(0, 1)$.

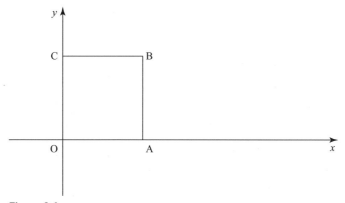

Figure 9.1

The unit square is the only two-dimensional shape that you will be expected to transform in the examination.

The following transformations of the unit square are the only ones that you will be expected to carry out.

Reflections

in the x axis   in the y axis   in the line $y = x$ in the line $y = -x$

Rotations about the origin

through 90°   through 180°   through 270°

NOTE Rotations are anti-clockwise unless stated otherwise.
Rotation of 270° is the same as rotation of 90° clockwise.

Enlargements, centre the origin

with positive scale factors   with negative scale factors

You will need to be able to work out the matrix that represents any of the above transformations. A method that can be used is shown in the following example.

EXAMPLE 9.6

Work out the matrix that represents each of the following transformations.

(i) Rotation through 270° about the origin.

(ii) Enlargement, centre the origin, scale factor 3.

SOLUTION

In both parts, consider the images of the vectors $\begin{pmatrix} 1 \\ 0 \end{pmatrix}$ and $\begin{pmatrix} 0 \\ 1 \end{pmatrix}$.

(i)

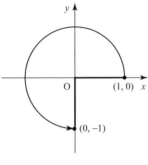

$$\begin{pmatrix} 1 \\ 0 \end{pmatrix} \longrightarrow \begin{pmatrix} 0 \\ -1 \end{pmatrix}$$

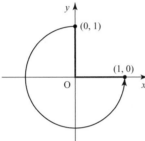

$$\begin{pmatrix} 0 \\ 1 \end{pmatrix} \longrightarrow \begin{pmatrix} 1 \\ 0 \end{pmatrix}$$

Figure 9.2

Matrix is $\begin{pmatrix} 0 & 1 \\ -1 & 0 \end{pmatrix}$.

(ii)

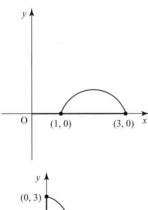

$$\begin{pmatrix} 1 \\ 0 \end{pmatrix} \longrightarrow \begin{pmatrix} 3 \\ 0 \end{pmatrix}$$

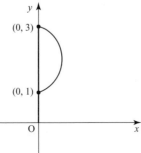

$$\begin{pmatrix} 0 \\ 1 \end{pmatrix} \longrightarrow \begin{pmatrix} 0 \\ 3 \end{pmatrix}$$

Matrix is $\begin{pmatrix} 3 & 0 \\ 0 & 3 \end{pmatrix}$.

Figure 9.3

EXAMPLE 9.7

The unit square OABC is transformed by the matrix $\begin{pmatrix} -1 & 0 \\ 0 & -1 \end{pmatrix}$ to OA′B′C′.

Show the image on a diagram, labelling each vertex.

SOLUTION

Method 1

Use the matrix to work out the image of each vertex

$$\begin{pmatrix} -1 & 0 \\ 0 & -1 \end{pmatrix}\begin{pmatrix} 0 \\ 0 \end{pmatrix} = \begin{pmatrix} 0 \\ 0 \end{pmatrix}$$
Image of O $(0, 0)$ is O $(0, 0)$.

$$\begin{pmatrix} -1 & 0 \\ 0 & -1 \end{pmatrix}\begin{pmatrix} 1 \\ 0 \end{pmatrix} = \begin{pmatrix} -1 \\ 0 \end{pmatrix}$$
Image of A $(1, 0)$ is A′ $(-1, 0)$.

$$\begin{pmatrix} -1 & 0 \\ 0 & -1 \end{pmatrix}\begin{pmatrix} 1 \\ 1 \end{pmatrix} = \begin{pmatrix} -1 \\ -1 \end{pmatrix}$$
Image of B $(1, 1)$ is B′ $(-1, -1)$.

$$\begin{pmatrix} -1 & 0 \\ 0 & -1 \end{pmatrix}\begin{pmatrix} 0 \\ 1 \end{pmatrix} = \begin{pmatrix} 0 \\ -1 \end{pmatrix}$$
Image of C $(0, 1)$ is C′ $(0, -1)$.

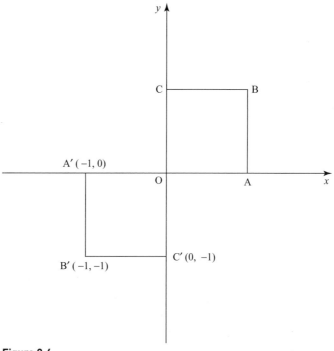

Figure 9.4

Method 2 (alternative method)

If the matrix is recognised as representing rotation through 180°, centre the origin, the unit square can be transformed and the above diagram is obtained.

1 Work out the matrix that represents each of the following transformations.

(i)   Reflection in the x axis.
(ii)   Rotation, centre O, through 90°.
(iii) Enlargement, scale factor 2, centre the origin.
(iv)   Reflection in the y axis.
(v)   Reflection in the line $y = x$.
(vi)   Rotation by 180°, centre the origin.
(vii) Reflection in the line $y = -x$.
(viii) Enlargement, scale factor -3, centre O.
(ix)   Enlargement, centre O, scale factor $\frac{1}{2}$.

2 The unit square OABC is transformed by the matrix $\begin{pmatrix} 0 & 1 \\ 1 & 0 \end{pmatrix}$ to OA′B′C′.

Show the image on a diagram, labelling each vertex.

3 The unit square OABC is transformed by the matrix $\begin{pmatrix} -\frac{1}{2} & 0 \\ 0 & -\frac{1}{2} \end{pmatrix}$ to OA′B′C′.

Show the image on a diagram, labelling each vertex.

4 The unit square OABC is transformed to OA′B′C′.

OA′B′C′ is shown on the diagram.

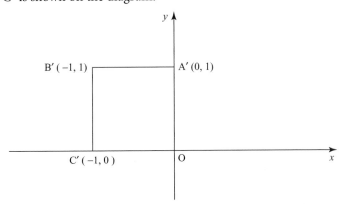

Work out the matrix for the transformation.

5 The unit square OABC is transformed by the matrix $\begin{pmatrix} 4 & 0 \\ 0 & 4 \end{pmatrix}$ to OA′B′C′.
Work out the area of OA′B′C′.

6 The unit square OABC is transformed by the matrix $\begin{pmatrix} k & 0 \\ 0 & k \end{pmatrix}$ to OA′B′C′.

The area of OA′B′C′ is 64 square units.

Work out the two possible values of k.

Combining transformations

Two transformations may be applied successively.

The two transformations can be combined to a single transformation that maps point A to point A″.

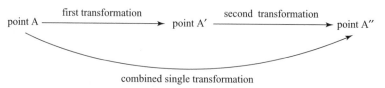

first transformation

second transformation

point A ⟶ point A′ ⟶ point A″

combined single transformation

Figure 9.5

When a transformation represented by matrix **P** is followed by a transformation represented by matrix **Q**, the matrix for the combined transformation is **QP**.

EXAMPLE 9.8

Point L is transformed by the matrix $\begin{pmatrix} 1 & 2 \\ 0 & 3 \end{pmatrix}$ to the point M.

Point M is then transformed by the matrix $\begin{pmatrix} 0 & -1 \\ 2 & -1 \end{pmatrix}$ to the point N.

Work out the matrix that transforms point L to point N.

> Note that the matrix for the second transformation is written first in the matrix for the combined transformation.

SOLUTION

Multiply the matrices in the correct order.

$$\begin{pmatrix} 0 & -1 \\ 2 & -1 \end{pmatrix}\begin{pmatrix} 1 & 2 \\ 0 & 3 \end{pmatrix} = \begin{pmatrix} 0 & -3 \\ 2 & 1 \end{pmatrix}$$

EXAMPLE 9.9

The unit square is transformed by the matrix $\begin{pmatrix} 0 & -1 \\ 1 & 0 \end{pmatrix}$ followed by a further transformation by the matrix $\begin{pmatrix} 1 & 0 \\ 0 & -1 \end{pmatrix}$.

Work out the matrix for the combined transformation and interpret the result geometrically.

SOLUTION

Multiply the matrices in the correct order

$$\begin{pmatrix} 1 & 0 \\ 0 & -1 \end{pmatrix}\begin{pmatrix} 0 & -1 \\ 1 & 0 \end{pmatrix} = \begin{pmatrix} 0 & -1 \\ -1 & 0 \end{pmatrix}$$

This is the transformation matrix for which

$$\begin{pmatrix} 1 \\ 0 \end{pmatrix} \rightarrow \begin{pmatrix} 0 \\ -1 \end{pmatrix} \quad \text{and} \quad \begin{pmatrix} 0 \\ 1 \end{pmatrix} \rightarrow \begin{pmatrix} -1 \\ 0 \end{pmatrix}.$$

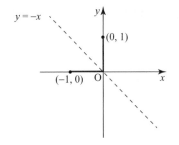

Figure 9.6

The combined matrix represents reflection in the line $y=-x$.

EXERCISE 9D

1 Point P $(3, -2)$ is transformed by the matrix $\begin{pmatrix} 1 & -1 \\ 0 & 1 \end{pmatrix}$ followed by a further transformation by the matrix $\begin{pmatrix} 0 & 2 \\ 1 & 0 \end{pmatrix}$.

(i) Work out the matrix for the combined transformation.

(ii) Work out the co-ordinates of the image point of P.

2 Point W $(-1, 4)$ is transformed by the matrix $\begin{pmatrix} 3 & -1 \\ -2 & 2 \end{pmatrix}$ followed by a further transformation by the matrix $\begin{pmatrix} 1 & 0 \\ 3 & -2 \end{pmatrix}$.

(i) Work out the matrix for the combined transformation.

(ii) Work out the co-ordinates of the image point of W.

3 The unit square is reflected in the x axis followed by a rotation through $180°$, centre the origin.

Work out the matrix for the combined transformation.

4 The unit square is enlarged, centre the origin, scale factor 2 followed by a reflection in the line $y = x$.

Work out the matrix for the combined transformation.

5 The unit square is rotated by $90°$, centre the origin, followed by a reflection in the y axis.

Work out the matrix for the combined transformation.

6 Matrix $\mathbf{P} = \begin{pmatrix} -1 & 0 \\ 0 & 1 \end{pmatrix}$

(i) Describe the transformation that this matrix represents.

(ii) Work out $\mathbf{P}^2$.

(iii) Use transformations to interpret your answer to (ii).

7 Matrix $\mathbf{D} = \begin{pmatrix} 0 & -1 \\ 1 & 0 \end{pmatrix}$ Matrix $\mathbf{E} = \begin{pmatrix} -1 & 0 \\ 0 & -1 \end{pmatrix}$

(i)   Describe the transformation that matrix **D** represents.

(ii)   Describe the transformation that matrix **E** represents.

(iii)   Work out **DE**.

(iv)   Describe the transformation that matrix **DE** represents.

(v)   Use transformations to interpret your answer to (iv).

(vi)   Use transformations to explain why **ED** = **DE**.

8 Use transformation matrices to prove that an enlargement, centre the origin, scale factor 3, followed by an enlargement, centre the origin, scale factor −2, is equivalent to an enlargement, centre the origin, scale factor k, where k is an integer. State the value of k.

KEY POINTS

1 To multiply a 2 × 2 matrix by a 2 × 1 matrix, each row of the 2 × 2 matrix is multiplied by the column of the 2 × 1 matrix. To multiply a 2 × 2 matrix by a 2 × 2 matrix, each row of the first 2 × 2 matrix is multiplied by each column of the second.

2 If two matrices are equal, the elements can be equated.

3 A point P (x, y) can be transformed to an **image** point P′ $(x′, y′)$.

If the transformation matrix is $\begin{pmatrix} a & b \\ c & d \end{pmatrix}$ then

$$\begin{pmatrix} a & b \\ c & d \end{pmatrix}\begin{pmatrix} x \\ y \end{pmatrix} = \begin{pmatrix} x′ \\ y′ \end{pmatrix}.$$

4 A transformation using matrix **A** followed by a transformation using matrix **B** is a combined transformation. The matrix for the combined transformation is **BA**.

Key words

Solve	Work out all solutions to an equation
Expand	Remove brackets
Expand and simplify	Remove brackets and collect like terms
Factorise	Write as a product
Show that	Show all relevant steps
Prove	Show all relevant steps (include explanations of facts used in geometrical proofs)
Explain	Give reasons, either in words or using mathematical symbols, or both
Work out the exact value	Give the answer as an integer, fraction, exact decimal, recurring decimal, in terms of π or as a surd
Give your answer in its simplest form	Cancel ratio or fraction answers
Draw (a graph)	Use axes on graph paper, plotting points accurately
Sketch (a graph)	Do not use graph paper. Use axes and show the correct shape in each quadrant. Label appropriate points (e.g. intersections with axes, stationary points)
State	Write the answer down (showing working is not necessary)

Exam-style paper

Paper 1   **Calculator NOT allowed** $1\frac{1}{2}$ **hours**

1   Match each graph with the correct equation.

Straight line of gradient -3

$x = -3$

$y = 3x^2$

Curve passing through $(3, 0)$

$7y + 4x = 12$

$y + 3x = 1$

Straight line passing through $(3, 0)$

$y = x^3 - 27$

     (3 marks)

2   $\begin{pmatrix} 4 & p \\ 1 & 3 \end{pmatrix} \begin{pmatrix} 5 \\ -2 \end{pmatrix} = \begin{pmatrix} 11 \\ -1 \end{pmatrix}$

   Work out the value of p.   (3 marks)

3   Work out the value of x.
   (a) $m^5 \times m^x = m^3$ (1 mark)
   (b) $(w^x)^6 = w^3$ (1 mark)
   (c) $\sqrt[x]{t^{12}} = t^4$ (1 mark)

4   **(a)** Expand $3x(5x + 7)$.   (1 mark)
   (b) Expand and simplify $(4 - 2x)(1 + 2x)$.   (3 marks)
   (c) When $x = -1$, work out the value of $\dfrac{3x(5x + 7)}{(4 - 2x)(1 + 2x)}$.   (2 marks)

5   $f(x)$ is a quadratic function.
   Here is a sketch of $y = f(x)$.
   $0 \leqslant f(x) \leqslant 8$

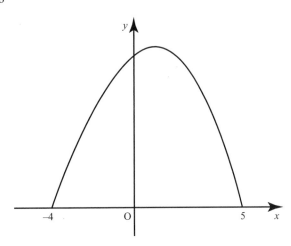

(a) State the domain of f(x). (1 mark)

(b) Work out the co-ordinates of the maximum point of $y = f(x)$. (2 marks)

(c) Write down the **number** of solutions there are to f(x) + 2 = 0. (1 mark)

6 The nth term of sequence A is $98n + 5$.

The nth term of sequence B is $n^2 - 94$.

Which term has the same value in each sequence? (4 marks)

7 A, B and C lie on a circle.

BD is a tangent.

AC is parallel to BD.

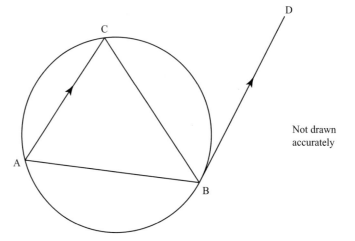

Not drawn
accurately

Prove that triangle ABC is isosceles. (3 marks)

8 Work out the equation of the line that is perpendicular to $2x + 3y = 5$
and crosses the x axis at $(-5, 0)$. (3 marks)

9 The diagram shows a cyclic quadrilateral.

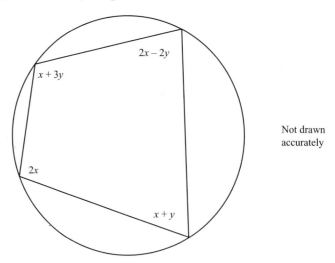

Not drawn
accurately

Work out x and y. (5 marks)

10 Show that the two solutions of $x^2 - 6x + 2 = 0$ add to make an integer. (5 marks)

11 A circle has centre C and passes through A $(-7, 3)$ and B $(5, 3)$.

AC = BC = 10

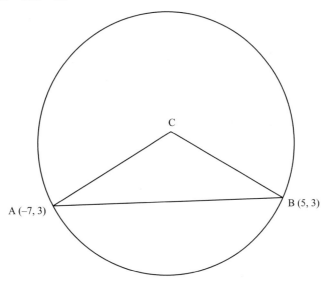

Not drawn accurately

Work out the equation of the circle. (4 marks)

12 (a) Use the factor theorem to show that $(y + 4)$ is a factor
of $y^3 + 4y^2 - 4y - 16$. (2 marks)

(b) Factorise fully $y^3 + 4y^2 - 4y - 16$. (3 marks)

13 (a) Factorise fully $t^3 - t^2$. (1 mark)

(b) Solve for $\quad 0° \leqslant x \leqslant 270° \quad \tan^3 x - \tan^2 x = 0$ (3 marks)

14 (a) What is the exact value of sin 60°? (1 mark)

(b)

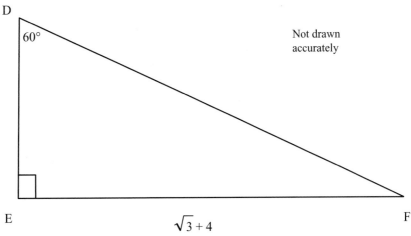

Not drawn accurately

Use your answer to **(a)** to work out the exact value of DF.

Give your answer in the form $a + b\sqrt{3}$. (5 marks)

15 The line $3y + x = 10$ and the circle $x^2 + y^2 = 20$ intersect at P and Q.

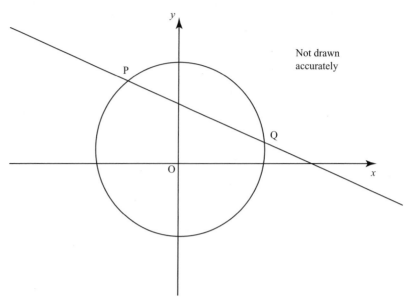

Not drawn accurately

Work out the co-ordinates of P and Q. (6 marks)

16 Work out the co-ordinates of the stationary points on the curve

$$y = \frac{1}{4}x^4 - \frac{4}{3}x^3 + 2x^2.$$

Determine the nature of each stationary point.

You **must** show your working. (6 marks)

Exam-style paper

Paper 2   **Calculator allowed**   **2 hours**

1 $f(x) = x^2 - 3$ for all values of x.

    (a) Work out $f(-2)$.   (1 mark)

    (b) Sketch the graph of $y = f(x)$.   (2 marks)

    (c) Write down the range of $f(x)$.   (1 mark)

2 $a : b = 2 : 3$

    (a) Write a in terms of b.   (1 mark)

    (b) Work out $5a + 2b : 4b$, giving your answer in the simplest form.   (2 marks)

3 P is $(2a, 8)$ and Q is $(6, 4b)$.

    The midpoint of PQ is M.

    x co-ordinate of M = y co-ordinate of M

    Show that $a = 2b + 1$.   (3 marks)

4 $f(x) = ax^2 + bx + c$ for all x values.

    $a \neq 0$

    Tick the correct statement for the graph of $y = f(x)$

	Always true	Sometimes true	Never true
(a) The graph intersects the y axis at $(0, c)$.	☐	☐	☐
(b) The graph intersects the x axis at two points.	☐	☐	☐
(c) The graph has a minimum point.	☐	☐	☐
(d) The graph has a point of inflection.	☐	☐	☐

    (4 marks)

5 $y = 4x^3 + x^2 - 7x$

    (a) Work out $\dfrac{dy}{dx}$.   (2 marks)

    (b) Work out the rate of change of y with respect to x when $x = 1.5$.   (2 marks)

6 C is the centre of the circle.
P is a point on the circumference.

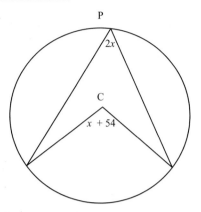

Work out the value of *x*. (3 marks)

7 *h* increased by 50% is equal to 60% of *m*.
Express *m* in terms of *h*. (2 marks)

8 A ship travels for 25 km on a bearing of 065° from A to B.
It then travels for 18 km from B to C.
Angle ABC = 90°

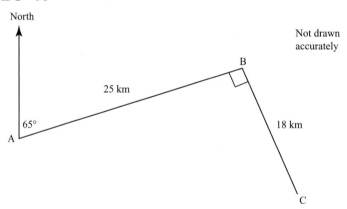

(a) Work out the distance AC. (3 marks)
(b) Work out the bearing of C from A. (4 marks)

9 PQR is a straight line.
PR = 3PQ

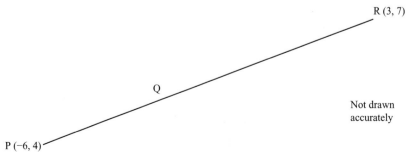

Work out the co-ordinates of Q. (4 marks)

10 Work out the matrix that represents a rotation through 180°, centre the origin. (2 marks)

11 Draw the graph of $y = g(x)$ where

$g(x) = 3x$ $0 \leqslant x < 2$

    $= 6$ $2 \leqslant x < 5$

    $= 16 - 2x$ $5 \leqslant x \leqslant 8$

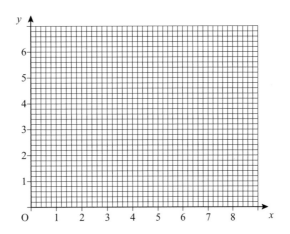

(3 marks)

12 (a) Write as a single power of x

$$\sqrt{\frac{x^{\frac{4}{3}} \times x^{\frac{8}{3}}}{x}}$$

(3 marks)

(b) Solve $x^{-\frac{1}{3}} = \frac{2}{5}$. (2 marks)

13 (a) Factorise fully $(a - b)^2 + (a - b)(a + 2b)$. (2 marks)

(b) Simplify fully $\dfrac{2c^4 - 5c^3}{4c^2 - 25}$. (3 marks)

14 Here is an L-shape.

All lengths are in centimetres.

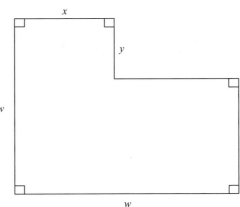

The shape has area A cm².

(a) Show that $A = w^2 + xy - wy$. (2 marks)

(b) Rearrange the formula to make y the subject. (3 marks)

15 Work out the x co-ordinates of the points on the curve $y = x^5 - x$ where the gradient is 79. (4 marks)

16 $(x + 4)^2 + p \equiv x^2 + qx + 28$
Work out the values of p and q. (3 marks)

17 (a) Sketch the curve $y = \cos x$ for $0° \leqslant x \leqslant 360°$. (2 marks)

(b) Solve $\cos x = \dfrac{\sqrt{3}}{2}$ for $0° \leqslant x \leqslant 360°$. (2 marks)

18 A paperweight is in the shape of a square-based pyramid.
The base ABCD has edge 5 cm.
The vertex V is directly above the centre of the base, E.
VE = 7 cm

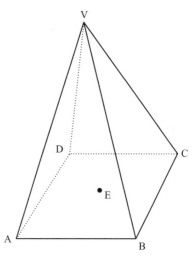

(a) Work out VA. (3 marks)
(b) Work out the angle between VA and ABCD. (3 marks)
(c) Work out the angle between VAB and ABCD. (2 marks)

19 (a) Here is a quadratic sequence.
  3   6   13   24   39
Work out an expression for the nth term. (4 marks)

(b) A different sequence has nth term $= \dfrac{3n + 2}{1 - 6n}$.
Prove that the limiting value of the nth term as $n \to \infty$ is $-\frac{1}{2}$. (3 marks)

20 A triangle and a rectangle are shown.
All dimensions are in centimetres.

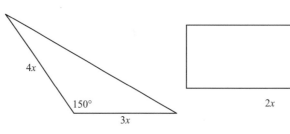

(a) Show that the area of the triangle is $6x^2$ cm^2 (2 marks)

(b) Work out the range of values of x for which

area of triangle < area of rectangle (5 marks)

21 Work out the equation of the tangent to the curve $y = (x + 5)(x - 3)$
at the point where $x = -3$. Give your answer in the
form $y = mx + c$. (5 marks)

22 Point P is transformed by the matrix $\begin{pmatrix} 3 & 1 \\ 6 & 3 \end{pmatrix}$, followed by a further

transformation by the matrix $\begin{pmatrix} -2 & 1 \\ 0 & -1 \end{pmatrix}$.

(a) Work out the matrix for the combined transformation. (2 marks)

(b) The image of point P after the combined transformation
is (2, 3). Work out the co-ordinates of P. (3 marks)

23 Prove that $\sin x \tan x \equiv \dfrac{1}{\cos x} - \cos x$. (3 marks)

24 $f(n) = n^3$ for all positive integer values of n.
Prove that $f(n + 1) - f(n - 1)$ is always even. (5 marks)

Answers

Chapter 1

Exercise 1A (Page 3)

1. (i) $5:2$
   (ii) $2:3$
   (iii) $11:2$
   (iv) $1:2$
   (v) $3:1$

2. (i) £69
   (ii) 260
   (iii) 11.2 cm

3. (i) 7163
   (ii) 6.72
   (iii) £6.30

4. (i) 84   (ii) £420
   (iii) £12   (iv) 12

5. (i) 741
   (ii) 3136.25
   (iii) £1314
   (iv) £48.53

6. (i) $\frac{52}{45}$
   (ii) $\frac{1}{32}$
   (iii) $\frac{53}{20}$

7. 35

8. (i) 10.7   (ii) 4.9
   (iii) 0.04   (iv) 0.60

9. 80

? (Page 4)

A small ice cream costs 80p, a large ice cream costs £1.20.

? (Page 4)

You just get $0 = 0$.

? (Page 5)

Express as a product of factors. Factorise *fully* means that you cannot split any of the factors into yet more factors.

Exercise 1B (Page 6)

1. (i) $10a - b - 2c$
   (ii) $6x - 3y - 4z$
   (iii) $19x + 5y$
   (iv) $p + 14q$
   (v) $5x$
   (vi) $2a^2 + 12a - 12$
   (vii) $3q^2 - 3p^2$
   (viii) $10fg + 10fh - 5gh$

2. (i) $2(4 - 5x^2)$
   (ii) $2b(3a + 4c)$
   (iii) $2a(a + 2b)$
   (iv) $pq(q^2 - p^2)$
   (v) $3xy(x + 2y^3)$
   (vi) $2pq(3p^2 - 2pq + q^2)$
   (vii) $3lm^2(5 - 3l^2m + 4lm^2)$
   (viii) $12a^4b^4(7a - 8b)$

3. (i) $4(5x - 4y)$
   (ii) $6(x + 1)$
   (iii) $z(x - y)$
   (iv) $2q(p - r)$
   (v) $k(l + n)$
   (vi) $-4(a + 2)$
   (vii) $3(x^2 + 2y^2)$
   (viii) $2(a + 4)$

4. (i) $10a^3b^4$
   (ii) $12p^3q^4r$
   (iii) lm^2n^2p
   (iv) $36r^4s^3$
   (v) $64ab^2c^2d^2e$
   (vi) $60x^3y^3z^3$
   (vii) $84a^5b^9$
   (viii) $42p^3q^8r^5$

5. (i) $2a$ (ii) pq
   (iii) $\frac{4b}{a}$ (iv) $\frac{bd}{ac}$
   (v) $\frac{2xy^2z}{3}$ (vi) $\frac{5}{2a^2b^2}$
   (vii) $\frac{7p^2r^3}{6q^4s^2}$

6. (i) $\frac{11a}{12}$ (ii) $\frac{13x}{20}$
   (iii) $\frac{7p}{12}$ (iv) $\frac{s}{3}$
   (v) $\frac{5b}{12}$ (vi) $\frac{7a}{3b}$
   (vii) $\frac{5q - 3p}{2pq}$ (viii) $-\frac{5x}{6y}$

? (Page 7)

An equation is how you use algebra to show that two expressions or numbers are equal, for example $5x + 2 = 3x + 8$. An equation must contain an equals sign.

When you solve an equation you find values for any variables in the equation.

? (Page 8)

It is the value of the variable that is required.

Exercise 1C (Page 9)

1. (i) $x = 7$ (ii) $a = -2$
   (iii) $x = 2$ (iv) $y = 2$
   (v) $c = 5$ (vi) $p = 10$
   (vii) $x = -5$ (viii) $x = -6$
   (ix) $y = 7$ (x) $k = 42$
   (xi) $t = 60$ (xii) $p = -55$
   (xiii) $p = 0$

2 (i) $2l + 2(l - 80) = 600$

  (ii) $l = 190$; Area $= 20\,900\,\text{m}^2$

3 (i) $2(j + 4) + j = 17$

  (ii) Louise and Molly, 7 years; Jonathan, 3 years

4 (i) $5c - a$

  (ii) $5c - 15 = 40$; $c = 11$

5 (i) John $(3m + x)$ years; Michael $(m + x)$ years where Michael is m years old now.

  (ii) $3m + x = 2(m + x)$; $x = m$

6 (i) $8a$

  (ii) $6a + 6$

  (iii) $a = 3$

7 (i) $m - 2,\ m - 1,\ m,\ m + 1,$ $m + 2$

  (ii) $m - 2 + (m - 1) + m +$ $(m + 1) + (m + 2) = 105$; $m = 21$

  (iii) 19, 20, 21, 22, 23

8 (i) $2(x + 2) = 5(x - 3)$; $x = 6\frac{1}{3}$

  (ii) $16\frac{2}{3}\,\text{cm}^2$

Exercise 1D (Page 11)

1 (i) $0.3b$ or $\dfrac{3b}{10}$

  (ii) $\dfrac{9y}{2}$

  (iii) $\dfrac{cd}{100}$

2 $66\frac{2}{3}\%$

3 (i) $1.2a$

  (ii) $1.05b$

  (iii) $0.65k$

  (iv) $0.98m$

4 $1.8a = 1.5b$

  $\dfrac{1.8}{1.5} = \dfrac{b}{a}$

  $1.2 = \dfrac{b}{a}$

5 60%

6 $8 : 12 : 27$

7 (i) $a = \dfrac{5b}{2}$

  (ii) $6 : 1$

  (iii) $5 : 4$

8 $15 : 8$

? **(Page 12)**

When the brackets are removed there are terms in x^2 and x and a number, but no other terms (e.g. no x^3, no $\sqrt{x}$, no $\dfrac{1}{x}$).

Exercise 1E (Page 13)

1 (i) $x^2 + 9x + 20$

  (ii) $x^2 + 4x + 3$

  (iii) $a^2 + 9a - 5$

  (iv) $6p^2 + 5p - 6$

  (v) $x^2 + 6x + 9$

  (vi) $4x^2 - 9$

  (vii) $14m - 3m^2 - 8$

  (viii) $12 + 4t - 5t^2$

  (ix) $16 - 24x + 9x^2$

  (x) $m^2 - 6mn + 9n^2$

2 (i) $x^5 - x^4 + 2x^3 - 3x^2 + x - 2$

  (ii) $x^6 + 2x^5 - 3x^4 - 4x^3 + 5x^2 + 6x - 3$

  (iii) $2x^5 - 4x^4 - x^3 + 11x^2 - 13x + 5$

  (iv) $x^6 - 1$

  (v) $x^3 + 4x^2 + x - 6$

  (vi) $2x^3 + 5x^2 - 14x - 8$

  (vii) $x^3 + 3x^2 + 3x + 1$

  (viii) $p^3 - 15p^2 + 75p - 125$

  (ix) $8a^3 + 36a^2 + 54a + 27$

  (x) $2x^3 - 17x - 18$

  (xi) $2x^2 - 2x$

? **(Page 15)**

A number of the form $\dfrac{a}{b}$ where a and b are integers. So a rational number can be a fraction or an integer (when $b = 1$); it can be positive or negative.

Exercise 1F (Page 16)

1 (i) $4\sqrt{2}$

  (ii) $5\sqrt{5}$

  (iii) $5\sqrt{3}$

  (iv) $\sqrt{2}$

  (v) $3\sqrt{3}$

  (vi) $7\sqrt{2} - 3$

  (vii) $10\sqrt{2}$

  (viii) $36 + 3\sqrt{3}$

  (ix) $16\sqrt{5}$

  (x) $\sqrt{3}$

2 (i) $3 - 2\sqrt{2}$

  (ii) $3 + 2\sqrt{5}$

  (iii) $3\sqrt{7} - 9$

  (iv) 2

  (v) $11 - \sqrt{2}$

  (vi) $5 - 3\sqrt{7}$

  (vii) $24 - 13\sqrt{3}$

  (viii) $8 - 2\sqrt{15}$

  (ix) $13\sqrt{2} - 17$

  (x) $17 + 12\sqrt{2}$

3 (i) $\dfrac{\sqrt{3}}{3}$ (ii) $\sqrt{5}$

  (iii) $\dfrac{4\sqrt{6}}{3}$ (iv) $\dfrac{\sqrt{6}}{3}$

  (v) 1 (vi) $\dfrac{\sqrt{21}}{7}$

  (vii) $3\sqrt{7}$ (viii) $\dfrac{\sqrt{5}}{3}$

  (ix) $\dfrac{\sqrt{15}}{5}$ (x) $\dfrac{\sqrt{2}}{2}$

Exercise 1G (Page 17)

1 (i) $\dfrac{10\sqrt{3} - 2\sqrt{6}}{23}$

  (ii) $\dfrac{4\sqrt{7} + \sqrt{14}}{14}$

  (iii) $\dfrac{9 - 3\sqrt{3}}{2}$

  (iv) $\dfrac{8 + 5\sqrt{2}}{7}$

  (v) $\dfrac{\sqrt{7} - 2}{3}$

  (vi) $10\sqrt{3} + 3 - 10\sqrt{2} - \sqrt{6}$

225

2 $12 + 9\sqrt{2}$

3 $18\sqrt{5} - 40$

4 $1 - \dfrac{1}{3}\sqrt{3}$

Chapter 2

? (Page 20)

Yes, except that the rows and columns could be interchanged.

? (Page 21)

Yes, but the brackets will be in the reverse order. (Work it through to check for yourself.)

? (Page 21)

No. It does not factorise.

Exercise 2A (Page 23)

1 (i) $(a + d)(b - c)$

  (ii) $(2x + w)(y + 1)$

  (iii) $(2p - 3r)(q - 4)$

  (iv) $(5 - 2n)(1 - m)$

2 (i) $(x + 2)(x + 3)$

  (ii) $(y - 1)(y - 4)$

  (iii) $(m - 4)^2$

  (iv) $(m - 3)(m - 5)$

  (v) $(x + 5)(x - 2)$

  (vi) $(a + 12)(a + 8)$

  (vii) $(x - 3)(x + 2)$

  (viii) $(y - 12)(y - 4)$

  (ix) $(k + 6)(k + 4)$

  (x) $(k - 12)(k + 2)$

  (xi) $(x + y)(x + 2y)$

  (xii) $(x + 5y)(x - y)$

  (xiii) $(a - 4b)(a + 3b)$

  (xiv) $(c - 3d)(c - 8d)$

3 (i) $(x + 2)(x - 2)$

  (ii) $(a + 5)(a - 5)$

  (iii) $(3 + p)(3 - p)$

  (iv) $(x + y)(x - y)$

  (v) $(t + 8)(t - 8)$

  (vi) $(2x + 1)(2x - 1)$

  (vii) $(2x + 3)(2x - 3)$

  (viii) $(2x + y)(2x - y)$

  (ix) $(4x + 5)(4x - 5)$

  (x) $(3a + 2b)(3a - 2b)$

  (xi) $(3a + 1)(a + 1)$

  (xii) $(4x + 5)(2x - 3)$

  (xiii) $(3p - 2)(p - 4)$

  (xiv) $(2 + 5y)(6 - 5y)$

4 (i) $(2x + 1)(x + 2)$

  (ii) $(2a - 3)(a + 7)$

  (iii) $(5p - 1)(3p + 1)$

  (iv) $(3x - 1)(x + 3)$

  (v) $(5a + 1)(a - 2)$

  (vi) $(2p - 1)(p + 3)$

  (vii) $(4x - 1)(2x + 3)$

  (viii) $(2a - 9)(a + 3)$

  (ix) $(3x - 5)^2$

  (x) $(2x + 5)(2x - 3)$

  (xi) $(2x + y)(x + 2y)$

  (xii) $(3x - y)(x + 2y)$

  (xiii) $(5a - 3b)(a - b)$

  (xiv) $(3c + 4d)(2c - d)$

5 (i) $x(x + 2)(x - 2)$

  (ii) $a^2(a + 4)(a - 4)$

  (iii) $y^3(3 + y)(3 - y)$

  (iv) $2x(x + 1)(x - 1)$

  (v) $p^2(2p + 3)(2p - 3)$

  (vi) $x(10 + x)(10 - x)$

  (viii) $2x(2x + 5y)(2x - 5y)$

Activity 2.1 (Page 23)

(i) 81 and a^4

(ii) $(a^2)^2 - 9^2$

(iii) $(a^2 + 9)(a^2 - 9)$

    $= (a^2 + 9)(a + 3)(a - 3)$

? (Page 24)

The subject appears only once in a formula, on its own on the left-hand side.

? (Page 24)

Omit it since length must be positive.

Exercise 2B (Page 25)

1 (i) $u = v - at$

  (ii) $a = \dfrac{v - u}{t}$;

  an equation of motion

2 $b = \dfrac{2A}{h}$; area of a triangle

3 $l = \dfrac{P - 2b}{2}$; perimeter of a rectangle

4 $r = \sqrt{\dfrac{A}{\pi}}$; area of a circle

5 $c = \dfrac{2A - bh}{h}$; area of a trapezium

6 $h = \dfrac{A - \pi r^2}{2\pi r}$; surface area of a cylinder with a base but no top

7 $l = \dfrac{\lambda e}{T}$; tension of a spring or string

8 (i) $u = \dfrac{2s - at^2}{2t}$

  (ii) $a = \dfrac{2(s - ut)}{t^2}$;
an equation of motion

9 $x = \dfrac{\sqrt{\omega^2 a^2 - v^2}}{\omega}$; speed of a particle on an oscillating spring

Exercise 2C (Page 26)

1 $m = \dfrac{2x}{3 - x}$

2 $y = \dfrac{2x}{5 - x}$

3 $b = -\dfrac{a}{7}$

4 $h = \dfrac{S - 2\pi r^2}{2\pi r}$

5 $x = \dfrac{1 - 2y}{y - 1}$

6 $c = \dfrac{1 - 2d}{d + 3}$

7 (i) $t = \dfrac{3x}{x - 1}$

  (ii) 4.5

8 (i) $p = \dfrac{2 - 3r}{2r - 3}$

  (ii) -1

Activity 2.2 (Page 26)

(i) $(x+3)(x+3) = x^2 + 3x + 3x + 9$
$= x^2 + 6x + 9$

(ii) $y = x^2 + 6x + 9$
$y = (x+3)^2$
$\sqrt{y} = (x+3)$
$\sqrt{y} - 3 = x$

Activity 2.3 (Page 26)

(i) $(x-5)(x-5) + 4$
$= x^2 - 5x - 5x + 25 + 4$
$= x^2 - 10x + 29$

(ii) $p = x^2 - 10x + 29$
$p = (x-5)^2 + 4$
$p - 4 = (x-5)^2$
$\sqrt{p-4} = x - 5$
$\sqrt{p-4} + 5 = x$

? (Page 26)

A fraction in arithmetic is one number divided by another number.

The definition of a fraction in algebra is the same but with 'number' replaced by 'expression'.

? (Page 26)

You can cancel a fraction in arithmetic when the numerator and denominator have a common factor.

It is the same for fractions in algebra.

A factor in arithmetic is a number that divides exactly into the given number, i.e. there is no remainder.

The definition of a factor in algebra is the same but with 'number' replaced by 'expression'.

? (Page 27)

x is not a factor of the numerator $(2x+2)$ or the denominator $(3x+3)$.

The correct answer involves factorising both the numerator and the denominator:
$$\frac{2(x+1)}{3(x+1)}$$
Cancelling $(x+1)$ gives $\frac{2}{3}$.

? (Page 27)

Neither a nor a^2 is a factor of the numerator and denominator.

The correct answer involves factorising to get
$$\frac{(a-3)(a+2)}{(a-3)(a-5)} = \frac{a+2}{a-5}$$

? (Page 28)

Individual terms have been cancelled rather than factors.

The correct answer is
$$\frac{(2n+3)(2n-3)}{(n+1)} \times \frac{(n+1)(n-1)}{(2n+3)}$$
$$= (2n-3)(n-1)$$

? (Page 28)

A denominator that is the same for both fractions. For example in
$$\frac{1}{2} + \frac{1}{x} = \frac{x}{2x} + \frac{2}{2x}$$
$$= \frac{x+2}{2x}$$
the common denominator is $2x$.

? (Page 29)

(a) 12

(b) $(x-1)(x+1)(x-3)$

Exercise 2D (Page 29)

1 (i) $\dfrac{1}{2}$

(ii) $\dfrac{4}{x+8}$

(iii) $\dfrac{3}{x-y}$

(iv) $\dfrac{2x}{3y}$

(v) $\dfrac{1}{3-p}$

(vi) $\dfrac{2b^2}{5a^2}$

(vii) $\dfrac{x-1}{2}$

(viii) $\dfrac{x}{x-y}$

(ix) $\dfrac{1}{a-3}$

(x) $\dfrac{3}{2}$

(xi) $\dfrac{3x-1}{3}$

(xii) $\dfrac{x}{2y}$

2 (i) $\dfrac{b}{2}$

(ii) x

(iii) $\dfrac{x}{8(x-1)}$

(iv) $2(a+1)$

(v) $\dfrac{(x-2)}{x(x+2)}$

(vi) $\dfrac{(2x-1)(x+2)}{(2x+1)(x-1)}$

(vii) $4(p+3)$

(viii) $\dfrac{3(x-1)(x^2-3)}{(x-3)^2}$

3 (i) $\dfrac{7a}{20}$

(ii) $-\dfrac{7}{3a}$

(iii) $\dfrac{(m-3n)}{(m+n)(m-n)}$

(iv) $\dfrac{5(p+2)}{(p-2)(2p+1)}$

(v) $\dfrac{(5a+1)}{a(a+1)(p-1)}$

(vi) 2

(vii) $\dfrac{1}{(p+1)(p-1)}$

(viii) $\dfrac{2(a^2+b^2)}{(a+b)(a-b)}$

? (Page 30)

When a fraction is simplified, the answer is an expression, but when an equation is solved the answer is the value of the variable.

? (Page 30)

If you multiplied both the numerator and the denominator, the multiplier would cancel and the fraction would be unchanged.

? (Page 30)

It allows you to cancel out all the fractions.

? (Page 31)

Not all of the left-hand side has been multiplied by 30.

? (Page 31)

It enables you to see what is best to multiply through by; in this case $2(a + 1)(a - 1)$, rather than $2(a + 1)(a^2 - 1)$.

Exercise 2E (Page 31)

1 (i) $x = \frac{5}{6}$

  (ii) $a = \frac{5}{8}$

  (iii) $x = \pm\frac{1}{\sqrt{3}}$

  (iv) $x = 1\frac{5}{13}$

  (v) $x = 2$ or $x = -6\frac{1}{3}$

  (vi) $a = -2$

  (vii) $p = \frac{1}{3}$ or $p = 3$

  (viii) $x = 0$ or $x = 3$

2   30 cm

Exercise 2F (Page 33)

1 $a = 4$ $b = -6$

2 $c = 2$ $d = 6$

3 $p = 6$ $q = -40$

4 $a = \frac{5}{2}$ $b = -\frac{33}{4}$

5 $p = 9$ $q = 2$

6 $c = \frac{9}{4}$ $d = \frac{1}{2}$

7 $a = 2$ $b = 8$ $c = -3$

8 $a = 5$ $b = 3$ $c = -35$

9 $p = 3$ $q = -2$ $r = 2$

10 $a = 3$ $b = -24$ $c = -47$

11 $a = 2$ $b = 4$ $c = 8$

12 $p = 23$ $q = 2$ $r = 3$

13 (i) $a = 4$ $b = 4$

  (ii) $x = \sqrt{y - 4} + 4$

14 (i) $p = 3$ $q = 1$ $r = -2$

  (ii) $x = \sqrt{\dfrac{y + 2}{3}} - 1$

Chapter 3

Exercise 3A (Page 36)

1 (i) -9 (ii) 0.2

  (iii) 15 (iv) -1

  (v) -1 (vi) 0

2 (i) 12 (ii) 75

  (iii) 3 (iv) -4

  (v) 12 (vi) -9

3 (i) $\dfrac{8}{3}$

  (ii) 2

  (iii) $-\dfrac{4}{7}$

4 (i) $6x - 2$

  (ii) $3x + 1$

  (iii) $3x^2 - 2$

5 (i) $9x^2 + 15x - 1$

  (ii) $x^2 + x - 7$

6 (i) 1.5

  (ii) 1.2

  (iii) 3

? (Page 36)

$\dfrac{1}{0}$ is not a real number

Activity 3.1 (Page 37)

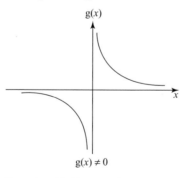

$g(x)$

$g(x) \neq 0$

Exercise 3B (Page 38)

1 (i) $f(x) < 6$

  (ii) $f(x) \geqslant 5$

  (iii) $f(x) \geqslant 2$

  (iv) $f(x) \geqslant 6$

  (v) $2 \leqslant f(x) \leqslant 10$

  (vi) $-3 < f(x) < 7$

  (vii) $f(x) \leqslant 11$

  (viii) $-9 \leqslant f(x) \leqslant 11$

2 (i) $0 \leqslant f(x) \leqslant 4$

  (ii) $0 < f(x) < 16$

  (iii) $f(x) \geqslant 0$

  (iv) $-1 \leqslant f(x) \leqslant 27$

3 (i)   Domain $1 \leqslant x \leqslant 5$

       Range $3 \leqslant f(x) \leqslant 8$

  (ii)   Domain $-4 \leqslant x \leqslant 4$

       Range $0 \leqslant f(x) \leqslant 2$

  (iii) Domain $-2 \leqslant x \leqslant 3$

       Range $0 \leqslant f(x) \leqslant 2$

? (Page 40)

Two points on the line *or* one point and the gradient of the line.

Activity 3.2 (Page 41)

Line A: 3

Line B: 0

Line C: $-\dfrac{2}{5}$

Line D: ∞

? (Page 41)

No, since

$$\frac{y_1 - y_2}{x_1 - x_2} = \frac{-(y_2 - y_1)}{-(x_2 - x_1)} = \frac{y_2 - y_1}{x_2 - x_1}$$

? (Page 44)

(i) $\dfrac{x}{4} + \dfrac{y}{3} = 1$

(ii) $a = 4, b = 3$

(iii) a is the intercept on the x axis and b is the intercept on the y axis.

Exercise 3C (Page 44)

1 (i) 2 (ii) -3

  (iii) $-\dfrac{11}{5}$ (iv) 3

  (v) $7\dfrac{1}{2}$ (vi) $2\dfrac{3}{5}$

  (vii) $-\dfrac{1}{5}$ (viii) $-3\dfrac{2}{3}$

2 (i)

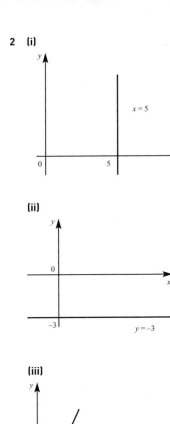

(ii)

(iii)

(iv)

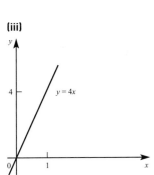

(v)

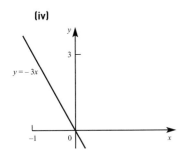

(vi)

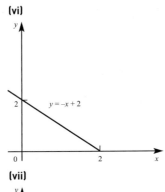

(vii)

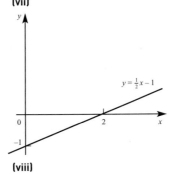

(viii)

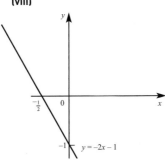

(ix)

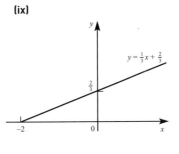

(x)

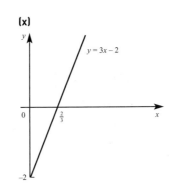

(xi)

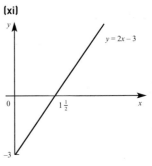

(xii)

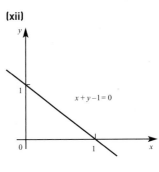

(xiii)

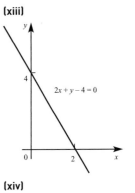

(xiv)

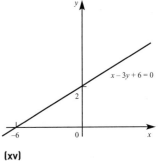

(xv)

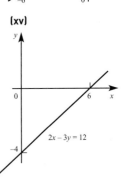

(xvi)

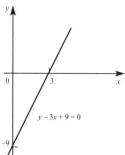

$y - 3x + 9 = 0$

(xvii)

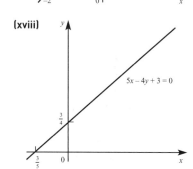

$3x = 2y - 6$

(xviii)

$5x - 4y + 3 = 0$

Exercise 3D (Page 49)

1　(a)　$x = -3$
　(b)　$y = 5$
　(c)　$y = 2x$
　(d)　$2x + y = 4$
　(e)　$2x + 3y = 12$
　(f)　$x = 5$
　(g)　$y = -3$
　(h)　$x + 2y = 0$
　(i)　$y = x + 4$
　(j)　$y = 2x - 6$

2　(i)　$y = 3x - 7$
　(ii)　$y = 2x$
　(iii)　$y = 3x - 13$
　(iv)　$4x - y - 16 = 0$
　(v)　$3x + 2y + 1 = 0$
　(vi)　$x + 2y - 12 = 0$

3　(i)　$y = x - 2$
　(ii)　$5x + 3y - 12 = 0$

(iii)　$y = x - 5$
(iv)　$3x + 5y - 12 = 0$
(v)　$x + 7y + 32 = 0$
(vi)　$y = 2x$

Activity 3.3 (Page 50)

x	-3	-2	-1	0	1	2	3	4
y	4	-1	-4	-5	-4	-1	4	11

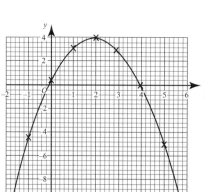

Activity 3.4 (Page 50)

x	-2	-1	0	1	2	3	4	5	6
y	-12	-5	0	3	4	3	0	-5	-12

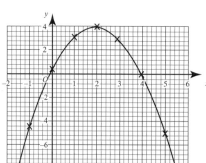

Exercise 3E (Page 52)

1　(a)　$y = x^2 - 2x - 3$
　(b)　$y = 5 - x^2$
2　(a)　$y = 4 - 7x - 2x^2$
　(b)　$y = 4x - x^2$
3　(i)　$(-1, 2)$
　(ii)　$x = -1$
　(iii)　$(0, 3)$

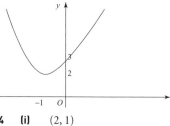

4　(i)　$(2, 1)$
　(ii)　$x = 2$
　(iii)　$(0, 5)$

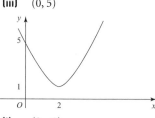

5　(i)　$(3, -2)$
　(ii)　$x = 3$
　(iii)　$(0, 7)$

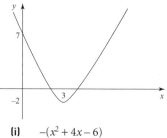

6　(i)　$-(x^2 + 4x - 6)$
　　　$= -((x + 2)^2 - 10)$
　　　$= 10 - (x + 2)^2$
　(ii)　$(-2, 10)$
　(iii)　$x = -2$
　(iv)　$(0, 6)$

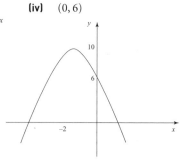

Exercise 3F (Page 56)

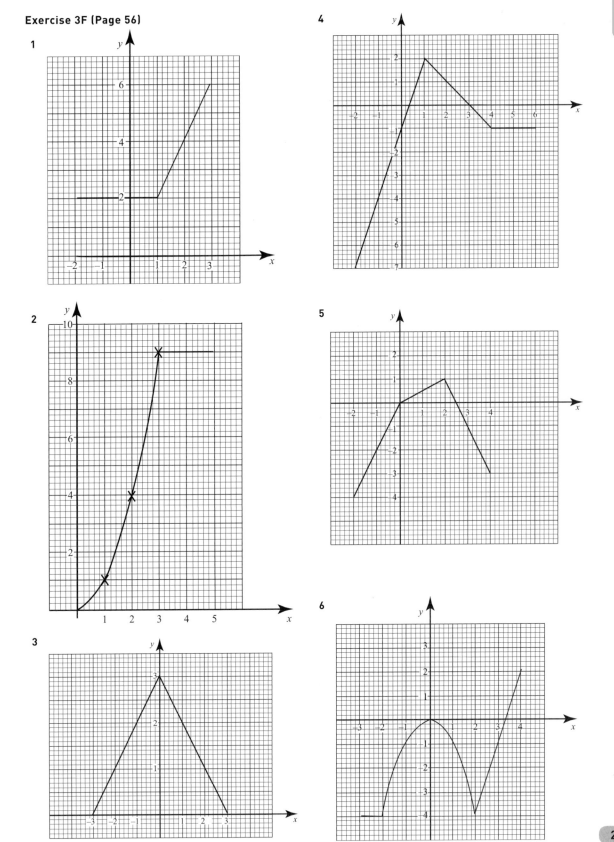

7 **(i)** $f(x) = x$ $0 \leqslant x < 3$

       $= 3$ $3 \leqslant x < 5$

       $= 2x - 7$ $5 \leqslant x \leqslant 7$

   (ii) $0 \leqslant f(x) \leqslant 7$

   (iii) $x = 6$

8 **(i)** $f(x) = 5$ $-3 \leqslant x < 1$

       $= 7 - 2x$ $1 \leqslant x < 3$

       $= x - 2$ $3 \leqslant x \leqslant 5$

   (ii) $1 \leqslant f(x) \leqslant 5$

   (iii) $x = 2, x = 5$

9 **(i)** $f(x) = x + 3$ $-3 \leqslant x < 0$

       $= 3$ $0 \leqslant x < 3$

       $= -\dfrac{3}{2}x + \dfrac{15}{2}$ $3 \leqslant x \leqslant 5$

   (ii) $\dfrac{33}{2}$

10 **(i)** $g(x) = 5x + 15$ $-3 \leqslant x < -2$

       $= 5$ $-2 \leqslant x < 2$

       $= -\dfrac{5}{2}x + 10$ $2 \leqslant x \leqslant 4$

   (ii) $\dfrac{55}{2}$

Chapter 4

Exercise 4A (Page 63)

1 **(i)** $x = 2$ or $x = 6$

   (ii) $m = 2$ (repeated)

   (iii) $p = 5$ or $p = -3$

   (iv) $a = -2$ or $a = -9$

   (v) $x = -2$ or $x = -\frac{1}{2}$

   (vi) $x = 1$ or $x = -1\frac{3}{4}$

   (vii) $t = \frac{1}{5}$ or $t = -\frac{1}{3}$

   (viii) $r = -\frac{1}{8}$ or $r = -\frac{2}{3}$

   (ix) $x = \frac{1}{3}$ or $x = -3$

   (x) $p = \frac{2}{3}$ or $p = 4$

2 **(i)** $x = 4.32$ or $x = -2.32$

   (ii) $x = 1.37$ or $x = -4.37$

   (iii) $x = 2.37$ or $x = -3.37$

   (iv) $x = 1.77$ or $x = -2.27$

   (v) $x = 1.68$ or $x = -2.68$

   (vi) $x = 2.70$ or $x = -3.70$

   (vii) $x = 4.24$ or $x = -0.24$

   (viii) $x = 3.22$ or $x = 0.78$

3 **(i)** $x = -0.23$ or $x = -1.43$

   (ii) $x = -0.41$ or $x = -1.84$

   (iii) $x = 0.34$ or $x = -5.84$

   (iv) $x = 1.64$ or $x = 0.61$

   (v) $x = 1.89$ or $x = 0.11$

   (vi) $x = -1.23$ or $x = -2.43$

4   3 cm, 4 cm, 5 cm

5 $x = 1.5$

6 $x = 9$

7 **(i)** $t = 1$ s and $t = 2$ s

   (ii) 3 seconds

8 **(i)** $0.5 \times (2x + 1) \times x = 68$

       $x^2 + 0.5x = 68$

       $2x^2 + x = 136$

       $2x^2 + x - 136 = 0$

   (ii) 17 cm

9 **(i)** **(a)** $(x + 6)$ cm

      (b) $(x - 10)$ cm

      (c) $(x - 16)$ cm

   (ii) $(x - 16) \times (x - 10) \times 8$

      $= 8(x^2 - 10x - 16x + 160)$

      $= 8(x^2 - 26x + 160)$

      $= 8x^2 - 208x + 1280$

   (iii) Length = 34 cm,

      width = 28 cm

? (Page 64)

Infinitely many. x can take any value and, in this example, the corresponding value of y is $4 - x$.

? (Page 67)

In this example the correct solution would be found, but in some cases, e.g. if the curve had equation $y^2 = 4x$, additional values that are not part of the solution can be obtained. Always substitute into the equation of the line. For example

$$y = x - 2$$
$$y^2 = 4x = 8$$

has $x = 2, y = 0$ and $x = 6, y = 4$ as its solution.

Substituting into the equation of the curve would also give the pair of values $x = 6, y = -4$.

? (Page 68)

You subtract if the coefficients of the variable to be eliminated have the same sign. You add if they have opposite signs.

Exercise 4B (Page 70)

1 **(i)** $x = 5, y = 2$

   (ii) $x = 4, y = -1$

   (iii) $x = 2\frac{1}{4}, y = 6\frac{1}{2}$

   (iv) $x = -2, y = -3$

   (v) $x = 1\frac{1}{2}, y = 4$

   (vi) $x = -\frac{1}{2}, y = -6\frac{1}{2}$

2 **(i)** $x = 2, y = 3$

   (ii) $x = 4, y = 3$

   (iii) $x = 6, y = 2$

   (iv) $x = -\frac{3}{7}, y = 3\frac{2}{7}$

   (v) $x = 2, y = 5$

   (vi) $x = -1, y = -2$

3 **(i)** $x = 1, y = 4$ or $x = 4, y = 1$

   (ii) $x = 2, y = 3$

      or $x = -\frac{2}{3}, y = \frac{1}{3}$

   (iii) $x = 4, y = -2$

      or $x = -1, y = -7$

   (iv) $x = 1, y = 5$

      or $x = 11, y = 25$

   (v) $x = 4, y = 2$

      or $x = -4, y = -2$

   (vi) $x = 1, y = -2$

      or $x = -2\frac{3}{7}, y = -\frac{2}{7}$

4 **(i)** $3c + 4l = 72, 5c + 2l = 64$;

      a chew costs 8p and a

      lollipop costs 12p.

   (ii) $x + 5m = 500, x + 7m =$

      660; $m = 80, x = 100$; £3.40

   (iii) $3c + 2n = 145, 2c + 5n =$

      225; $n = 35, c = 25$; £1.65

   (iv) $2a + c = 3750, a + 3c =$

      3750; $c = 750, a = 1500$;

      £67.50

5   A(3, 4), B(4, 3)

? (Page 71)

The answer is zero in both cases.

? (Page 72)

The x^3 term on the left-hand side is x^3 and on the right-hand side is kx^3.

? (Page 73)

±1 and ±3 are the only factors of -3.

? (Page 73)

$f(1) = -4$

No, since you would only try factors of the constant term -1.

Exercise 4C (Page 74)

1. (i) Factor
   (ii) No
   (iii) No
   (iv) Factor
   (v) Factor
   (vi) Factor

2. (i) $(x-1)(x+1)(x-3)$
   (ii) $(x+1)(x+2)(x-3)$
   (iii) $x(x+1)(x-2)$
   (iv) $(x+1)(x+2)(x-5)$
   (v) $(x-2)(x+4)(x-3)$
   (vi) $(x+1)(x-1)(x+5)$
   (vii) $(x-2)(x+2)^2$
   (viii) $(x-1)(x+3)^2$
   (ix) $(x-1)^2(x+5)$
   (x) $(x+1)(x+2)(x+4)$

3. (i) 1   3 -2
   (ii) 2 -1 -4
   (iii) -1 -3 6
   (iv) 2   3 -2
   (v) 1   0.303 -3.30
   (vi) -2 3.45 -1.45

4. -5

5. (i) $(x-2)$
   (ii) $p=0$ $q=-7$

6. (i) $k=-7$
   (ii) $x=1, x=-3$

7. (i) $\dfrac{8}{x^2}$

(ii) $(x \times x) + 4\left(x \times \dfrac{8}{x^2}\right)$

$$= x^2 + 4\left(\dfrac{8}{x}\right)$$

$$= x^2 + \dfrac{32}{x}$$

(iii) $x^2 + \dfrac{32}{x} = 24$

$x^3 + 32 = 24x$

$x^3 - 24x + 32 = 0$

(iv) $x = 4, x = 1.46$

? (Page 75)

An equation contains an $=$ sign and any solution will consist of one or more particular values of any variables involved.

An inequality contains any of the signs $<, \leqslant, >, \geqslant$ and any solution will consist of a range of values of its variable(s).

? (Page 75)

$8 \times 10^7 \leqslant x \leqslant 3.8 \times 10^8$

? (Page 76)

An inequality may be rearranged using addition, subtraction, multiplication by a positive number and division by a positive number in the same way as an equation.

Multiplication or division by a negative number reverses the inequality.

? (Page 76)

$2 < 3$, but $-2 > -3$; $5 > 1$, but $-5 < -1$.

Exercise 4D (Page 77)

1. (i) $x < 5$
   (ii) $x \geqslant 2$
   (iii) $y \leqslant 4$
   (iv) $y < 4$
   (v) $x \geqslant -3$
   (vi) $b \geqslant -3$
   (vii) $x > 3$
   (viii) $x < 12$

   (ix) $x \geqslant -5$
   (x) $x \leqslant -4$
   (xi) $2 \leqslant x \leqslant 4$
   (xii) $2 \leqslant x \leqslant 5$
   (xiii) $-3 < x < 1$
   (xiv) $1 < x < 2$

2. $-5 < p - q < 1$

3. $-1 < x + y < 7$

4. (i) $-2 \leqslant a + b \leqslant 9$
   (ii) $-2 \leqslant a - b \leqslant 9$

5. (i) $-4 \leqslant a + b \leqslant 10$
   (ii) $-13 \leqslant a - b \leqslant 1$
   (iii) $-9 \leqslant 2a + 3b \leqslant 30$

6. (i) always
   (ii) never
   (iii) sometimes
   (iv) sometimes
   (v) never
   (vi) always

7. (i) always
   (ii) always
   (iii) never
   (iv) sometimes
   (v) never
   (vi) sometimes

8. $x > 4$

Exercise 4E (Page 80)

1. (i) $x < 1$ or $x > 5$
   (ii) $-4 \leqslant a \leqslant 1$
   (iii) $-1\frac{1}{2} < y < 1$
   (iv) $-2 \leqslant y \leqslant 2$
   (v) $x < 2$ or $x > 2$
   (vi) $1 \leqslant p \leqslant 2$
   (vii) $a < -3$ or $a > 2$
   (viii) $-4 \leqslant a \leqslant 2$
   (ix) $y < -1$ or $y > \frac{1}{3}$
   (x) $y \leqslant -1$ or $y \geqslant 5$

2. $x^2 - 5x > 0$

3. $p^2 - p > 0$

Activity 4.1 (Page 80)

(i) a^3 $a^0 = 1$

(ii) a^0 $a^{-2} = \dfrac{1}{a^2}$

(iii) a^1 $a^{\frac{1}{2}}$ is the square root of a.

(iv) a^1 $a^{\frac{1}{3}}$ is the cube root of a.

Exercise 4F (Page 82)

1 (i) x^4 (ii) x^{-3}

   (iii) $x^{\frac{5}{2}}$ (iv) x^6

   (v) x^4 (vi) x^2

   (vii) x^{-1} (viii) x^{10}

   (ix) x^2

2 (i) 9 (ii) -8

   (iii) $\dfrac{1}{9}$ (iv) $\dfrac{1}{4}$

   (v) $\dfrac{1}{64}$ (vi) $\dfrac{1}{8}$

   (vii) 8 (viii) 9

   (ix) $\dfrac{5}{3}$ (x) 9

   (xi) $\dfrac{27}{8}$ (xii) $\dfrac{1}{10}$

3 (i) $x^2 + x$

   (ii) $x - 1$

   (iii) $x - x^3$

   (iv) $x^{-5} + x^{-4}$

   (v) $x + x^3$

   (vi) $x^3 - 1$

Exercise 4G (Page 84)

1 $2m + 14 - 10 - 2m = 4$

2 $5c - 15 + 3c + 21 = 8c + 6$
   $= 8(c + 6)$ Multiple of 2 so even

3 $y^2 + 3y + 6y + 18 - y^2 = 9y + 18$
   $= 9(y + 2)$

4 (i) $(n + 1)^2 = (n + 1)(n + 1)$
      $= n^2 + n + n + 1$
      $= n^2 + 2n + 1$

   (ii) $(n + 1)^2 + (n - 1)^2$
      $= n^2 + 2n + 1 + n^2 - 2n + 1$
      $= 2n^2 + 2$
      $= 2(n^2 + 1)$ Multiple of 2
              so even

   (iii) $(n + 1)^2 - (n - 1)^2$
      $= n^2 + 2n + 1 - (n^2 - 2n + 1)$
      $= n^2 + 2n + 1 - n^2 + 2n - 1$
      $= 4n$

5 (i) $(x + 1)^2 + 4$

   (ii) $(x + 1)^2 \geqslant 0$ for all values of x
      Adding 4 means always > 0

6 $(y - 5)^2 + 1$ $(y - 5)^2 \geqslant 0$ for all values of y
   Adding 1 means always > 0

7 $27m^3 - 9m^2 + 9m^2 = 27m^3$
                 $= (3m)^3$

8 $\dfrac{6(p - 3)}{2(p - 3)} = 3$

9 $\dfrac{a(a + b)}{b(a + b)} = \dfrac{a}{b}$
   Positive $\div$ negative $=$ negative

10 $f(4x) = (4x)^2 + 2(4x)$
          $= 16x^2 + 8x$
          $= 8x(2x + 1)$ $k = 8$

Exercise 4H (Page 86)

1 (i) $4n + 6$

   (ii) $7n - 5$

   (iii) $2n - 7$

   (iv) $25n - 25$

   (v) $8n - 19$

   (vi) $0.5n + 2.5$

   (vii) $50 - 10n$

   (viii) $10 - 3n$

   (ix) $1\frac{1}{2} - \frac{1}{2}n$

   (x) $-2.5 - 1.5n$

2 (i) 589

   (ii) -308

   (iii) -1792

3 250.5

4 $9 - 2n + 6 - 3n = 15 - 5n$

5 (i) $p = -52$ $q = 18$

   (ii) $36n - 88$

Exercise 4I (Page 88)

1 (i) $n^2 + 2n + 1$

   (ii) $n^2 + 3n - 4$

   (iii) $n^2 + 6n - 3$

   (iv) $3n^2 + 4n + 1$

   (v) $2n^2 + 3n - 1$

   (vi) $2n^2 - 6n$

   (vii) $-n^2 + 2n + 10$

   (viii) $-2n^2 + 100$

2 (i) $4n - 3$

   (ii) $16n^2 - 24n + 9$

3 (i) Other methods are possible.
     nth term $= an^2 + bn + c$
     when $n = 1$, the term is 2
       $2 = a + b + c$ (1)
     when $n = 2$, the term is 7
       $7 = 4a + 2b + c$ (2)
     when $n = 3$, the term is 14
       $14 = 9a + 3b + c$ (3)
     subtracting (1) from (2)
       $5 = 3a + b$ (4)
     subtracting (2) from (3)
       $7 = 5a + b$ (5)
     subtracting (4) from (5)
       $2 = 2a$ so $a = 1$
     Substitute in (4)
       $b = 2$
     substitute in (1)
       $c = -1$
     nth term $= n^2 + 2n - 1$

   (ii) $n^2 + 2n + 2$

4 (i) Other methods are possible.
     nth term $= an^2 + bn + c$
     work out up to the second
     differences

     -1 1 3 5
         2 2 2

     Divide the second
     difference by 2
       $2 \div 2 = 1$
     This will be the coefficient of
       $n^2 : a = 1$
     subtract n^2 from the
     sequence
       -6 -10 -14 -18 -22
     The nth term of this linear
     sequence is $-4n - 2$
     nth term $= n^2 - 4n - 2$

   (ii) $3n^2 - 12n - 6$

   (iii) $3n^2 - 12n + 9$

Activity 4.2 (Page 89)

(i)   0.75   2   2.25   2.4
      2.5   2.571   2.625
      2.667   2.7   2.727   2.75
      2.769   2.786   2.8   2.813

(ii) 2.857   2.903   2.927
     2.941   2.970   2.985
     2.994

(iii) Terms are increasing in size and getting closer to 3.

Exercise 4J (Page 90)

1 (i) $\dfrac{2}{3}$ $\quad$ $\dfrac{3}{5}$ $\quad$ $\dfrac{4}{7}$

(ii) 12th

2 (i) 15th

(ii) $\dfrac{4n-1}{2n-5} = 1$

$4n - 1 = 2n - 5$

$2n = -4$

$n = -2$

n has to be a positive integer

3 (i) 2 $\qquad$ **(ii)** 1

(iii) $\dfrac{1}{3}$ $\qquad$ **(iv)** $\dfrac{1}{2}$

(v) $\dfrac{3}{4}$ $\qquad$ **(vi)** -1

(vii) $-\dfrac{1}{2}$ $\qquad$ **(viii)** 3

4 $\dfrac{5+\frac{1}{n}}{2-\frac{1}{n}}$

As $n \to \infty$ $\quad \dfrac{1}{n} \to 0$

$\dfrac{5+\frac{1}{n}}{2-\frac{1}{n}} \to \dfrac{5}{2}$

5 $\dfrac{\frac{10}{n}-6}{8-\frac{3}{n}}$

As $n \to \infty$ $\quad \dfrac{10}{n} \to 0$

and $\dfrac{3}{n} \to 0$

$\dfrac{\frac{10}{n}-6}{8-\frac{3}{n}} \to \dfrac{-6}{8} = -\dfrac{3}{4}$

Chapter 5

? (Page 95)

When the increase in x is the same for both lines, then the increase in y is also the same for both lines.

Activity 5.1 (Page 95)

(i) As figure 5.2

(ii) $\angle ABE = \angle BCD$ and
$\angle BCD + \angle CBD = 90°$
$\Rightarrow \angle ABE = \angle CBD = 90°$
i.e. $\angle ABC = 90°$

(iii) Depends on the individual sketch.

(iv) Follows from **(iii)**.

? (Page 98)

$\sqrt{4a^2 + 16b^2}$
$= \sqrt{4\left(a^2 + 4b^2\right)}$
$= 2\sqrt{a^2 + 4b^2}$

Exercise 5A (Page 99)

1 (i) (a) $-\dfrac{1}{2}$

(b) $\sqrt{80} = 4\sqrt{5}$

(c) $(6, 7)$

(ii) (a) $\dfrac{1}{3}$

(b) $\sqrt{90} = 3\sqrt{10}$

(c) $\left(1\frac{1}{2}, 8\frac{1}{2}\right)$

(iii) (a) $\dfrac{5}{11}$

(b) $\sqrt{146}$

(c) $\left(7\frac{1}{2}, -2\frac{1}{2}\right)$

(iv) (a) $-\dfrac{1}{3}$

(b) $\sqrt{490} = 7\sqrt{10}$

(c) $\left(-2\frac{1}{2}, -3\frac{1}{2}\right)$

(v) (a) $-\dfrac{2}{15}$

(b) $\sqrt{229}$

(c) $\left(7, 7\frac{1}{2}\right)$

(vi) (a) $-\dfrac{5}{13}$

(b) $\sqrt{194}$

(c) $\left(\frac{1}{2}, 2\frac{1}{2}\right)$

(vii) (a) 5

(b) $\sqrt{26}$

(c) $\left(-\frac{1}{2}, -6\frac{1}{2}\right)$

(viii) (a) $\dfrac{3}{11}$

(b) $\sqrt{130}$

(c) $\left(5\frac{1}{2}, 1\frac{1}{2}\right)$

2 (i) Gradient $AB = -1$;
gradient $AC = 1$;
product $= -1$

(ii) $AB = \sqrt{32}$; $AC = \sqrt{8}$;
$BC = \sqrt{40}$;
$BC^2 = AB^2 + AC^2$

---

3 Gradient $AB = -\dfrac{1}{2}$;
gradient $AC = 2$;
$AB = AC = \sqrt{20}$

4 (i) 19.73 units

(ii) 9 units²

5 (i) $PQ = \sqrt{173}$; $QR = \sqrt{173}$;
$RS = \sqrt{173}$; $PS = \sqrt{173}$

(ii) $\left(3\frac{1}{2}, \frac{1}{2}\right)$

(iii) Gradient $PQ = -\dfrac{2}{13}$;
gradient $QR = -\dfrac{13}{2}$, so
PQ is not perpendicular to
QR; rhombus

6 (i)

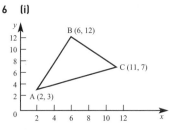

(ii) $AB = AC = \sqrt{97}$;
$BC = \sqrt{50}$

(iii) $\left(8\frac{1}{2}, 9\frac{1}{2}\right)$

(iv) 32.5 units²

7 (i) $\left(-\frac{1}{2}, 2\right)$

(ii) $(0, -1)$

8 (i) Gradient $AB = -2$;
gradient $BC = \frac{1}{2}$

(ii) $(7, 4)$

9 (i) $q = 2$

(ii) $1 : 2$

10 (i)

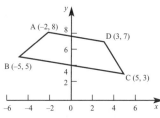

(ii) Gradient $AD =$ gradient
$BC = -\dfrac{1}{5}$; Gradient
$AB \neq$ gradient DC.

(iii) $(8, 6)$

Exercise 5B (Page 102)

1 (i) $0, \infty$; perpendicular

(ii) $2, -2$; neither

(iii) $-\frac{1}{3}, 2$; perpendicular

(iv) $1, 1$; parallel

(v) $-4, -3$; neither

(vi) $-1, 1$; perpendicular

(vii) $\frac{1}{2}, \frac{1}{2}$; parallel

(viii) $-\frac{1}{3}, 3$; perpendicular

(ix) $\frac{1}{2}, -2$; perpendicular

(x) $-\frac{2}{3}, -\frac{2}{3}$; parallel

(xi) $-\frac{1}{3}, -3$; neither

(xii) $\frac{2}{5}, -\frac{2}{5}$; perpendicular

2 (i) $y = 3x - 7$

(ii) $y = 2x$

(iii) $y = 3x - 13$

(iv) $4x - y - 16 = 0$

(v) $3x + 2y + 1 = 0$

(vi) $x + 2y - 12 = 0$

3 (i) $x + 2y = 0$

(ii) $x + 3y - 12 = 0$

(iii) $y = x - 4$

(iv) $x + 2y + 1 = 0$

(v) $2x - 3y - 6 = 0$

(vi) $x - 2y - 2 = 0$

4 (i) 4

(ii) $(4, 3)$

(iii) $x + 4y - 16 = 0$

5 (i)

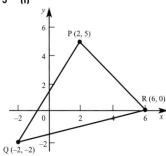

(ii) $L(0, 1\frac{1}{2}), M(2, -1),$
$N(4, 2\frac{1}{2})$

(iii) LR: $x + 4y - 6 = 0$
MP: $x = 2$
NQ: $3x - 4y - 2 = 0$

(iv) Substitute $x - 2$ and $y = 1$
into the three equations
LR $x + 4y - 6 = 2 + 4 - 6 = 0$
MP $x = 2$
NQ $3x - 4y - 2 = 6 - 4 - 2$
$= 2$

6 (i)

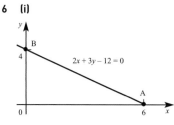

(ii) $A(6, 0), B(0, 4)$

(iii) 12 units²

(iv) $3x - 2y = 0$

(v) $AB = \sqrt{52}$ units; shortest
distance $= 3.33$ units (2 d.p.)

7 (i)

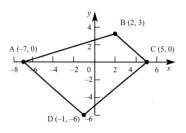

(ii) AB: $\frac{1}{3}$; BC: -1;
CD: 1; DA: -1

(iii) AB: $x - 3y + 7 = 0$
BC: $x + y - 5 = 0$
CD: $x - y - 5 = 0$
DA: $x + y + 7 = 0$

(iv) AB: $\sqrt{90}$ units
BC: $3\sqrt{2}$ units
CD: $6\sqrt{2}$ units
DA: $6\sqrt{2}$ units

(v) 54 units²

? (Page 104)

You need to choose a scale that makes
it easy to plot the points and read off
the co-ordinates of the point of
intersection. It is particularly difficult to
get an accurate solution when it is not
represented by a point on the grid.

? (Page 105)

You can always join two points with a
straight line. Using three points alerts
you if one of your calculated points
is wrong.

? (Page 105)

They won't intersect if they are parallel.

Exercise 5C (Page 105)

1 (i) $x = 1, y = 0$

(ii) $x = -1, y = 4$

(iii) $x = 3, y = 2$

(iv) $x = \frac{1}{2}, y = -2$

2 (i)

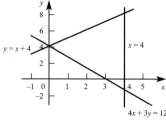

(ii) $(4, 8)$ at the intersection of
$x = 4$ and $y = x + 4$
$(4, -1\frac{1}{3})$ at the intersection
of $x = 4$ and $4x + 3y = 12$
$(0, 4)$ at the intersection of
$y = x + 4$ and $4x + 3y = 12$

(iii) $18\frac{2}{3}$ units²

3 (i)

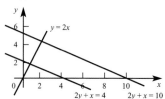

The lines look parallel.
They have the same
gradient.

(ii) This line looks
perpendicular to the first
two lines. The first two lines have a gradient of $-\frac{1}{2}$
and the third line has a
gradient of $+2$. The product of the gradients is -1
so they are perpendicular.

(iii) $\left(\frac{4}{5}, 1\frac{3}{5}\right)$ at the intersection of $y = 2x$ and $2y + x = 4$

$(2, 4)$ at the intersection of $y = 2x$ and $2y + x = 10$

Activity 5.2 (Page 107)

$AE = x_2 - x_1 \quad BE = y_2 - y_1$

$$\frac{AC}{AB} = \frac{p}{p + q}$$

Triangles ACD and ABE are similar.

$$\frac{AD}{AE} = \frac{AC}{AB} \text{ so } \frac{AD}{x_2 - x_1} = \frac{p}{p + q}$$

$$AD = \frac{p}{p + q}(x_2 - x_1)$$

x co-ordinate of C is

$$x_1 + \frac{p}{p + q}(x_2 - x_1)$$

$$= \frac{(p + q)x_1 + p(x_2 - x_1)}{p + q}$$

$$= \frac{(px_1 + qx_1 + px_2 - px_1)}{p + q}$$

$$= \frac{qx_1 + px_2}{p + q}$$

Also

$$\frac{CD}{BE} = \frac{AC}{AB} \text{ so } \frac{CD}{y_2 - y_1} = \frac{p}{p + q}$$

$$CD = \frac{p}{p + q}(y_2 - y_1)$$

y co-ordinate of C is

$$y_1 + \frac{p}{p + q}(y_2 - y_1)$$

$$= \frac{(p + q)y_1 + p(y_2 - y_1)}{p + q}$$

$$= \frac{(py_1 + qy_1 + py_2 - py_1)}{p + q}$$

$$= \frac{qy_1 + py_2}{p + q}$$

Exercise 5D (Page 108)

1 (i) $(5, 12)$

(ii) $(9, 1)$

(iii) $(4, 1)$

(iv) $\left(\frac{7}{5}, 17\right)$

(v) $(-10, -11)$

2 (i) $(14, 8)$

(ii) $(-2, 9)$

(iii) $(1, 3)$

(iv) $\left(-1, -\frac{7}{5}\right)$

(v) $(7, 3)$

3 (i) $5 : 4$

(ii) $(7, -8)$

4 $\left(-\frac{3}{2}, 2\right)$

5 $\left(\frac{13}{4}, 4\right)$

Exercise 5E (Page 112)

1 (i) $(x - 1)^2 + (y - 2)^2 = 9$

(ii) $(x - 4)^2 + (y + 3)^2 = 16$

(iii) $(x - 1)^2 + y^2 = 25$

(iv) $(x + 2)^2 + (y + 2)^2 = 4$

(v) $(x + 4)^2 + (y - 3)^2 = 1$

2 (i) (a) $(0, 0)$

(b) 5

(c)

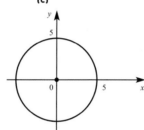

(ii) (a) $(3, 0)$

(b) 3

(c)

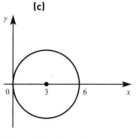

(iii) (a) $(-4, 3)$

(b) 5

(c)

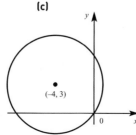

(iv) (a) $(-1, -6)$

(b) 6

(c)

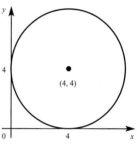

(v) (a) $(4, 4)$

(b) 4

(c)

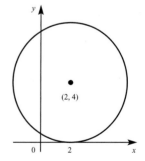

3 $(x - 2)^2 + (y + 3)^2 = 5$

4 (i) $(3, 1)$

(ii) $\sqrt{26}$

(iii) $(x - 3)^2 + (y - 1)^2 = 26$

5 Centre $(2, 4)$, radius 4

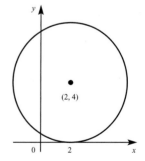

Exercise 5F (Page 115)

1 $\frac{1}{5}$

2 $(5, 0)$

3 $-\frac{3}{2}$

4 $y = -x + 7$

5 $y = \frac{3}{4}x - \frac{25}{4}$

6 $(x - 2)^2 + (y - 3)^2 = 25$

Chapter 6

Activity 6.1 (Page 120)

1   1   4   9   16   25   36   49   64
    81   100   121   144   169   196
    225   256   289   324   361   400
    441   484   529   576   625

$10^2 = 6^2 + 8^2$ $15^2 = 9^2 + 12^2$
$20^2 = 12^2 + 16^2$ $25^2 = 15^2 + 20^2$
$13^2 = 5^2 + 12^2$ $17^2 = 8^2 + 15^2$
$25^2 = 7^2 + 24^2$

Right-angled triangles can be made with sides the lengths of the numbers used.

Exercise 6A (Page 122)

1   (i) $x = 28°$ $y = 25°$
    (ii) $x = 113°$
    (iii) $x = 62°$ $y = 48°$
    (iv) $x = 118°$ $y = 18°$
    (v) $x = 57.5°$
    (vi) $19°$

2   38

3   42

4   $x = 36$ $y = 18$

Exercise 6B (Page 126)

These solutions may not be unique.

1   Angle ABC = 90 (angle in a semicircle)
    $x + y + 90 = 180$ (angle sum of triangle)
    $x = 90 - y$

2   Angle CBF = x (alternate angles)
    $x + 2x + y = 180$ (angle sum of triangle)
    $3x + y = 180$

3   Angle YAB = b (angles in the same segment)
    angle AYB = 90 (angle in a semicircle)
    $a + b + 90 = 180$ (angle sum of triangle)
    $a + b = 90$

4   Angle CDB = a (base angles of isosceles triangle)
    angle ABF = a (corresponding angles)
    angle ABC = a (alternate angles)
    angle ABC = angle ABF

5   Angle PTC = 90 (tangent is perpendicular to radius)
    angle PCT + 90 + 2y = 180 (angle sum of triangle)
    angle PCT = 90 − 2y
    angle TMN = 45 − y (angle at circumference is half angle at centre)

6   Angle ACB = angle DBA (alternate segment theorem)
    angle ACB = angle BAD (base angles of isosceles triangle)
    angle DBA = angle BAD
    Triangle ABD is isosceles as base angles are equal

7   Angle EDG = 180 − y (opposite angles of cyclic quadrilateral)
    angle CDG = 130 − y
    angle CGD = 130 − y (base angles of isosceles triangle)
    $x + 130 - y + 130 - y = 180$ (angle sum of triangle)
    $x + 260 - 2y = 180$
    $x = 2y - 80$

8   Reflex angle PCR = 2y (angle at centre is double angle at circumference)
    angle PCR = 360 − 2y (angles at a point)
    $x + x + y + 360 - 2y = 360$ (angle sum of quadrilateral)
    $2x = y$

? (Page 129)

No: since they are defined using the sides of a right-angled triangle they are restricted to $0 < \theta < 90°$.

? (Page 130)

You need at least 3 decimal places:
$\tan^{-1} 0.714 = 35.5°$, but
$\tan^{-1} 0.71 = 35.4°$.

? (Page 131)

The best function would be tan θ, since this does not use the value of h that you calculated earlier.

Exercise 6C (Page 131)

1   (i)   11.2 cm
    (ii)   7.7 cm
    (iii)   12.1 cm
    (iv)   15.1 cm
    (v)   6.8 cm
    (vi)   7.7 cm

2   (i)   30.6°
    (ii)   50.4°
    (iii)   55.7°
    (iv)   41.4°
    (v)   45.0°
    (vi)   64.2°

3   (i)   63.6°
    (ii)   14.9 cm
    (iii)   9.1 cm

4   4.5 m

5   78.2 m

6   282.7 m

7   33.7°

8   (i)   119 km
    (ii)   33°
    (iii)   333 km h^{-1}

? (Page 134)

The results would be unchanged

Exercise 6D (Page 135)

1   (i) $5 + \sqrt{3}$
    (ii) $3 + 2\sqrt{3}$
    (iii)   5
    (iv) $\dfrac{9}{2}$

2   $\cos 30° = \dfrac{y}{6\sqrt{3}}$
    $\dfrac{\sqrt{3}}{2} = \dfrac{y}{6\sqrt{3}}$
    $\dfrac{\sqrt{3}}{2} \times 6\sqrt{3} = y$
    $9 = y$

3   $\sin 45° = \dfrac{\sqrt{8} + \sqrt{2}}{p}$
    $\dfrac{1}{\sqrt{2}} = \dfrac{\sqrt{8} + \sqrt{2}}{p}$
    $p = \sqrt{2}\left(\sqrt{8} + \sqrt{2}\right)$
    $p = \sqrt{16} + 2$
    $p = 4 + 2$
    $p = 6$

4 $9 + 6\sqrt{3}$

5 $2\sqrt{6}$

❓ (Page 136)

On the surface of the Earth (or just above it) the lines of latitude do not represent the shortest distance between two points (unless those points are on the equator). In general, aircraft fly long distances along the most economical route.

❓ (Page 138)

One possible example is a ramp used for disabled access to a building.

❓ (Page 140)

Possible answers

The shelves of a bookcase are *parallel*.

The side of a filing cabinet meets the floor *in a line*.

Exercise 6E (Page 144)

1   **(i)**   14.1 cm

    (ii)   17.3 cm

    (iii)   35.3°

2   **(i)**   3 cm

    (ii)   72.1°

    (iii)   76.0°

3   **(i)**   18.4°

    (ii)   13 cm

    (iii)   17.1°

    (iv)   Half way along

4   **(i)**   75 m

    (ii)   67.5 m

    (iii)   42°

5   **(i)**   33.4 m

    (ii)   66.7 m

    (iii)   115.6 m

    (iv)   22.8°

6   **(i)**   28.3 cm

    (ii)   42.4 cm

    (iii)   40.6 cm

7   **(i)**   41.8°

    (ii)   219 m

    (iii)   186 m

    (iv)   51.7°

8   **(i)**   1.57 m

    (ii)   1.547 m

    (iii)   3.05 m

9   **(i)**   15 m

    (ii)   16.4 m

    (iii)   65.4°

    (iv)   69.9°

10   **(i)**   5.2 cm

    (ii)   5.2 cm

    (iii)   54.7°

    (iv)   16.9 cm

Chapter 7

❓ (Page 149)

Yes, it is possible provided that the definitions are changed to ones that do not require that the angle is in a right-angled triangle.

Activity 7.1 (Page 151)

The curve continues in the same manner repeating the wave pattern every 360° both to the right and the left.

❓ (Page 152)

Undefined means that you cannot find a value for it. When $\theta = 90°$, $x = 0$ and $\cos\theta = 0$, so neither definition works since you cannot divide by zero. $\tan\theta$ is also undefined for $\theta = 90° \pm$ any multiple of 180°.

❓ (Page 152)

It is a line that is very close to the shape of the curve for large values of x or y.

❓ (Page 152)

The period is 180° since it repeats itself every 180°.

For $-90 \leqslant \theta \leqslant 0°$, rotate the part of the curve for $0° \leqslant \theta \leqslant 90°$ through 180° about the origin. This gives one complete branch of the curve.

Translating this branch through multiples of 180° to the right or left gives the rest of the curve.

Activity 7.2 (Page 153)

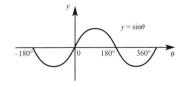

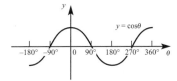

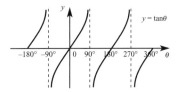

Exercise 7A (Page 155)

Answers given to 3 significant figures.

1   **(i)**   9.85 cm²

    (ii)   19.5 cm²

    (iii)   15.2 cm²

    (iv)   20.5 cm²

2   127 cm²

3   **(i)**   23.8 cm²

    (ii)   5.56 cm

    (iii)   126 cm²

4   **(i)**   308 cm²

    (ii)   325

    (iii)   There is likely to be a lot of wastage when tiles are cut for the edges, so he will need more tiles.

5   173 cm²

❓ (Page 156)

It is easier to solve an equation involving fractions if the unknown quantity is in the numerator.

❓ (Page 158)

$$\frac{\sin z}{6} = \frac{\sin 78°}{8} \Rightarrow Z = 47.2°$$

or $z = 132.8°$, but $132.8°$ is too large to fit into a triangle where one of the other angles is $78°$.

Exercise 7B (Page 158)

1 (i) 4.6 m

   (ii) 11.0 cm

   (iii) 5.6 cm

2 (i) 57.7°

   (ii) 16.5°

   (iii) 103.3°

   (Reject 76.7° since the angle in the diagram is obtuse.)

Exercise 7C (Page 161)

1 (i) 6.4 cm

   (ii) 8.8 cm

   (iii) 13.3 cm

2 (i) 41.4°

   (ii) 107.2°

   (iii) 90°

3 9.1 cm, 12.3 cm

4 (i) 10 cm

   (ii) 111.8°

5 55.8°

? (Page 164)

You know the lengths of all three sides of triangle ABC so there is only one possible value for $\angle A$. Using the cosine rule confirms that $\angle A = 62°$.

? (Page 164)

The cosine rule involves three sides and one angle and you want to find an angle and know three sides. The sine rule involves two angles and two sides and you do not know any angles.

Exercise 7D (Page 164)

1 12.2 cm

2 6.1 km

3 (i) 26.5 m

   (ii) 19.4 m

4 (i) 57.1°, 57.1°, 122.9°, 122.9°

   (ii) 14.5 cm

5 (i) 10.2 km

   (ii) 117°

6 (i) 29.9 km

   (ii) 12.9 km h^{-1}

7 BD = 2.1 m, EG = 2.1 m

8 4.8 km

? (Page 166)

The equation will have infinitely many roots since the curve continues to oscillate and the line $y = 0.5$ crosses it infinitely many times.

? (Page 167)

$293.6° = -66.4° + 360°$

Exercise 7E (Page 168)

1 (i) 60°, 300°

   (ii) 45°, 225°

   (iii) 60°, 120°

   (iv) 210°, 330°

   (v) 90°, 270°

   (vi) 101.3°, 281.3°

   (vii) 0°, 180°

   (viii) 122.7°, 237.3°

   (ix) 90°

2 (i) $\theta = 48.2°$ or $311.8°$

   (ii) $\theta = 45.6°$ or $134.4°$

   (iii) $\theta = 69.4°$ or $249.4°$

   (iv) $\theta = 236.4°$ or $303.6°$

   (v) $\theta = 113.6°$ or $246.4°$

   (vi) $\theta = 150.9°$ or $330.9°$

3 (i) $\theta = 60°, 120°, 240°$ or $300°$

   (ii) $\theta = 45°, 135°, 225°$ or $315°$

   (iii) $\theta = 45°, 135°, 225°$ or $315°$

4 (i) $(2x-1)(x+1)$

   (ii) $x = 0.5$ or -1

   (iii) (a) $\theta = 30°, 150°$ or $270°$

       (b) $\theta = 60°, 180°$ or $300°$

   (c) $\theta = 26.6°, 135°, 206.6°$ or $315°$

5 (i) 0° 180° 360° 71.6° 251.6°

   (ii) 45° 135° 225° 315°

   (iii) 70.5° 289.5° 180°

   (iv) 90° 210° 330°

6 (i) 60° 240°

   (ii) 30° 150°

   (iii) 45° 315°

   (iv) 60° 120°

   (v) 0° 180° 360° 45° 225°

   (vi) 30° 330°

Exercise 7F (Page 171)

1 (i) (a) $2\sin^2\theta - \sin\theta - 1 = 0$

       (b) $\theta = 90°, 210°$ or $330°$

   (ii) (a) $\cos^2\theta - \cos\theta - 2 = 0$

       (b) $\theta = 180°$

   (iii) (a) $2\cos^2\theta + \cos\theta - 1 = 0$

       (b) $\theta = 60°, 180°$ or $300°$

   (iv) (a) $\sin^2\theta - \sin\theta = 0$

       (b) $\theta = 0°, 90°, 180°$ or $360°$

   (v) (a) $2\sin^2\theta + \sin\theta - 1 = 0$

       (b) $\theta = 30°, 150°$ or $270°$

2 (i) (a) $\cos^2\theta + 2\cos\theta - 2 = 0$

       (b) $\theta = 42.9°$

   (ii) (a) $\sin^2\theta + \sin\theta - 1 = 0$

       (b) $\theta = 38.2°$ or $141.8°$

   (iii) (a) $\cos^2\theta + 3\cos\theta - 1 = 0$

       (b) $\theta = 72.4°$

3 (i) $\tan\theta = 2$

   (ii) $\theta = 63.4°$

4 (i) $\theta = 153.4°$ or $333.4°$

   (ii) $\theta = 0°, 30°, 180°, 330°$ or $360°$

   (iii) $\theta = 14.5°$ or $165.5°$

5 (i) $\sin^2 x$

   (ii) $1 - \sin^2 x$

   (iii) $2 - 3\sin x - 2\sin^2 x$

6 $3\sin^2 x + 6\sin x - 6\sin x + 3\cos^2 x$
   $= 3\sin^2 x + 3\cos^2 x$
   $= 3(\sin^2 x + \cos^2 x)$
   $= 3$

7 (i)

$$\tan x \sqrt{1 - \sin^2 x} \equiv \tan x \sqrt{\cos^2 x}$$
$$\equiv \tan x \cos x$$
$$\equiv \frac{\sin x}{\cos x} \cos x$$
$$\equiv \sin x$$

(ii)
$$\frac{1 - \cos^2 x}{1 - \sin^2 x} \equiv \frac{\sin^2 x}{\cos^2 x}$$
$$\equiv \tan^2 x$$

(iii) $(1 + \sin x)(1 - \sin x)$
$$\equiv 1 - \sin x + \sin x - \sin^2 x$$
$$\equiv 1 - \sin^2 x$$
$$\equiv \cos^2 x$$

(iv)
$$\frac{2 \sin x \cos x}{\tan x} \equiv \frac{2 \sin x \cos x}{\frac{\sin x}{\cos x}}$$
$$\equiv \frac{2 \sin x \cos^2 x}{\sin x}$$
$$\equiv 2 \cos^2 x$$
$$\equiv 2(1 - \sin^2 x)$$
$$\equiv 2 - 2 \sin^2 x$$

Chapter 8

? (Page 178)

Yes: drawing chords from P to points to the left of P will again give a sequence that eventually gives the gradient of the tangent. Activity 8.1 does this in greater detail.

Activity 8.1 (Page 179)

Taking $R_1 = (2, 4)$, $R_2 = (2.5, 6.25)$, $R_3 = (2.9, 8.41)$, $R_4 = (2.99, 8.9401)$ and $R_5 = (2.999, 8.994\,001)$ gives the gradient sequence 5, 5.5, 5.9, 5.99, 5.999. Again the sequence seems to converge to 6.

Activity 8.2 (Page 180)

(i) The gradient of the chord is $4 + h$.
The gradient of the tangent is 4.

(ii) The gradient of the chord is $-2 + h$.
The gradient of the tangent is -2.

(iii) The gradient of the chord is $-6 + h$.
The gradient of the tangent is -6.

In each case the gradient of the tangent is twice the value of the x co-ordinate.

Exercise 8A (Page 181)

1 (i) Gradient 34.481, 32.241…, 32.024…, approaching a limit of 32.

(ii) Gradient 113.521, 108.541…, 108.054…, approaching a limit of 108.
−3.439, −3.940…, −3.994…, approaching a limit of −4.

2 The gradient of the chord is $2x + h$, with a limit of $2x$.

Activity 8.3 (Page 182)

(i), (ii)

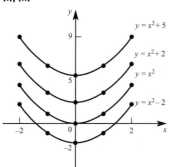

(iii) When $x = 0$, the gradients of all three curves are zero.
When $x = 1$, the tangents to the three curves are parallel, so the gradients are the same.
When $x = -1$, the tangents to the three curves are parallel, so the gradients are the same.

(iv) When $y = x^2 + c$, where c is a constant, $\dfrac{dy}{dx} = 2x$, so the value of c does not affect the value of $\dfrac{dy}{dx}$. This shows that the value of $\dfrac{dy}{dx}$ for all three curves in **(i)** and **(ii)** will be the same for any particular value of x.

Exercise 8B (Page 183)

1 (i) $\dfrac{dy}{dx} = 4x^3$

(ii) $\dfrac{dy}{dx} = 6x^2$

(iii) $\dfrac{dy}{dx} = 10x$

(iv) $\dfrac{dy}{dx} = 63x^8$

(v) $\dfrac{dy}{dx} = -18x^5$

(vi) $\dfrac{dy}{dx} = 0$

(vii) $\dfrac{dy}{dx} = 10$

(viii) $\dfrac{dy}{dx} = 10x^4 + 8x$

(ix) $\dfrac{dy}{dx} = 12x^3 + 8$

(x) $\dfrac{dy}{dx} = 3x^2$

(xi) $\dfrac{dy}{dx} = 1 - 15x^2$

(xii) $\dfrac{dy}{dx} = 15x^4 + 16x^3 - 6x$

(xiii) $\dfrac{dy}{dx} = 12x^2 + 2$

(xiv) $\dfrac{dy}{dx} = 2$

(xv) $\dfrac{dy}{dx} = 5x^4 + 36x^2 + 3$

(xvi) $\dfrac{dy}{dx} = 15x^4$

(xvii) $\dfrac{dy}{dx} = \frac{3}{4} p^2$

(xviii) $\dfrac{dy}{dx} = 3x^2 + 84x - 5$

(xix) $\dfrac{dy}{dx} = 2\pi$

(xx) $\dfrac{dy}{dx} = 2\pi x$

2 (i) $y = 18x^2$

(ii) $36x$

3 (i) $y = \dfrac{4}{3}\pi(2x)^3$
$$= \frac{4}{3}\pi \times 8x^3$$
$$= \frac{32}{3}\pi x^3$$

(ii) 128π

Exercise 8C (Page 184)

1 (i) $3x^2 + 2$

(ii) $18x^2 - 16x$

(iii) $2x + 5$

(iv) $2x + 7$

(v) $12x^2 + 4x^3 - 5x^4$

(vi) $\dfrac{5x^4 + 3x^2}{4}$

2 (i) $2x - 3$

(ii) $5x^4 + 1$

(iii) $16x^3$

(iv) $6x - 5$

(v) $2x + 1$

(vi) $4x^3$

3 54

4 1

5 -7

6 10

Exercise 8D (Page 187)

1 (i) $\dfrac{dy}{dx} = 5 - 2x$

(ii) -1

(iii) $x + y - 9 = 0$

(iv) $x - y + 3 = 0$

2 (i) (a) $\dfrac{dy}{dx} = 6x - 3x^2$

(b) 0

(c) $y = 4$

(d) $x = 2$

(ii) (a) $(3, 0)$

(b) -9

(c) $9x + y = 27$

(iii) $y = 0$

3 (i) $(1, 0)$

(ii) $y = 2x - 2$

(iii) $x + 2y - 2 = 0$

(iv) $Q(0, -2), R(0, \frac{1}{2})$;

$1\frac{1}{4}$ units^2

4 (i) $\dfrac{dy}{dx} = 3x^2 - 6x + 4$

(ii) (a) 5

(b) $y = 4x - 3$

(c) $x + 4y - 22 = 0$

(iii) $x = -1, x = 3$

5 (i) $\dfrac{dy}{dx} = 3x^2 - 18x + 23$

(ii) -1

(iii) $x + y = 5$

(iv) $(4, -3)$

(v) $x + y = 1$

6 (i) $2p - q = 16$

(ii) $\dfrac{dy}{dx} = 3x^2 - p$

(iii) $p = 12$

(iv) $(-2, 24)$

(v) $(0, 8)$

(vi) $x - 12y + 96 = 0$

7 (i) $y = 3x - 5$

(ii) $-\dfrac{1}{3}$

(iii) $\left(\dfrac{1}{3}, -1\dfrac{2}{9}\right)$

8 (i) $\dfrac{dy}{dx} = 10 - 2x$

(ii) $2x + y - 15 = 0$

(iii) $x - 2y = 0$

(iv) The normal

9 (i) Substituting $x = 0$
$y = 0 - 0 + 0 = 0$
Substituting $x = 1$
$y = 1.5 - 3.5 + 2 = 0$

(ii) At $(0, 0)$ the tangent is
$y = 2x$ and the normal is
$x + 2y = 0$.

At $(1, 0)$ the tangent is
$x + 2y - 1 = 0$ and the
normal is $2x - y - 2 = 0$.

Exercise 8E (Page 190)

1 (i) $x > 0$

(ii) All x values

(iii) $x > -1$

(iv) $x > \frac{3}{2}$

(v) $x > -\frac{2}{3}$

(vi) $x > -2$

(vii) $x < 0$ or $x > 4$

(viii) $x < -5$ or $x > 1$

(ix) $x < -1$ or $x > 3$

2 (i) $x < 0$

(ii) $x < 3$

(iii) $x < -1$

(iv) $x > 2$

(v) All x values

(vi) $x < -\frac{1}{2}$

(vii) $-2 < x < 0$

(viii) $-3 < x < 4$

(ix) $x < -3$ or $x > 3$

---

3 $x^2 + 4x + 7 = (x + 2)^2 + 3$
$(x + 2)^2 \geqslant 0$ for all x values.
Adding 3 means always positive,
so increasing function.

4 $3x^2 - 12x + 27 = 3(x^2 - 4x + 9)$
$= 3((x - 2)^2 + 5)$
$= 3(x - 2)^2 + 15$
$3(x - 2)^2 \geqslant 0$ for all x values.
Adding 15 means always
positive, so increasing function.

5 $-2 - 3x^2$
$-3x^2 \leqslant 0$ for all x values.
Subtracting -2 means always
negative, so decreasing function.

Activity 8.4 (Page 190)

(i)

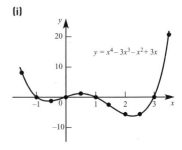

(ii) Three

(iii) Zero

(iv) Minimum near $(-0.5, -1.3)$,
maximum near $(0.5, 0.9)$,
minimum near $(-2.3, -6.9)$

(v) No, for example $x = -1.5$ and
$x = 3.5$ give higher points.

(vi) No. $\dfrac{dy}{dx} = 4x^3 - 9x^2 - 2x + 3$ and
this does not equal zero at the
points plotted.

(vii) About -6.9

? (Page 190)

The gradient is positive both to the
left and to the right of D.

Activity 8.5 (Page 191)

When $x = 0°$ the gradient is zero. It then
decreases through negative values and
is least when $x = 90°$. It increases to zero
when $x = 180°$ and continues to increase
through positive values until it is
greatest when $x = 270°$. The gradient
then decreases to zero when $x = 360°$.

? (Page 194)

There are no more values when $\frac{dy}{dx} = 0$, so there are no more turning points. As x increases beyond the point where $x = 2$, $\frac{dy}{dx}$ takes positive values and so the curve will cross the x axis again. To the left of $x = -2$ the gradient is always negative, giving a further point of intersection with the x axis.

? (Page 194)

(i) The curve crosses the x axis when $x^3 - 12x + 3 = 0$. This does not factorise, so the values of x cannot be found easily.

(ii) Only when the equation obtained when $y = 0$ factorises.

Exercise 8F (Page 195)

1 (i) (a) $\frac{dy}{dx} = 1 - 4x$; $x = \frac{1}{4}$

(b) Max

(c) $y = 1\frac{1}{8}$

(d)

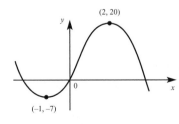

(ii) (a) $\frac{dy}{dx} = 12 + 6x - 6x^2$;
$x = -1, x = 2$

(b) Min when $x = -1$,
max when $x = 2$

(c) $x = -1, y = -7$;
$x = 2, y = 20$

(d)

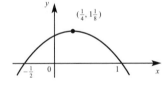
$(2, 20)$
$(-1, -7)$

(iii) (a) $\frac{dy}{dx} = 3x^2 - 8x$; $x = 0$,
$x = 2\frac{2}{3}$

(b) Max when $x = 0$,
min when $x = 2\frac{2}{3}$

(c) $x = 0, y = 9$;
$x = 2\frac{2}{3}, y = -\frac{13}{27}$

(d)

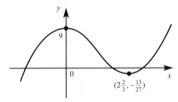
9
$(2\frac{2}{3}, -\frac{13}{27})$

(iii) Gradients of the lines are
$2 \quad -\frac{1}{2} \quad -\frac{1}{2}$ and 2
Two lines each with gradient 2 will be parallel
Two lines each with gradient $-\frac{1}{2}$ will be parallel
Pairs of links with gradient 2 and $-\frac{1}{2}$ will be perpendicular, so form a rectangle.

(iv) (a) $\frac{dy}{dx} = 4x^3 - 6x^2 + 2x$; $x = 0$,
$x = \frac{1}{2}, x = 1$

(b) Min when $x = 0$,
max when $x = \frac{1}{2}$,
min when $x = 1$

(c) $x = 0, y = 0$; $x = \frac{1}{2}, y = \frac{1}{16}$;
$x = 1, y = 0$

(d)

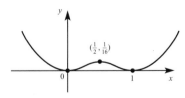
$(\frac{1}{2}, \frac{1}{16})$

(v) (a) $\frac{dy}{dx} = 4x^3 - 16x$; $x = -2$,
$x = 0, x = 2$

(b) Min when $x = -2$,
max when $x = 0$,
min when $x = 2$

(c) $x = -2, y = -12$; $x = 0$,
$y = 4$; $x = 2, y = -12$

(d)

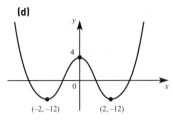
4
$(-2, -12)$ $(2, -12)$

(vi) (a) $\frac{dy}{dx} = 3x^2 - 48$; $x = -4, x = 4$

(b) Max when $x = -4$,
min when $x = 4$

(c) $x = -4, y = 128$;
$x = 4, y = -128$

(d)

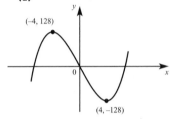
$(-4, 128)$
$(4, -128)$

(vii) (a) $\frac{dy}{dx} = 3x^2 + 12x - 36$;
$x = -6, x = 2$

(b) Max when $x = -6$,
min when $x = 2$

(c) $x = -6, y = 241$;
$x = 2, y = -15$

(d)

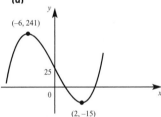
$(-6, 241)$
25
$(2, -15)$

(viii) (a) $\frac{dy}{dx} = 6x^2 - 30x + 24$;
$x = 1, x = 4$

(b) Max when $x = 1$,
min when $x = 4$

(c) $x = 1, y = 19$;
$x = 4, y = -8$

(d)

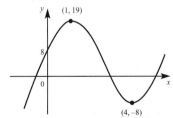
$(1, 19)$
8
$(4, -8)$

2 (i) $p = 4, q = -3$

(ii) $y = 1\frac{1}{3}, x = \frac{2}{3}$

3 (i) Min at $(-\frac{1}{2}, -\frac{5}{16})$, max at $(0, 0)$, min at $(1, -2)$

(ii)

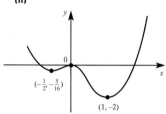

Exercise 8G (Page 197)

1 (i) (a) $\dfrac{dy}{dx} = 3x^2 + 12x + 12;$

$x = -2$

(b) Point of inflection

(c) $x = -2, y = 0$

(d)

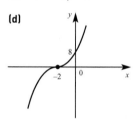

(ii) (a) $\dfrac{dy}{dx} = 12x^3 + 12x^2;$

$x = -1, x = 0$

(b) Min when $x = -1$, point of inflection when $x = 0$

(c) $x = -1, y = -1;$

$x = 0, y = 0$

(d)

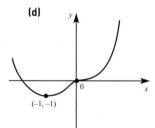

(iii) (a) $\dfrac{dy}{dx} = 12x^2 - 4x^3;$

$x = 0, x = 3$

(b) Point of inflection when $x = 0$, max when $x = 3$

(c) $x = 0, y = 3;$

$x = 3, y = 30$

(d)

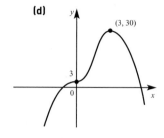

(iv) (a) $\dfrac{dy}{dx} = 15x^4 - 15x^2;$

$x = -1, x = 0, x = 1$

(b) Max when $x = -1$, point of inflection when $x = 0$, min when $x = 1$

(c) $x = -1, y = 2;$

$x = 0, y = 0;$

$x = 1, y = -2$

(d)

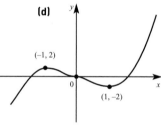

(v) (a) $\dfrac{dy}{dx} = 24x^2 - 16x^3;$

$x = 0, x = 1\frac{1}{2}$

(b) Point of inflection when $x = 0$; max when $x = 1\frac{1}{2}$

(c) $x = 0, y = 0;$

$x = 1\frac{1}{2}, y = 6\frac{3}{4}$

(d)

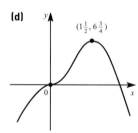

(vi) (a) $\dfrac{dy}{dx} = 3x^2 - 6x + 3;$

$x = 1$

(b) Point of inflection when $x = 1$

(c) $x = 1, y = 2$

(d)

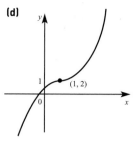

2 (i) Point of inflection at $(1, 3)$

(ii) The curve is the same shape as the curve in question 1**(vi)**, translated up one unit.

3 (i) $p + q = -3$

(ii) $4p + 3q = 0$

(iii) $p = 9, q = -12$

(iv) Minimum turning point

(v) Point of inflection at $(0, 0)$

Chapter 9

Activity 9.1 (Page 203)

$$\mathbf{A} = \begin{pmatrix} 2 & 4 \\ -3 & 1 \end{pmatrix} \quad \mathbf{B} = \begin{pmatrix} 1 & 2 \\ 3 & -4 \end{pmatrix}$$

$$\mathbf{AB} = \begin{pmatrix} 14 & -12 \\ 0 & -10 \end{pmatrix}$$

$$\mathbf{BA} = \begin{pmatrix} -4 & 6 \\ 18 & 8 \end{pmatrix}$$

? (Page 203)

An infinite number of answers.

The answer to **PQ** and **QP** will always be $\begin{pmatrix} 1 & 0 \\ 0 & 1 \end{pmatrix}$

e.g. $\mathbf{P} = \begin{pmatrix} 3 & 5 \\ 1 & 2 \end{pmatrix} \quad \mathbf{Q} = \begin{pmatrix} 2 & -5 \\ -1 & 3 \end{pmatrix}$

Exercise 9A (Page 203)

1 (i) $\begin{pmatrix} 8 & 12 \\ 4 & 4 \end{pmatrix}$

(ii) $\begin{pmatrix} 0 & 0 \\ -6 & -10 \end{pmatrix}$

(iii) $\begin{pmatrix} 23 \\ 10 \end{pmatrix}$ **(iv)** $\begin{pmatrix} 2 \\ -5 \end{pmatrix}$

(v) $\begin{pmatrix} 0 \\ 11 \end{pmatrix}$ **(vi)** $\begin{pmatrix} 4 \\ -7 \end{pmatrix}$

(vii) $\begin{pmatrix} 5 & 3 \\ 1 & 1 \end{pmatrix}$

(viii) $\begin{pmatrix} -4 & -6 \\ 7 & 10 \end{pmatrix}$

(ix) $\begin{pmatrix} -12 & 4 \\ 15 & -7 \end{pmatrix}$

(x) $\begin{pmatrix} -18 & -2 \\ 3 & -1 \end{pmatrix}$

(xi) $\begin{pmatrix} 0 & 0 \\ -11 & -14 \end{pmatrix}$

(xii) $\begin{pmatrix} 0 & 0 \\ -3 & -5 \end{pmatrix}$

(xiii) $\begin{pmatrix} 3 & -7 \\ 3 & -3 \end{pmatrix}$

(xiv) $\begin{pmatrix} 0 & 0 \\ -3 & 11 \end{pmatrix}$

2 **(i)** −1 **(ii)** 6
(iii) 0.5 **(iv)** 1.5
(v) 7 **(vi)** −2

3 **(i)** $x = 4$ $y = 2$
(ii) $x = -1$ $y = -2$
(iii) $x = 3$ $y = -5$
(iv) $x = -3$ $y = 7$

4 **(ii)** $2x - y = -4$
(iii) $x = -1$ $y = 2$

5 **(i)** $a = 3$ $b = 5$
(ii) $a = -2$ $b = 4$
(iii) $a = 1$ $b = -5$
(iv) $a = 2$ $b = 2$

Activity 9.2 (Page 205)

(i) (3, 2) (−1, 5) (6, 0) (−3, −4)
and (x, y)
No transformation has occurred

(ii) (2, −1) (−4, −3) (0, −4) (−5, 1)
and $(x, -y)$
Reflection in the x axis

Exercise 9B (Page 205)

1 (20, 8) **2** (9, −16)
3 (13, −1) **4** −2 **5** 9
6 $a = -3$ $b = 3$
7 $c = 1$ $d = -2$
8 $\begin{pmatrix} 0 & -1 \\ -1 & 0 \end{pmatrix}\begin{pmatrix} 0 & -1 \\ -1 & 0 \end{pmatrix} = \begin{pmatrix} 1 & 0 \\ 0 & 1 \end{pmatrix}$
9 5

Exercise 9C (Page 209)

1 **(i)** $\begin{pmatrix} 1 & 0 \\ 0 & -1 \end{pmatrix}$ **(ii)** $\begin{pmatrix} 0 & -1 \\ 1 & 0 \end{pmatrix}$
(iii) $\begin{pmatrix} 2 & 0 \\ 0 & 2 \end{pmatrix}$ **(iv)** $\begin{pmatrix} -1 & 0 \\ 0 & 1 \end{pmatrix}$
(v) $\begin{pmatrix} 0 & 1 \\ 1 & 0 \end{pmatrix}$ **(vi)** $\begin{pmatrix} -1 & 0 \\ 0 & -1 \end{pmatrix}$
(vii) $\begin{pmatrix} 0 & -1 \\ -1 & 0 \end{pmatrix}$
(viii) $\begin{pmatrix} -3 & 0 \\ 0 & -3 \end{pmatrix}$ **(ix)** $\begin{pmatrix} \frac{1}{2} & 0 \\ 0 & \frac{1}{2} \end{pmatrix}$

2

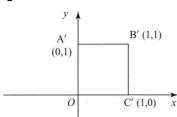

3

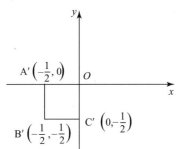

4 $\begin{pmatrix} 0 & -1 \\ 1 & 0 \end{pmatrix}$
5 16 sq units **6** 8 or −8

Exercise 9D (Page 211)

1 **(i)** $\begin{pmatrix} 0 & 2 \\ 1 & -1 \end{pmatrix}$ **(ii)** (−4, 5)

2 **(i)** $\begin{pmatrix} 3 & -1 \\ 13 & -7 \end{pmatrix}$ **(ii)** (−7, −41)

3 $\begin{pmatrix} -1 & 0 \\ 0 & 1 \end{pmatrix}$ **4** $\begin{pmatrix} 0 & 2 \\ 2 & 0 \end{pmatrix}$

5 $\begin{pmatrix} 0 & 1 \\ 1 & 0 \end{pmatrix}$

6 **(i)** Reflection in the y axis
(ii) $\begin{pmatrix} 1 & 0 \\ 0 & 1 \end{pmatrix}$
(iii) Two successive reflections in the y axis takes you back to the original position.

7 **(i)** Rotation through 90°, centre O
(ii) Rotation through 180°, centre O
(iii) $\begin{pmatrix} 0 & 1 \\ -1 & 0 \end{pmatrix}$
(iv) Rotation through 270°, centre O
(v) Rotation through 180°, centre O followed by rotation through 90°, centre O is equivalent to rotation through 270°, centre O.
(vi) **ED** is a rotation through 90°, centre O followed by rotation through 180°, centre O.
This is also equivalent to a rotation through 270°, centre O, the same as **DE**.

8 $\begin{pmatrix} -2 & 0 \\ 0 & -2 \end{pmatrix}\begin{pmatrix} 3 & 0 \\ 0 & 3 \end{pmatrix} = \begin{pmatrix} -6 & 0 \\ 0 & -6 \end{pmatrix}$
$\begin{pmatrix} -6 & 0 \\ 0 & -6 \end{pmatrix}$ represents an enlargement, centre O, scale factor −6 $k = -6$

Exam-style papers

Paper 1 (Page 215)

1. Box 1 → $y + 3x = 1$

   Box 2 → $y = x^3 - 27$

   Box 3 → $7y + 4x = 12$

2. 4.5

3. (a) -2 (b) $\frac{1}{2}$

   (c) 3

4. (a) $15x^2 + 21x$

   (b) $4 + 6x - 4x^2$

   (c) 1

5. (a) $-4 \leqslant x \leqslant 5$

   (b) $\left(\frac{1}{2}, 8\right)$ (c) 0

6. 99th term = 9707

7. Angle DBC = angle ACB

   alternate angles

   angle DBC = angle CAB

   alternate segment theorem

   triangle ABC isosceles

   base angles equal

8. $y = \frac{3}{2}x + \frac{15}{2}$

9. $x = 54$ $y = 18$

10. $x = \dfrac{--6 \pm \sqrt{36 - 8}}{2}$

    $= \dfrac{6 \pm \sqrt{28}}{2}$

    $\text{Sum} = \dfrac{6 + \sqrt{28}}{2} + \dfrac{6 - \sqrt{28}}{2}$

    $3 + 3 = 6$, which is an inteqes

11. $(x + 1)^2 + (y - 11)^2 = 100$

12. (a) $(-4)^3 + 4(-4)^2 - 4(-4) - 16$

    $= -64 + 64 + 16 - 16 = 0$

    (b) $(y + 4)(y + 2)(y - 2)$

13. (a) $t^2(t - 1)$

    (b) $0°\ 45°\ 180°\ 225°$

14. (a) $\dfrac{\sqrt{3}}{2}$

    (b) $2 + \frac{8}{3}\sqrt{3}$

15. P $(-2, 4)$ Q $(4, 2)$

16. $(0, 0)$ minimum

    $(2, \frac{4}{3})$ point of inflection

Paper 2 (Page 219)

1. (a) 1

   (b)

   (c) $f(x) \geqslant -3$

2. (a) $a = \dfrac{2b}{3}$ (b) $4 : 3$

3. $\dfrac{2a + 6}{2} = \dfrac{8 + 4b}{2}$

   $2a + 6 = 8 + 4b$

   $2a = 8 + 4b - 6$

   $2a = 4b + 2$

   $a = 2b + 1$

4. (a) Always true

   (b) Sometimes true

   (c) Sometimes true

   (d) Never true

5. (a) $12x^2 + 2x - 7$

   (b) 23

6. $x = 18$ 7. $m = \dfrac{5h}{2}$

8. (a) 30.8 km

   (b) 100.8°

9. $(-3, 5)$

10. $\begin{pmatrix} -1 & 0 \\ 0 & -1 \end{pmatrix}$

11.
    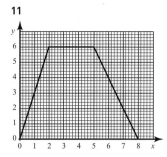

12. (a) $x^{\frac{3}{2}}$

    (b) $x = \dfrac{125}{8}$

13. (a) $(a - b)(2a + b)$

    (b) $\dfrac{c^3}{2c + 5}$

14. (a) $w(w - y) + xy = w^2 - wy + xy$

    (b) $y = \dfrac{A - w^2}{x - w}$

15. 2 and -2

16. $p = 12$ $q = 8$

17. (a)
    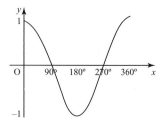

    (b) 30° and 330°

18. (a) 7.84 cm

    (b) 63.2°

    (c) 70.3°

19. (a) $2n^2 - 3n + 4$

    (b) $\dfrac{3 + \frac{2}{n}}{\frac{1}{n} - 6}$

    As $n \to \infty$

    $\dfrac{2}{n} \to 0$ and $\dfrac{1}{n} \to 0$

    $\dfrac{3 + \frac{2}{n}}{\frac{1}{n} - 6} \to \dfrac{3}{-6} = -\dfrac{1}{2}$

20. (a) $\frac{1}{2} \times 4x \times 3x = 6x^2$

    (b) $0 < x < \frac{3}{2}$

21. $y = -4x - 20$

22. (a) $\begin{pmatrix} 0 & 1 \\ -6 & -3 \end{pmatrix}$

    (b) $\left(-\frac{3}{2}, 2\right)$

23. $\sin x \tan x = \sin x \dfrac{\sin x}{\cos x}$

    $= \dfrac{\sin^2 x}{\cos x}$

    $= \dfrac{1 - \cos^2 x}{\cos x}$

    $= \dfrac{1}{\cos x} - \dfrac{\cos^2 x}{\cos x}$

    $= \dfrac{1}{\cos x} - \cos x$

24. $(n + 1)^3 = n^3 + 3n^2 + 3n + 1$

    $(n - 1)^3 = n^3 - 3n^2 + 3n - 1$

    $(n + 1)^3 - (n - 1)^3 = 6n^2 + 2$

    $= 2(3n^2 + 1)$

    Multiple of 2, so always even.

Index